Contents

It's an exciting year ahead. And as a National Trust member, there's lots for you to look forward to.

Whether you're out exploring the places we care for, or delving into stories, recipes and collections online at **nationaltrust.org.uk**, there's more than one way to make the most of being a member.

This year, why not rediscover everything you love about your favourite places? Or pay a visit to the places you've always wanted to go. There's so much to explore, and it all starts from these pages.

Inside, you'll find we've introduced a new pawprint rating system for helping you decide the best places to visit with dogs – from great locations for a morning walk to dog-friendly days out.

This handbook provides you with all the inspiration you need to choose your next visit and learn more about the places we look after. Without your support, we wouldn't be able to care for them.

Thank you.

A year to look forward to

From Her Majesty The Queen's Platinum Jubilee to the Birmingham 2022 Commonwealth Games, it looks set to be a year of celebration, and we're looking forward to playing our part.

From the Industrial Revolution to J. M. W. Turner, the Giant's Causeway and The Beatles, the places we look after have played an incredible role in our nations' history. And they're full of extraordinary stories for you to discover.

Your handbook has been created to help you explore more of what you love. Whether that means rediscovering your favourite places all over again, or visiting new places on your to-do list, I hope it will be an inspiring companion for all your adventures this year.

As ever, I want to say a huge thank you for your support. Without it, we couldn't protect nature, beauty and history for everyone, for ever.

Thank you,

Hilary McGrady
Director-General

Mendips, the childhood home of John Lennon, in Liverpool

What's online?

- opening dates, prices and all visiting details
- access information
- things to see and do
- eating, drinking and shopping
- holiday cottages, hotels, bothies and campsites
- our 'Land Map' – everything looked after by the Trust
- how to get more involved

What's in your handbook?

- who we are and what we do
- descriptions and photographs of places we look after
- how to contact and visit them
- opening times
- maps showing all these places
- a pawprint rating system for choosing a dog-friendly place to visit

And the best ways to get to it:

1. **National Trust website**
   Browse specific web pages for the place you want to visit
2. **National Trust app**
   For all the up-to-date details on your phone, scan this QR code to download the app now

If you'd prefer not to go online, or it's tricky to do so where you are, call 0344 800 1895.

Together, we care for places

Find out how you've helped already, and what more you can do to make a difference:
nationaltrust.org.uk/donate

Poldhu Cove, Cornwall

so that **people and nature can thrive**

Thank you for joining Europe's biggest conservation charity. Thank you for getting involved, thank you for making a difference.

Nature, beauty, history

Many millions share the belief that nature, beauty and history are for everyone. So we look after the nation's coastline, historic sites, countryside and green spaces, ensuring everyone benefits.

From wild and precious places to the world outside your window, the National Trust offers access, enjoyment and a chance for everyone to help out.

Nature and the historic environment are under threat. They're essential to everyone, they enrich people's lives and are part of the fabric of society and they urgently need more care.

With our staff, members, volunteers and supporters, we are the biggest conservation charity in Europe. Everyone can get involved, everyone can make a difference.

Discover more about the art and collections we care for at **nationaltrust.org.uk/art-and-collections**

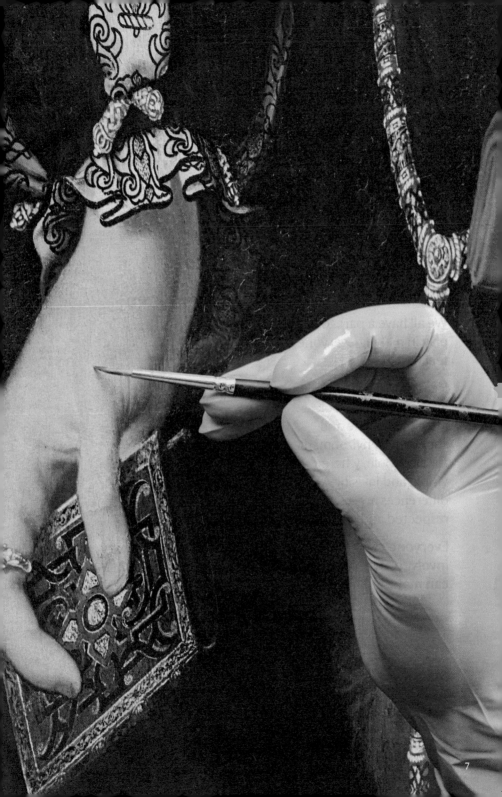

for everyone

When we say 'for everyone', we mean it.

We believe, as did our founders, that nature, beauty and history are for everyone.

We all have a part to play in making everyone feel welcome.

Help us make sure that all the places we look after offer a safe and supportive environment for all people, where visible and invisible differences are respected and valued.

Everyone can get involved, everyone can make a difference.

In the Great Hall
at Cotehele, Cornwall

for ever

**When we say 'for ever',
we mean it.**

'For ever' means that through
wars, pandemics, recessions
and all our darkest times, the
National Trust has still been
here, caring for the places that
people love. And we have to
adapt and respond to what
people most need from us in
changing times.

The founders of the Trust knew
that the only way to protect
precious places for ever – and
people's access to them – was
to own them. And they had
the foresight to guarantee this
'for ever' ownership through
a crucial Act of Parliament
in 1907.

Your membership will carry on
making a difference to people's
lives far into the future.

We're committed to improving
access everywhere, but
every place is different.
Find out more here:
nationaltrust.org.uk/access

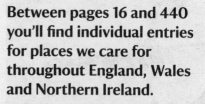

Planning your visit

Between pages 16 and 440 you'll find individual entries for places we care for throughout England, Wales and Northern Ireland.

On these pages, you'll find descriptions, photographs and maps of the places, as well as information about opening times and a pawprint rating system for helping you decide the best places to visit with dogs. **You can read more about this on page 12.**

All the changeable details to do with visiting these places – their opening dates and times, prices, facilities, events, dog access and so on – are now held online to make sure they're always up-to-date. See page 3 for the best ways to get to this information. And you can always call **0344 800 1895** if you can't get online.

Getting there

Every place entry includes its address, contact details and postcode. We'll always let you know if satnavs have difficulties with the postcode, and provide you with written directions. Locations of the places we look after are shown on maps in each chapter.

And not just by car

Many places are easy to get to by train, bus, walking or cycling. Check our website for details of the place you want to visit, or use **traveline.info** (England and Wales) or **translink.co.uk** (Northern Ireland) for public transport, and **sustrans.org.uk** for cycle routes.

If you'd like a free copy of our **Getting Here Guide** – with directions and details of public transport, cycling and walking routes – call **0344 800 1895**, or go to **nationaltrust.org.uk/membership-enquiries** to download a pdf.

We also print an **Access Guide**, showing which facilities we have at which places, such as powered mobility vehicles and 'Changing Places'. Download a pdf from **nationaltrust.org.uk/access** or call **0344 800 1895** for a printed copy.

We're working towards every place featured in the handbook having its own access statement on the website.

What kind of place is it?

To help you plan your visit, you'll find a list of **facility and place icons** at the start of each place entry, and a list of **access icons** at the end. The key for all of these is on the inside back cover. There are also more details on the website and app.

You'll always find toilets and parking at the places we look after, unless we tell you otherwise.

Members park free

As a member of the National Trust, you can also park for free at our coastal and countryside car parks. You'll find a list of these at the back of the handbook and online at **nationaltrust.org.uk/carparks**

More useful links

Online shop
nationaltrust.org.uk/shop

Holidays
nationaltrust.org.uk/holidays

1947 **Why the date?** This gives you the year that a place came into the care of the Trust. You can find more details on **ntlandmap.org.uk**

Welcoming you and your dog

Dogs are welcome at the National Trust. But every place we look after is different, and some are much better for visiting with dogs than others. You've asked us to help you plan your visit, whether you're bringing a dog or hoping to avoid them. That's why we've introduced three ratings of dog-friendliness.

Top tips on visiting with dogs

- Before you visit with your dog, please check the website of the place you're heading to. Sometimes, seasonal restrictions can mean changes to where your dog is allowed to go.

- We welcome assistance dogs at every place we look after, except the Farne Islands. Dogs are welcome on a lead on some boat trips and on Longstone (although not inside the lighthouse). They're not allowed anywhere else on the Farnes.

- If you see this icon, it means we only allow assistance dogs.

- Please be a responsible owner. You can find out more about our canine code at **nationaltrust.org.uk/forthglade**

In partnership with

Forthglade

We've rated every place we look after for its dog-friendliness

Let them stretch their legs with a walk in Croome's parkland, Worcestershire

Standard 🐾

Dogs are welcome here, but facilities are limited. They'll be able to stretch their legs in the car park and walk in the nearby open spaces, depending on the season.

Explore the grounds with your dog at Dunster Castle, Somerset

Good 🐾 🐾

These places have water bowls, dog bins and dog-friendly walks. You'll be able to take your dog into some areas, but not everywhere. If there's a food and beverage outlet, you can have a cup of tea with them, probably outside.

Take time out together in the Coach House Café at Hatchlands Park, Surrey

Best 🐾 🐾 🐾

The very best places for a day with your dog. You'll be able to take your dog to most areas, including indoors for a cup of tea and a treat. There'll be clearly signed dog zones and dog-friendly experiences.

For more ideas on planning a dog-friendly day at the places we care for, visit **nationaltrust.org.uk/ for-dog-walkers**

Did you know?

There are three historic houses –
in North Wales, North Yorkshire
and Buckinghamshire – where you
can go and stay the night, with all
profits going to the Trust to fund
our conservation work.
If you've ever dreamt of sleeping
in a National Trust house,
then read on.

Historic House Hotels Ltd
was founded in 1979 to rescue
and restore run-down country
houses, and give them a new
life as hotels. In 2008 the hotels
were given to us to ensure their
long-term protection.

Each has its own character and
atmosphere. But all three share
that feeling of staying in a private
country house, with the smell
of woodsmoke from open fires,
grand sweeping staircases, trays
of afternoon tea, and beautiful
gardens to stroll through in
the evening.

Middlethorpe Hall, just outside York

Bodysgallen Hall, near Llandudno

Hartwell House, Buckinghamshire

Afternoon tea at Hartwell House

To find out more, have a look at the hotels' main entries on pages 118, 348 and 379, or visit **historichousehotels.com**

Walking towards the pump
house at Wheal Coates

Cornwall

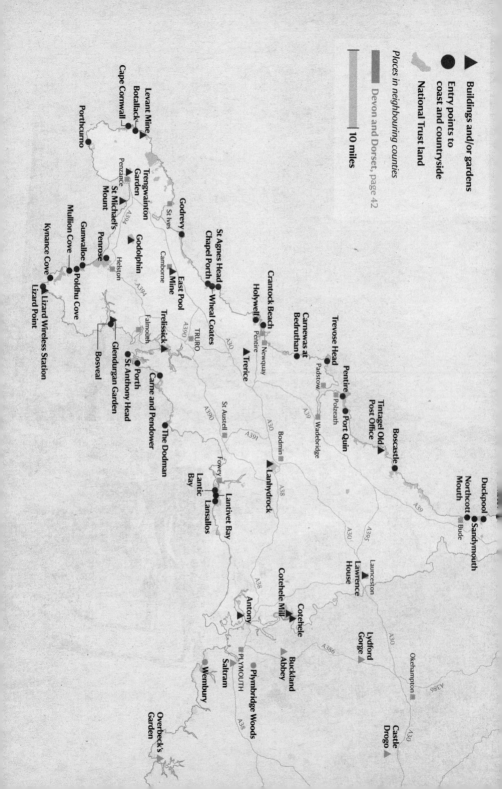

Places in neighbouring counties
Devon and Dorset, page 42

Buildings and/or gardens

Entry points to
coast and countryside

National Trust land

10 miles

Cape Cornwall
Levant Mine
Botallack
Porthcurno
Penzance
Trengwainton
Garden
St Michael's
Mount
Godrevy
St Ives
Godolphin
Helston
Camborne
East Pool
Mine
St Agnes Head
Chapel Porth
Wheal Coates
Crantock Beach
Holywell
Pentire
Newquay
Carnewas at
Bedruthan
Trevose Head
Padstow
Port Quin
Pentire
Polzeath
Wadebridge
Tintagel Old
Post Office
Boscastle
Northcott
Mouth
Duckpool
Sandymouth
Bude
Kynance Cove
Mullion Cove
Gunwalloe
Poldhu Cove
Penrose
Lizard Wireless Station
Lizard Point
Bosveal
Glendurgan Garden
Trelissick
Falmouth
Porth
St Anthony Head
Carne and Pendower
The Dodman
TRURO
Trerice
St Austell
Bodmin
Lanhydrock
Fowey
Lantic
Bay
Lantivet Bay
Lansallos
Launceston
Lawrence
House
Lydford
Gorge
Okehampton
Castle
Drogo
Cotehele Mill
Antony
Cotehele
Buckland
Abbey
PLYMOUTH
Plymbridge Woods
Saltram
Wembury
Overbeck's
Garden

A30
A394
A391
A390
A39
A38
A395
A386
A30
A386
A38

Antony

Torpoint, Cornwall PL11 2QA

`1961`

Centuries-old portraits preside over glimpses of present-day life in this house full of personal treasures, which is still lived in today by the Carew Pole family. Playful topiary, a cone-shaped fountain and intriguing sculptures accompany sweeping views in the garden. Antony is a great place to lose track of time.

Parking: 250 yards.

Access:

Find out more: 01752 812191 or antony@nationaltrust.org.uk
nationaltrust.org.uk/antony

Antony		M	T	W	T	F	S	S
5 Apr–31 May	12–5*	·	T	W	T	·	·	·
1 Jun–31 Aug	12–5*	·	T	W	T	·	·	S
1 Sep–27 Oct	12–5*	·	T	W	T	·	·	·

*House: open 12:30 to 4:30; also open Good Friday, Easter Sunday, 1 May and Bank Holidays, excluding Christmas and New Year.

The garden at Antony in June

Boscastle

near Tintagel, Cornwall

`1955`

Boscastle: the snaking inlet to the harbour

There has been a fishing and trading port here for centuries, with boats coming and going between the high cliffs that guard the snaking harbour entrance. Much of Boscastle can be discovered on foot, with footpaths leading in all directions. You can walk in the footsteps of the young Thomas Hardy through the wildlife-rich ancient woodland in the Valency Valley, or explore the rare medieval field system known as 'the Forrabury Stitches' high above the village. The striking lookout building on Willapark headland, and the historic churches of Minster and Forrabury, are nearby. **Note**: toilet by main car park (not National Trust).

Satnav: use PL35 0HD. **Parking**: 100 yards, pay and display, not National Trust (charge including members).

Dog rating: 🐾 🐾 **Good** – Welcome on walks and in café courtyard.

Access:

Boscastle: crossing the River Valency

Find out more: 01840 250010 or
boscastle@nationaltrust.org.uk
nationaltrust.org.uk/boscastle

Boscastle		M	T	W	T	F	S	S
Shop and café								
1 Jan–3 Apr	10:30–4*	M	T	W	T	F	S	S
4 Apr–30 Oct	10–5*	M	T	W	T	F	S	S
31 Oct–31 Dec**	10:30–4*	M	T	W	T	F	S	S

*Café: closes 30 minutes earlier.
**Closed 25 and 26 December.

Bosveal

near Mawnan Smith,
Falmouth, Cornwall 1980

Walks take in wooded valleys, secluded
coves and soft, sheltered shores of
the Helford River and Falmouth Bay.
Note: toilets at nearby Glendurgan Garden.
For satnav use TR11 5JR. Holiday cottages
at Bosloe and Durgan.

Find out more: 01326 252020 or
bosveal@nationaltrust.org.uk
nationaltrust.org.uk/bosveal

Botallack

on the Tin Coast, near St Just, Cornwall

1995 [icons]

On the wild Tin Coast, the famed Crowns
engine houses cling to the foot of the cliffs
in a landscape transformed by its industrial
past. From here Cornish miners changed
the world, and today it's part of the
Cornish Mining World Heritage Site.
Note: industrial landscape with mine shafts
and exposed cliffs – please keep to paths.

Satnav: use TR19 7QQ. Beware, some
satnavs misdirect. Keep to the B3306 until
you reach Botallack village. **Parking**: just
beyond Botallack Count House.

The Crowns engine houses cling
to the cliffs at Botallack

Dog rating: ✿ **Standard** – Welcome on
short leads. Please take care near mine
shafts and cliff edges.

Access: [icons]

Find out more: 01736 786934 or
botallack@nationaltrust.org.uk
nationaltrust.org.uk/botallack

Botallack
Please check for café and toilet opening times.

Cape Cornwall

on the Tin Coast, near St Just, Cornwall

1987 🏠🏕️⛰️🦆🎪

The Kenidjack Valley and Cape Cornwall

The distinctive headland of Cape Cornwall juts out into the ocean where two great bodies of water meet. Once a heavily industrialised landscape, it is now part of the Cornish Mining World Heritage Site, and a wild and rugged home to the many seabirds that nest on the Brisons Rocks. **Note**: narrow lanes, unsuitable for caravans. Industrial landscape – please keep to paths for your own safety.

Satnav: use TR19 7NN for Cape Cornwall car park. Beware some satnavs misdirect. Follow the signs in St Just town to Cape Cornwall. **Parking**: at Cape Cornwall, Porth Nanven (Cot Valley) and Ballowall.

Dog rating: 🐾 **Standard** – Welcome, but not on beach and slipway from Easter to October.

Access: ♿

Find out more: 01736 786934 or capecornwall@nationaltrust.org.uk **nationaltrust.org.uk/cape-cornwall**

Cape Cornwall

Café (not National Trust): open March to October, Wednesday to Sunday (subject to change).

Carne and Pendower

near Veryan, Cornwall

1961 🏠🏕️⛰️🦆🎪

Two neighbouring beaches with fine stretches of sand and rock pools, popular with families. Walks along the coast and inland reveal the area's wildlife – great for butterflies in summer and birds in winter. Lots of history to discover nearby, from Bronze Age to Cold War. **Note**: seasonal toilets in both car parks. Accessible toilet and parking spaces at Carne.

Satnav: for Carne use TR2 5PF; Pendower TR2 5PF (turn right at sign for Pendower Beach). **Parking**: car parks at both Carne and Pendower.

Dog rating: 🐾 **Standard** – Seasonal dog restrictions on beaches (please keep under control near livestock).

Access:

Find out more: 01872 501062 or carne@nationaltrust.org.uk **nationaltrust.org.uk/carne-and-pendower**

Carne and Pendower

Narrow access lanes. Both beaches very busy at peak times.

Pendower Beach, adjacent to Carne Beach

Carnewas at Bedruthan

near Padstow, Cornwall

1930 ⚡☕🏠⛩

Carnewas at Bedruthan: view from the cliffs

Clifftop with spectacular views of giant rock stacks striding across Bedruthan Beach (not National Trust). For a longer walk, follow the coast path to Park Head and the sheltered cove of Porth Mear. Spring and autumn squill carpet these clifftops, and birds nesting from March include linnets, stonechats and skylarks.
Note: no beach access and unsafe to enter the sea at any time.

Satnav: use PL27 7UW. **Parking**: on site.

Dog rating: 🐾 🐾 **Good** – Welcome under control.

Access: 🅿♿🚾♿🅿➡

Find out more: 01208 863046 or carnewas@nationaltrust.org.uk
nationaltrust.org.uk/carnewas-at-bedruthan

Carnewas at Bedruthan		M	T	W	T	F	S	S
Shop								
2 Apr–30 Oct	10:30–5	M	T	W	T	F	S	S
Tea-room								
1 Jan–6 Feb	11–3*						S	S
12 Feb–30 Oct	10:30–5*	M	T	W	T	F	S	S
5 Nov–18 Dec	11–3						S	S
27 Dec–31 Dec	11–3		T	W	T	F	S	

*Tea-room: 1 January to 27 March, open 11 to 4.
Toilets: limited winter opening. Cliff staircase currently closed: no access to beach.

Chapel Porth

near St Agnes, Cornwall

1957 🏠♿⛱⚡☕⛩

At the foot of a steep valley between high heathery cliffs, Chapel Porth Beach is a shingle strip at high tide and a huge expanse of sand at low tide. The area is steeped in mining history, with many remains to be discovered on walks.
Note: seasonal toilets. Take care not to get cut off by incoming tide. Seasonal lifeguards.

Satnav: use TR5 0NS. **Parking**: car park (very busy at peak times), accessed down single track with passing places. Additional parking at nearby Wheal Coates and St Agnes Head.

Dog rating: 🐾 **Standard** – Seasonal dog ban on the beach (Easter Sunday to 30 September inclusive).

Access: 🅿♿🚾♿

Find out more: 01872 552412 or chapelporth@nationaltrust.org.uk
nationaltrust.org.uk/chapel-porth

Chapel Porth
Café (tenant-run), open most days.

Looking down on Chapel Porth

Cotehele

St Dominick, near Saltash,
Cornwall PL12 6TA

1947 🏠🏚️✿♨️🍽️☕🗃️△🚶

This rambling granite and slate-stone home, high above the River Tamar, was built by the Edgcumbes and remained in their family for nearly 600 years. Time has stood still. The hall, with its ancient timber roof and displays of weaponry, and the warren of tapestry-clad rooms beyond have changed little since Tudor times. The 5-hectare (12-acre) garden features historic daffodils, terraces, ponds and orchards with 150 local apple varieties. The Valley Garden, with medieval stewpond and dovecote, leads to Cotehele Quay – thriving in Victorian times – where you'll find the 1899 Tamar sailing barge *Shamrock*, lime kilns and Discovery Centre. **Note**: the house has no electricity, so feel free to bring a torch.

Satnav: follow to St Mellion or St Ann's Chapel, then follow signs.
Parking: at house and on quay.

The Great Hall, above, at mainly Tudor Cotehele, below

Dog rating: 🐾 🐾 **Good** – Welcome on estate walks and restaurant (assistance dogs only in house, formal garden and orchards).

Access: 🅿️ 🐕 🚾 ♿ 🖼️ 🪑 👓 🅰️ ♿ ♿ ➡️

Find out more: 01579 351346 or cotehele@nationaltrust.org.uk
nationaltrust.org.uk/cotehele

Cotehele		M	T	W	T	F	S	S
House								
5 Mar–30 Oct	11–4	M	T	W	T	F	S	S
Garden, estate, restaurant and shop								
1 Jan–4 Mar	10–4*	M	T	W	T	F	S	S
5 Mar–30 Oct	10–5	M	T	W	T	F	S	S
31 Oct–31 Dec**	10–4*	M	T	W	T	F	S	S

*Shop: opens 11. Bull Pen Gallery: open, check for details.
**Christmas Garland in December, check before visiting; everything closed 25 and 26 December.

Cotehele Mill

St Dominick, near Saltash,
Cornwall PL12 6TA

1947 🏠♿🚻

A peaceful walk alongside the Morden
stream from Cotehele Quay takes you to
the restored 19th-century Cotehele Mill.
Traditional woodworker and potter on
site, as well as recreated wheelwright's,
saddler's and blacksmith's workshops.
Note: nearest toilets at Cotehele Quay.

Parking: on Cotehele Quay (at the Mill
by arrangement only). Shuttlebus from
Cotehele house (dependent on
volunteer availability).

Dog rating: 🐾 **Standard** – Welcome
(assistance dogs only in bakery and Mill).

Access: 🅿♿💻♿♿

Find out more: 01579 350606 (Mill).
01579 351346 (Cotehele) or
cotehele@nationaltrust.org.uk
nationaltrust.org.uk/cotehele-mill

Cotehele Mill		M	T	W	T	F	S	S
5 Mar–2 Oct	11–4:30	M	T	W	T	F	S	S
3 Oct–30 Oct	11–4	M	T	W	T	F	S	S

Wheelwright's workshop at Cotehele Mill

Crantock Beach

near Newquay, Cornwall

1956 🏰🚻

Crantock Beach is a popular expanse of
golden sand. Wonderful walking country –
through the dunes on Rushy Green, along
the banks of the Gannel Estuary, or
around the headland of West Pentire.
Note: danger, unpredictable currents
and sheer drops from dunes.

Satnav: use TR8 5RN for Crantock Beach
and TR8 5QS for Treago Mill. **Parking**: on
site (2.1-metre height restriction barrier
when unmanned) and at Treago Mill for
Polly Joke Beach (also known as Porth Joke).

Dog rating: 🐾 **Standard** – Welcome
under control.

Access: 🅿♿

Find out more: 01208 863046 or
crantockbeach@nationaltrust.org.uk
nationaltrust.org.uk/crantock-beach

Crantock Beach
Toilets: limited winter opening.

The Dodman

Penare, near Gorran Haven, Cornwall 1919

The highest headland on Cornwall's south
coast, with Iron Age ramparts. Great walking,
wildlife and beaches. **Note**: footpaths
to Hemmick Beach and Dodman Point.
For satnav use PL26 6NY – go past
Treveague Farm and continue down hill.

Find out more: 01872 501062 or
thedodman@nationaltrust.org.uk
nationaltrust.org.uk/the-dodman

Duckpool

near Bude, Cornwall ☐ 1960

Remote beach with rock pools at the mouth of the wooded Coombe Valley, overlooked by cliffs carpeted with wild flowers.
Note: for satnav use EX23 9JN.

Find out more: 01208 863046 or
duckpool@nationaltrust.org.uk
nationaltrust.org.uk/duckpool

East Pool Mine

near Redruth, Cornwall

☐ 1967 🏚 🏠 🚹 ✈

East Pool celebrates the extraordinary lives of people who worked at the very heart of what is now the Cornish Mining World Heritage Site. With two beam engines, preserved in their engine houses, this is a place for all the family to discover the dramatic story of Cornish mining.

Satnav: for main site, use TR15 3NH; for Trevithick Cottage use TR14 0QG.
Parking: for main site, use Morrisons' car park (far end).

Access: 🅿 🅿 🔠 🔍 🚹 ♿ ➡

Inside Taylor's Engine House at East Pool Mine

Find out more: 01209 315027 or
eastpool@nationaltrust.org.uk
Trevithick Road, Pool, Cornwall TR15 3NP
nationaltrust.org.uk/east-pool-mine

East Pool Mine	M	T	W	T·	F	S	S
Mine and Taylor's Engine House							
1 Mar–29 Oct* Tour		·	T	W	T	F	S
Trevithick Cottage							
13 Apr–26 Oct* Tour**		·		W	·	·	·

*Booking essential. **Opening arrangements not confirmed at time of print, please check before visiting.

Glendurgan Garden

Mawnan Smith, near Falmouth, Cornwall TR11 5JZ

☐ 1962 🏚 ❄ 🎣 ⛴ ☕ 🅿 🏠 ✈

Exploring lush Glendurgan Garden

A distinctive and exotic valley garden created in the 1820s by Quakers Alfred and Sarah Fox. Visitors can explore Glendurgan's three valleys, which run down to the sheltered beach at Durgan, on the Helford River. There's a puzzling maze, created by the Foxes to entertain their 12 children and family, and the Giant's Stride, a giant maypole swing popular with both adults and children. You can enjoy camellias, magnolias and primroses in early spring, then rhododendrons and bluebells in May, followed by the exotic greens of summer and dramatic autumn colour in the trees. **Note**: steep paths, steps, uneven terrain.

Parking: on site.

Access: 🅿️ 🚾 ♿ 🤱 ♿

Find out more: 01326 252020 or
glendurgan@nationaltrust.org.uk
nationaltrust.org.uk/glendurgan

Glendurgan Garden		M	T	W	T	F	S	S
19 Feb–31 Jul	10:30–5*	·	T	W	T	F	S	S
1 Aug–31 Aug	10:30–5*	M	T	W	T	F	S	S
1 Sep–30 Oct	10:30–5*	·	T	W	T	F	S	S

*Tea-house: opens 10. Last entry one hour before closing.
Closes dusk if earlier. Open Bank Holiday Mondays. Gates to
Durgan Village are locked 30 minutes before closing.

**The boat shelter, above, and laurel
maze, below, at Glendurgan Garden**

Godolphin

Godolphin Cross, Helston,
Cornwall TR13 9RE

2000 🏠 🏛️ ♣ 🛶 ☕ ⛱️ ♿ 👤

Hidden in shaded woodland, Godolphin
escaped modernisation and contemporary
fashions. The granite-faced terraces and
sunken lawns of the Side Garden have seen
little change since the 16th century, and
Victorian farm buildings tell the story of
Godolphin as a tenant farm. The estate,
once busy with prosperous tin mines, is
now part of the Cornish Mining World
Heritage Site and is wonderful walking
country, rich in archaeology, rare plants
and wildlife. There are panoramic views
from the top of Godolphin Hill. The
historic house is a holiday home, where
you can stay and experience the
splendour that mining riches bought.
Note: house is open to visitors on limited
dates between holiday bookings.

Parking: 300 yards.

Dog rating: ♣ ♣ **Good** – Welcome
outdoors and in tea-room on short leads.

Access:

Find out more: 01736 763194 or
godolphin@nationaltrust.org.uk
nationaltrust.org.uk/godolphin

Godolphin		M	T	W	T	F	S	S
Garden, farm buildings and tea-room								
1 Jan–31 Jan	10–4	M	T	W	T	F	S	S
1 Feb–31 Oct	10–5	M	T	W	T	F	S	S
1 Nov–31 Dec*	10–4	M	T	W	T	F	S	S
Estate								
Open all year	Dawn–dusk	M	T	W	T	F	S	S
House								
Limited opening**								

*Closed 24 and 25 December. **House: open to visitors
between holiday lets on limited dates – first Saturday to
Thursday of every month (except January).

**Godolphin: the house, opposite, courtyard
and Godolphin Hill, this page**

Godrevy

near Hayle, Cornwall 1939

Sandy beach on St Ives Bay with rock pools
and towering cliffs. Footpaths weave
through this wildlife-rich headland.
Note: unstable cliffs and incoming tides.
Toilets open in top field. For satnav use
TR27 5ED. Café (concession).

Find out more: 01872 552412 or
godrevy@nationaltrust.org.uk
nationaltrust.org.uk/godrevy

Gunwalloe

near Helston, Cornwall 1974

Two family-friendly beaches and reedbeds
rich in wildlife. Between the two coves a
medieval church shelters behind Castle
Mound. **Note**: for satnav use TR12 7QE.
Church Cove seasonal dog ban.
Kiosk open seasonally.

Find out more: 01326 222170 or
gunwalloe@nationaltrust.org.uk
nationaltrust.org.uk/gunwalloe

Holywell

near Newquay, Cornwall

1951

Classic north Cornish beach, with a sweep
of golden sand and a towering dune system.
There's lots of history to discover, including
the remains of an Iron Age castle on
Kelsey Head, a Bronze Age barrow on
Cubert Common and the holy well
in a cave on the beach.

Holywell, with Carter's Rocks just offshore

Satnav: use TR8 5PF. **Parking:** on site.

Dog rating: ❀ ❀ **Good** – Welcome everywhere, including the beach, but under close control (especially around livestock).

Access: 🅿️♿

Find out more: 01208 863046 or holywell@nationaltrust.org.uk
nationaltrust.org.uk/holywell

Holywell
Toilets: limited winter opening.

Kynance Cove

on the Lizard peninsula, Cornwall 1935

It's a ⅓-mile walk through Lizard heathland down to this famous beach, with its serpentine stacks, islands and caves.
Note: steep, uneven beach path. For satnav use TR12 7PJ. Extremely busy in summer. Seasonal dog ban (July and August). Café (concession) open seasonally.

Find out more: 01326 222170 or kynancecove@nationaltrust.org.uk
nationaltrust.org.uk/kynance-cove

Lanhydrock

Bodmin, Cornwall

1953 🏛️🏠🎡🎣☕🏚️📷🎪

A family-friendly cycle route at Lanhydrock, above. There are more than 50 rooms to discover in the house, opposite

A tragic fire in 1881 meant that the Agar-Robartes family had to rebuild most of their 17th-century home. Out of the ashes came the country house you see today, a fine example of a High Victorian Arts and Crafts interior. Discover the story of the Agar-Robartes in the elegant luxury of the family rooms, and the lives of the staff who lived and worked here. Outside is a garden, full of colour all year round and famed for its magnolias and ancient woodlands with miles of footpaths to explore. The off-road cycle trails have different routes to suit all levels of experience, and you can even hire a bike when you get here.

Satnav: use PL30 4AB (1 Double Lodges).
Parking: 600 yards.

Dog rating: ❀ **Standard** – Dog-friendly walks throughout the estate (assistance dogs only in house and garden).

Access: 🅿️ ♿ 👶 🚻 🅿️♿ 📷 ♿ ⏱️ 🚶 ⬍ 🚶
♿ ➡️ ♿

Find out more: 01208 265950 or
lanhydrock@nationaltrust.org.uk
Bodmin, Cornwall PL30 5AD
nationaltrust.org.uk/lanhydrock

Lanhydrock		M	T	W	T	F	S	S
House and garden								
1 Mar–31 Oct	11–5:30*	M	T	W	T	F	S	S
Refreshments								
Open all year	9:30–5**	M	T	W	T	F	S	S

*Garden opens 10:30. House and garden: March and
October, close 5. **Refreshments: October to February,
10 to 4. Last house ticket available 45 minutes before
closing. Everything closed 25 and 26 December.

Lansallos

between Polperro and Polruan, Cornwall

1936

Walking down towards the beach at Lansallos

Between Polperro and Polruan on a long stretch of unspoilt coast loved by walkers, with abundant wild flowers and birds. From Lansallos church, a path ambles down the valley to a west-facing sandy beach. Perfect for day visits or book a stay in the holiday cottages or campsite here. **Note**: nearest toilets at Lantivet Bay car park.

Satnav: use PL13 2PX for Lansallos.
Parking: at Lansallos.

Dog rating: ❖ **Standard** – Welcome, under close control around livestock.

Find out more: 01726 870146 or lansallos@nationaltrust.org.uk
nationaltrust.org.uk/lansallos

Lansallos
No camping in the car park.

Lantic Bay

near Polruan, Cornwall 1959

Secluded bay, clifftop views and footpaths around Pencarrow Head. **Note**: beach is down a very steep path with steps. Beware of rip tides. Nearest toilets at Lantivet. For satnav use PL23 1NP.

Find out more: 01726 870146 or lanticbay@nationaltrust.org.uk
nationaltrust.org.uk/lantic-bay

Lantivet Bay

between Polruan and Lansallos, Cornwall 1976

A path leads down through open fields. Explore the small rocky coves below or the coast path along the clifftop. **Note**: for satnav use PL23 1NP.

Find out more: 01726 870146 or lantivetbay@nationaltrust.org.uk
nationaltrust.org.uk/lantivet-bay

Lawrence House

9 Castle Street, Launceston, Cornwall PL15 8BA 1964

This Georgian town house, now a museum, hosts special exhibitions. Large display of costumes and a children's toy room. **Note**: leased to Launceston Town Council. Open 28 March to 29 October, Monday to Saturday, 10:30 to 4:30.

Find out more: 01566 773277 or lawrencehouse@nationaltrust.org.uk
nationaltrust.org.uk/lawrence-house

Levant Mine and Beam Engine

on the Tin Coast, near Pendeen,
St Just, Cornwall

1967

High on the cliffs of the Tin Coast is
Levant, part of the Cornish Mining World
Heritage Site. At its heart is an 1840s
beam engine, run on steam. You can
discover how Cornish miners, engineers
and inventors risked everything in
pursuit of mineral riches under the sea.
Note: exposed clifftop location, uneven
ground/mine ruins. Limited space in
engine house and small staircases.

Parking: at Geevor Tin Mine, Pendeen,
TR19 7EW (½-mile walk via coastal path).

Access:

Find out more: 01736 786156 or
levant@nationaltrust.org.uk
nationaltrust.org.uk/levant-mine

Levant Mine		M	T	W	T	F	S	S
1 Mar–31 Oct	Tour	M	T	W	T			S

Entry by booked tour only (places limited).
Geevor car park open to 5.

**Levant Mine and Beam Engine
on the dramatic Tin Coast**

Lizard Point

on the Lizard peninsula,
near Helston, Cornwall

1935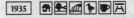

Old Lizard Lifeboat Station
at Polpeor Cove, Lizard Point

This is mainland Britain's most southerly
point, infamous as a site of shipwrecks in
the past and overlooking what is still one
of the busiest shipping lanes in the world.
The cliffs and farmland are incredibly
rich in wildlife, and in early summer the
wild flowers are at their best. From the
Wildlife Watchpoint you can spot seals
and occasionally dolphins, as well as the
iconic Cornish choughs that breed close
by. At Bass Point, a short walk along
the coast path, you'll find the tiny
Lizard Wireless Station.

Satnav: use TR12 7NT.
Parking: at Lizard Point.

Dog rating: 🐾 **Standard** – Welcome
on leads, please note that livestock
graze in some areas.

Wild seas at Lizard Point

Access: 🅿️ ♿ 🚻 ♿ ➡️

Find out more: 01326 222170 or
lizard@nationaltrust.org.uk
nationaltrust.org.uk/lizard-point

Lizard Wireless Station

Bass Point, Lizard,
near Helston, Cornwall 1996

The oldest surviving wireless station in the
world – a tiny hut on the cliffs where
Marconi conducted his world-changing
experiments. **Note:** best access by foot
from Lizard Point car park (TR12 7NT),
1 mile along coast path. Please check the
website for opening arrangements.

Find out more: 01326 222170 or
lizardwirelessstation@nationaltrust.org.uk

Morwenstow

near Bude, Cornwall 1956

Coastal realm of a great Victorian
character – Parson Hawker. Hawker's Hut,
driftwood-built, is on the cliff edge near
his church. **Note:** sorry no toilet.
For satnav use EX23 9SR.

Find out more: 01208 863046 or
morwenstow@nationaltrust.org.uk
nationaltrust.org.uk/morwenstow

Mullion Cove

on the Lizard peninsula,
near Helston, Cornwall 1945

Originally built in the 1890s, the picturesque
harbour at Mullion Cove shelters a small
fishing fleet from powerful westerly storms.
Note: toilets open seasonally. For satnav
use TR12 7ES. National Trust campsite
nearby at Teneriffe Farm.

Find out more: 01326 222170 or
mullioncove@nationaltrust.org.uk
nationaltrust.org.uk/mullion-cove

Northcott Mouth

near Bude, Cornwall 1981

Quiet and ruggedly beautiful, this small
rocky beach opens up to expansive
sand and rock pools as the tide drops.
Note: sorry no toilet. Lifeguards in high
season. For satnav use EX23 9ED.

Find out more: 01208 863046 or
northcottmouth@nationaltrust.org.uk
nationaltrust.org.uk/northcott-mouth

Penrose

near Helston and Porthleven, Cornwall

| 1974 |

Home to Loe Pool, Cornwall's largest natural lake, Penrose is a mix of woods, farmland, parkland, walled garden, cliffs and beaches: a great place to explore. There are 16 miles of bridleways and footpaths, including a trail around the pool and many coast-path links. **Note**: to maintain the sense of peace, fishing and recreational activities aren't allowed on the pool.

Satnav: use TR13 0RA for Fairground car park and TR13 0RD for Penrose Hill car park. **Parking**: several small car parks around Loe Pool, plus Fairground car park in Helston (not National Trust).

Dog rating: 🐾 **Standard** – Welcome under control in park – please note, livestock graze in fields. Seasonal ban on beaches (July and August).

Access: ▶

Find out more: 01326 222170 or penroseestate@nationaltrust.org.uk
nationaltrust.org.uk/penrose

Running along the coast path at Penrose near Porthleven

Pentire

near Wadebridge, Cornwall

| 1936 |

Pentire: Port Quin Bay from The Rumps

Carpeted with wild flowers, the farmed headlands of Pentire and The Rumps command views from Tintagel to Trevose Head. Remnants of Iron Age ramparts and an abundance of birds and wildlife can be seen from footpaths that crisscross the headland. There are also accessible paths and an orchard for picnics.

Satnav: use PL27 6QY for Pentireglaze; PL27 6QZ for Lundy Bay. **Parking**: at Pentireglaze (main car park), Lead Mines, Pentire Farm (limited) and Lundy Bay. Also at Polzeath (not National Trust).

Dog rating: 🐾 🐾 **Good** – Welcome, but under control around livestock and ground-nesting birds.

Access:

Find out more: 01208 863046 or pentire@nationaltrust.org.uk

Pentire		M	T	W	T	F	S	S
Café								
1 Jan–3 Apr*	10:30–4						S	S
4 Apr–30 Oct	10–4	M	T	W	T	F	S	S
5 Nov–18 Dec	10:30–4						S	S
29 Dec–31 Dec	10:30–4				T	F	S	

*Café: 12 to 20 February, open daily.
Toilets: limited winter opening.

Poldhu Cove

near Mullion, Cornwall

1984

This unspoilt beach, above, is popular with locals and visitors. The beach, dunes and reedbeds are designated a Site of Special Scientific Interest for their rich wildlife. Nearby, the Marconi Monument and visitor centre celebrate Poldhu's role as the site of the first transatlantic wireless signal. **Note**: beach is lifeguarded in peak season.

Satnav: use TR12 7JB. **Parking**: on site, not National Trust (charge including members).

Dog rating: ❖ **Standard** – Welcome on coast path. Council-enforced beach ban (1 July to 31 August).

Access: 🅿️ ➡️

Find out more: 01326 222170 or poldhucove@nationaltrust.org.uk
nationaltrust.org.uk/poldhu-cove

Port Quin

near Wadebridge, Cornwall 1936

Sheltered inlet on outstanding stretch of unspoilt coast. **Note**: for satnav use PL29 3SU.

Find out more: 01208 863046 or portquin@nationaltrust.org.uk
nationaltrust.org.uk/port-quin

Porth

on the Roseland peninsula, near Portscatho, Cornwall 1958

The creekside and coastal footpaths are great for walking and wildlife-spotting, or spend the day on the beach at Towan. **Note**: for satnav use TR2 5EX. Café (not National Trust): check before visiting for opening times.

Find out more: 01872 501062 or porth@nationaltrust.org.uk
nationaltrust.org.uk/porth

Porthcurno

near Penzance, Cornwall 1994

Popular sandy beach on a turquoise bay. Great for watching birds and spotting marine wildlife from the cliffs above. **Note**: for satnav use TR19 6JX. Car park (not National Trust) gets very busy in summer, please consider alternative means of transport.

Find out more: 01736 761853 or porthcurno@nationaltrust.org.uk
nationaltrust.org.uk/porthcurno

St Agnes Head

near St Agnes, Cornwall 1967

A network of paths weaves through a mosaic of gorse and heather. Walk the clifftops or St Agnes Beacon. **Note**: for satnav use TR5 0NU.

Find out more: 01872 552412 or stagneshead@nationaltrust.org.uk
nationaltrust.org.uk/st-agnes-head

St Anthony Head

on the Roseland peninsula,
near Portscatho, Cornwall

**St Anthony Head, above, and the
Battery Observation Post, below**

Standing guard on the eastern entrance
to Falmouth Harbour, the headland has
been strategically important for centuries,
commanding magnificent views up the
Fal Estuary and across Falmouth Bay
towards the Lizard. Discover historic
fortifications and military buildings
from various eras with places to stop
for picnics and bird watching.

Satnav: use TR2 5HA. **Parking:** on site.

Dog rating: ✿ **Standard** – Welcome,
but please be aware of wildlife.

Access:

Find out more: 01872 501062 or
stanthonyhead@nationaltrust.org.uk
nationaltrust.org.uk/st-anthony-head

St Michael's Mount

Marazion, Cornwall TR17 0HS

**The sea rises over the cobbled causeway
leading to St Michael's Mount**

This iconic rocky island, crowned by a
medieval church and castle, is home to
the St Aubyn family and a 30-strong
community of islanders. Visiting the Mount,
you are immersed in history, islanders' tales
and legends, such as the famous 'Jack the
Giant Killer'. There's a subtropical terraced

Check opening dates and times before you set out: nationaltrust.org.uk

St Michael's Mount: looking up at the iconic castle from its subtropical terraced garden, opposite, and the rocky island and village, above, as seen from Marazion

garden to explore, and spectacular views of Mount's Bay and the Lizard from the castle battlements. If the tide is high, you can take an evocative boat trip to the island harbour; at low tide you walk across the ancient cobbled causeway from Marazion on the mainland, as pilgrims have done for centuries. **Note**: steep climb to the castle on uneven, cobbled pathway. St Aubyn Estates/National Trust partnership.

Parking: numerous spaces in Marazion, opposite St Michael's Mount, not National Trust (charge including members).

Access:

Find out more: 01736 710265 (information, tides and boats) or stmichaelsmount@nationaltrust.org.uk Estate Office, King's Road, Marazion TR17 0EL
nationaltrust.org.uk/st-michaels-mount

St Michael's Mount

Opening arrangements subject to tides (please check stmichaelsmount.co.uk). Tickets must be booked via website before visiting. If boat tickets are required you will be prompted at time of booking.

Sandymouth

near Bude, Cornwall

1978

A popular destination, yet Sandymouth remains unspoilt and breathtakingly beautiful. You'll find an extreme difference between the beach at low tide – when it is a huge sweep of sand and rocky outcrops – and at high tide, when it shrinks back to a pebbly cove, backed by twisted cliffs.

Satnav: use EX23 9HW. **Parking**: on site.

Dog rating: 🐾 🐾 **Good** – Welcome everywhere, including the beach, but under close control (especially around livestock).

Access:

Find out more: 01208 863046 or sandymouth@nationaltrust.org.uk
nationaltrust.org.uk/sandymouth

Sandymouth

Toilets: limited winter opening. Café (tenant-run): open daily April to October, with reduced winter opening, telephone 01288 354286 for details.

Sandymouth: popular yet unspoilt

Tintagel Old Post Office

Fore Street, Tintagel, Cornwall PL34 0DB

| 1903 |

The cottage garden hidden at the back of Tintagel Old Post Office

A medieval manor house in miniature, at more than 600 years old this is one of Cornwall's oldest domestic buildings. Used by a number of businesses throughout the Victorian period, its final function was as the village's letter-receiving office. The cottage garden hidden at the back offers a welcome retreat.

Parking: pay and display village car parks, not National Trust (charges including members). Nearest Trust parking at Glebe Cliff in Tintagel, ½ mile.

Access:

Find out more: 01840 770024 or tintageloldpo@nationaltrust.org.uk **nationaltrust.org.uk/tintagel-old-post-office**

Tintagel Old Post Office		M	T	W	T	F	S	S
4 Mar–1 Nov	11–4	M	T	·	·	F	S	S

Trelissick

Feock, near Truro, Cornwall TR3 6QL

| 1955 |

Set on its own peninsula, Trelissick enjoys panoramic views over the Fal Estuary, and the south terrace provides the perfect setting to enjoy the ever-changing seascape and countryside. Visitors can explore meandering paths through the garden, leading to exotic planting and formal lawns with herbaceous borders bursting with colour. There are also longer walks to discover through the historic park and woodland, which sweep down towards the estuary, and along Lamouth Creek to the Iron Age promontory fort and 18th-century quay at Roundwood. **Note**: gallery run by Cornwall Crafts Association.

Parking: 80 yards.

Dog rating: ❀ ❀ **Good** – Welcome in the park and woodland walks (assistance dogs only in garden).

Trelissick: heading down towards the beach

Historic woodland at Trelissick

Access:

Find out more: 01872 862090 or
trelissick@nationaltrust.org.uk
nationaltrust.org.uk/trelissick

Trelissick		M	T	W	T	F	S	S
Garden, café, shop, gallery and bookshop								
Open all year	10–5*	M	T	W	T	F	S	S
Parkland and walks								
Open all year	Dawn–dusk	M	T	W	T	F	S	S

*1 January to 27 February and 31 October to 31 December:
closes 4:30. Garden closes dusk if earlier. House: seasonal
opening (check before visiting). Everything closed
25 and 26 December.

Trengwainton Garden

Madron, near Penzance,
Cornwall TR20 8RZ

1961	✿ 🍴 📷 ⛺ 🔧

Moisture-loving plants hug the banks of
a stream at Trengwainton Garden

Nestled between the moors and the sea,
the mild climate at Trengwainton – 'Home
of springs' – nurtures an award-winning
plant collection. A garden of contrasts, it
has winding wooded paths that climb to an
open, grassy terrace with sea views across
Mount's Bay. A gentle stream runs through
the centre and the carriage drive is
bordered by colourful stream-side planting
and meadows. Ten sections of walled
gardens each have their own unique
character, including the kitchen
garden built in 1815 to the dimensions
of Noah's Ark.

Parking: 150 yards.

Dog rating: 🐾 🐾 **Good** – Welcome on leads in garden, shop and café garden (assistance dogs only in café and bookshop).

Access: 🅿️ 🐕 🚾 🚶 🏛️ 🖼️ 📷 ♿ ➡️

Find out more: 01736 363148 or trengwainton@nationaltrust.org.uk
nationaltrust.org.uk/trengwainton

Trengwainton Garden		M	T	W	T	F	S	S
13 Feb–30 Oct	10–5	M	T	W	T			S
Open Good Friday.								

Trengwainton Garden bathed in summer sunshine, above, and in winter, below

Trerice

near Newquay, Cornwall

1953 🏛️ 🏠 🍀 ☕ 🍴 📷 🏹 🐕

Once the Cornish seat of the Arundell family, Trerice remains little changed since it was built in 1573, thanks to long periods under absentee owners. With golden stone, ornate gables and a magnificent hall window, Trerice is a grand Elizabethan house on a small scale. From the highest point of the garden, views stretch out over a landscape rich in history. Shouts of excitement ring out from the kayling lawn as the Cornish game of 'kayles' is played, bringing back some of the bustle and noise that must have typified Trerice's time as a working manor farm. **Note**: we occasionally need to close parts or all of Trerice for private functions.

Trevose Head

near Padstow, Cornwall

2016

Jutting into the Atlantic, Trevose Head commands views for miles along the coast. Exposed western cliffs contrast starkly with a gentler eastern coastline. Home of Trevose Lighthouse (owned by Trinity House) and Padstow Lifeboat Station, it's also famed for nesting corn buntings and skylarks, and rare plants like wild asparagus. **Note**: sorry no toilet. Be careful of the sheer-sided round hole and quarry near Dinas Head.

Satnav: use PL28 8SL. **Parking**: on site. Open all year at scenic car park; summer car park for beaches open 20 March to 31 October.

Dog rating: 🐾 🐾 **Good** – Welcome under control on footpaths (ground-nesting birds).

Find out more: 01208 863046 or trevosehead@nationaltrust.org.uk
nationaltrust.org.uk/trevose

Trerice, this page and opposite: a small-scale version of a grand Elizabethan house

Satnav: enter Kestle Mill via A3058, not postcode. **Parking**: 300 yards.

Access: 🅿️ 🚪 🚾 ♿ 🔊 📷 🔦 🅰️ ♿ 👟 ♿ ➡️

Find out more: 01637 875404 or trerice@nationaltrust.org.uk
Kestle Mill, near Newquay,
Cornwall TR8 4PG
nationaltrust.org.uk/trerice

Trerice		M	T	W	T	F	S	S
26 Feb–30 Oct	10:30–5*	M	T	W	T	F	S	S
5 Nov–11 Dec**	11–4						S	S
17 Dec–23 Dec**	11–4	M	T	W	T	F	S	S

*House, shop and café: close 4:30. **Selected rooms, garden, shop and restaurant open.

Wheal Coates

near St Agnes, Cornwall 1956

Dramatic mining ruins hugging the heather and gorse-carpeted clifftops. Footpaths lead to St Agnes Head and down to Chapel Porth. **Note**: for satnav use TR5 0NT.

Find out more: 01872 552412 or whealcoates@nationaltrust.org.uk
nationaltrust.org.uk/wheal-coates

Looking up at the dramatic stone
exterior of Castle Drogo, Devon

Devon and Dorset

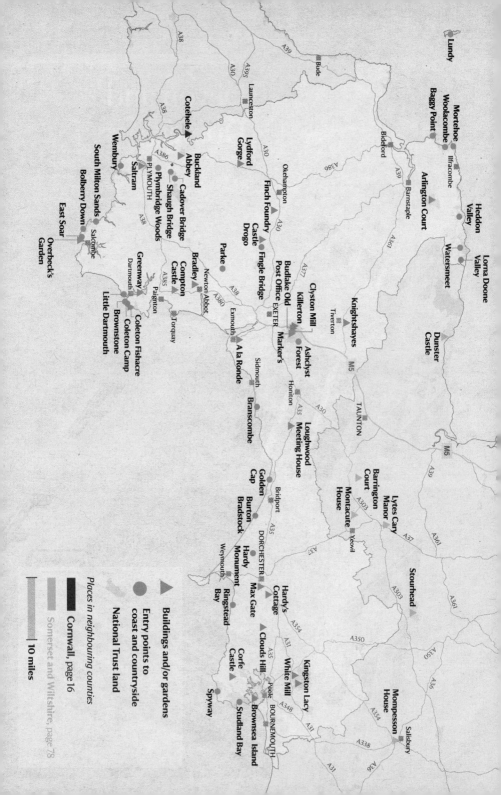

Places in neighbouring counties

Cornwall, page 16

Somerset and Wiltshire, page 78

Buildings and/or gardens

Entry points to coast and countryside

National Trust land

10 miles

Lundy

Mortehoe
Woolacombe
Baggy Point

Heddon
Valley

Lorna Doone
Valley

Watersmeet

Arlington Court

Ilfracombe

Bideford

Barnstaple

Dunster
Castle

Bude

Launceston

Cotehele

Lydford
Gorge

Buckland
Abbey
Cadover Bridge
Plymbridge Woods
Shaugh Bridge
Saltram
PLYMOUTH

Wembury
South Milton Sands
Bolberry Down

East Soar
Garden

Overbeck's
Garden

Salcombe

Greenway
Dartmouth
Coleton Fishacre
Coleton Camp
Brownstone
Little Dartmouth

Compton
Castle
Bradley
Paignton

Torquay

Newton Abbot

Parke

Finch Foundry

Castle
Drogo

Fingle Bridge

Okehampton

Budlake Old
Post Office
Killerton
EXETER
Clyston Mill
Marker's

Exmouth

A la Ronde

Sidmouth

Branscombe

Budlake Old
Post Office

Ashclyst
Forest

Knightshayes

Tiverton

Loughwood
Meeting House

Honiton

TAUNTON

Golden
Cap

Burton
Bradstock

Bridport

Barrington
Court

Montacute
House

Lytes Cary
Manor

Yeovil

Stourhead

Weymouth

Hardy
Monument

DORCHESTER

Max Gate

Ringstead
Bay

Hardy's
Cottage

Clouds Hill

White Mill
Corfe
Castle

Kingston Lacy

Mompesson
House

Salisbury

Spyway

Brownsea Island
Studland Bay

BOURNEMOUTH
Poole

A la Ronde

Exmouth, Devon

1991

Another world awaits inside this 1790s 16-sided house. Walls are decorated with feathers, shells and pictures made of seaweed and sand, and every space contains mementoes from the travels of Jane and Mary Parminter, the creators of this extravaganza. Outside, there's an orchard, hay meadow and colourful borders. **Note**: small and delicate rooms. Photography welcome without flash.

Satnav: postcode unreliable, enter Summer Lane. **Parking**: on site.

Dog rating: 🐾 🐾 **Good** – Dogs on leads welcome everywhere (assistance dogs only in house).

Access: 🅿️ 🚗 ♿ 🚻 💻 🪑 🚶 🪜 ♿ 👥 ➡️

Find out more: 01395 265514 or alaronde@nationaltrust.org.uk
Summer Lane, Exmouth, Devon EX8 5BD
nationaltrust.org.uk/a-la-ronde

A la Ronde		M	T	W	T	F	S	S
13 Apr–30 Oct	10:30–3:30	·	·	W	T	F	S	S

House: last entry one hour before closing.

A la Ronde, Devon: quirky and captivating

Arlington Court and the National Trust Carriage Museum

Arlington, near Barnstaple, Devon EX31 4LP

1949 🏛️ 🏠 ♣️ 🐾 ☕ 📷 🗄️ 🚪

Arlington Court and the National Trust Carriage Museum in Devon

Hidden in the lichen-draped landscape of North Devon, Arlington is a surprise and a delight. The starkly classical exterior of the house gives no clue to what lies inside – recently redisplayed to share the passions of the Chichester family who lived here. The stable block houses a nationally important display of more than 40 carriages, from grand state coaches to humble governess cars. The garden is restored to its colourful Victorian glory, and the conservatory's exotic plantings reveal the Chichesters' world travels.

The austere exterior of Arlington Court, top, and the opulent White Drawing Room, above

Satnav: from South Molton, don't turn left into unmarked lane (deliveries only).
Parking: 150 yards.

Dog rating: 🐾 🐾 🐾 **Best** – Welcome on leads in garden, Carriage Museum and wider estate.

Access: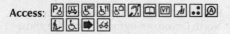

Find out more: 01271 850296 or arlingtoncourt@nationaltrust.org.uk
nationaltrust.org.uk/arlington

Arlington Court		M	T	W	T	F	S	S
19 Feb–10 Apr	11–3:30*	·	·	·	·	·	S	S
11 Apr–30 Oct	11–4*	M	T	W	T	F	S	S
5 Nov–18 Dec	11–3:30*	·	·	·	·	·	S	S

*Garden and tea-room: open 10. House: access at quiet times may be via guided tour. Wider estate open all year, dawn to dusk.

Baggy Point

near Croyde, Devon

1939

Baggy Point is the impressive headland at Croyde, once owned by the Hyde family and overlooking one of the best surfing beaches in the South West. Huge coastal views out to Lundy Island, great walking and opportunities to climb, surf and coasteer make it a must-do destination for anyone visiting North Devon. Baggy Point also appeals to lovers of wildlife and nature – keep a look out for seals and porpoises, and be sure not to miss the wildflower meadow and orchard next to the car park. **Note**: toilets and outdoor shower in courtyard beside car park.

The impressive headland of Baggy Point in Devon

Satnav: use EX33 1PA.
Parking: in Moor Lane. Electric vehicle charging points available.

Dog rating: ❀ ❀ ❀ **Best** – Welcome on leads (except for seasonal ban on Croyde Beach, May to September).

Access: P♿ 🚻♿ ♿ ➡

Find out more: 01271 891970 or baggypoint@nationaltrust.org.uk
nationaltrust.org.uk/baggy-point

Baggy Point		M	T	W	T	F	S	S
Sandleigh tea-room								
19 Feb–27 Feb	10:30–4	M	T	W	T	F	S	S
5 Mar–27 Mar	10:30–4	.	.	.	.	.	S	S
1 Apr–31 Aug	10:30–5	M	T	W	T	F	S	S
1 Sep–31 Oct	10:30–4	M	T	W	T	F	S	S
5 Nov–18 Dec	10:30–4	.	.	.	.	.	S	S
19 Dec–31 Dec*	10:30–4	M	T	W	T	F	S	S

*Closed 25 and 26 December.

Bolberry Down

between Salcombe and Hope Cove, near Malborough, Devon

 1938 🏕 ⛰ ⛱

Majestic rugged cliffs at Bolberry Down in Devon

The starting point for a spectacular stretch of coast between Salcombe and Hope Cove, including the headlands of Bolt Head and Bolt Tail and the sandy beach at Soar Mill Cove. The majestic rugged cliffs have claimed countless ships over the centuries. There's an easy-access clifftop route.

Satnav: use TQ7 3DY. **Parking**: at Bolberry Down or Hope Cove (not National Trust).

Dog rating: ❀ **Standard** – Welcome (on leads where animals grazing).

Access: P♿ 🚶 ➡

Find out more: 01752 346585 or bolberrydown@nationaltrust.org.uk
nationaltrust.org.uk/bolberry-down

Bradley

Newton Abbot, Devon

| 1938 |

Surrounded by riverside meadows and woodland, this unspoilt medieval manor house is still a relaxed family home. There are original features to look out for, such as the medieval cat hole and drip stones, as well as the peaceful chapel that was licensed for services in 1428.
Note: sorry no toilet.

Satnav: TQ12 1LX directs to gate lodge.
Parking: blue badge parking only on site (please call 07745 236836). Car parks in town centre not National Trust (charge including members). Nearest public car park at Wolborough Street (TQ12 1JW).

Dog rating: ✿ **Standard** – Welcome in meadows and woodland. Assistance dogs only in garden and house.

Access:

Find out more: 01803 661907 or bradley@nationaltrust.org.uk
Totnes Road, Newton Abbot,
Devon TQ12 6BN
nationaltrust.org.uk/bradley

Bradley		M	T	W	T	F	S	S
5 Apr–27 Oct	Tour		T	W	T			

Open for guided tours on certain days (please call for details).

Medieval Bradley in Devon

Branscombe

on the Jurassic Coast, near Seaton, Devon

| 1965 |

Branscombe on Devon's Jurassic Coast

Nestling in a valley that reaches down to the sea on East Devon's dramatic Jurassic Coast, the village of Branscombe is surrounded by picturesque countryside with miles of tranquil walking through woodland, farmland and beach. Charming thatched houses, forge and restored watermill add to the timeless magic of the place. **Note**: nearest toilets (not National Trust) at information point, village hall and beach car park.

Satnav: use EX12 3DB. **Parking**: next to Old Forge, limited spaces. Also village hall and beach car parks (neither National Trust).

Dog rating: ✿ **Standard** – Welcome on leads in the Old Bakery garden, orchard, beach and wider countryside.

Access:

Find out more: 01752 346585 or branscombe@nationaltrust.org.uk
nationaltrust.org.uk/branscombe

Branscombe

Old Bakery Tea-room and Manor Mill: opening arrangements not confirmed at time of print, please check before visiting. Forge (tenant-run): open daily, 9 to 4:30 (excluding Tuesday, 9 to 12:30). For further information, call 01297 680481.

Brownsea Island

Poole Harbour, Poole, Dorset

1962

The perfect day's adventure, this island wildlife sanctuary is easy to get to but feels like a million miles away as soon as you step ashore. Wander through sheltered woodland, sweeping shorelines and dramatic clifftops, spotting wildlife as you go, including our rare resident red squirrels. The internationally important lagoon also plays host to thousands of birds that fly in from distant lands throughout the season. As the birthplace of Scouting and Guiding, the island is the perfect place for your very own outdoor adventure with free family trails, natural play area and historic campsite. **Note**: wheelchair ferry service available. Donation to enter the Dorset Wildlife Trust area. No castle access.

Brownsea Island, Dorset: a rare red squirrel, above, and intrepid explorers, below

Discovering Brownsea Island

Satnav: use BH15 1HP for Poole Quay.
Parking: at Poole Quay, not National Trust (charge including members).

Access: 🏳️♿🚻♿🔍🔊📷♿♿➡️

Find out more: 01202 707744 or
brownseaisland@nationaltrust.org.uk
nationaltrust.org.uk/brownsea-island

Brownsea Island		M	T	W	T	F	S	S
19 Mar–30 Oct	10–5	M	T	W	T	F	S	S

Ferry service from Poole Quay, charge including members
(see website for details).

Brownstone

Brownstone Road, Kingswear,
Devon TQ6 0EH 1981

Spectacular views on a coastal walk that
leads to a rare Second World War gun
battery at Froward Point. **Note**: naturally
uneven coastal paths, steep in places – be
aware of cliff edges.

Find out more: 01803 752776 (rangers) or
brownstone@nationaltrust.org.uk
nationaltrust.org.uk/brownstone

Buckland Abbey

Yelverton, Devon

1948 🏠🏠✳️♣️🛍️🍴📷🚻🍽️

Hundreds of years ago, Cistercian monks
chose this tranquil valley as the perfect
spot in which to worship, farm their estate
and trade. The Abbey, later converted into a
house, today combines furnished rooms
with museum galleries, bringing to life the
story of how seafaring adventurers Sir
Richard Grenville and Sir Francis Drake
changed the shape of Buckland Abbey and
the fate of England. Outdoors you'll find
the formal Elizabethan garden, walled
kitchen garden and Cider House garden;
the impressive medieval Great Barn;
orchards and woodland walks with
far-reaching views and late spring bluebells.

Satnav: follow brown signs, not satnav.
Parking: 150 yards.

Dog rating: ✤ **Standard** – Welcome on
leads on three estate walks and in café
(assistance dogs only in garden).

Buckland Abbey, Devon: the house,
above, and garden, below

Access:

Find out more: 01822 853607 or
bucklandabbey@nationaltrust.org.uk
Yelverton, Devon PL20 6EY
nationaltrust.org.uk/buckland-abbey

Buckland Abbey		M	T	W	T	F	S	S
Abbey, estate, garden, shop and café								
19 Feb–30 Oct	10–5*	M	T	W	T	F	S	S
3 Dec–31 Dec**	10–4*	M	T	W	T	F	S	S
Estate, garden, shop and café								
1 Jan–13 Feb	10–4	·	·	·	·	·	S	S

Last entry to whole site one hour before closing. *Abbey:
opens 11. **Everything closed 25 and 26 December; estate,
garden, shop and café: 29 October to 4 December, open
weekends only, 10 to 4.

Burton Bradstock

on the Jurassic Coast, near Bridport, Dorset

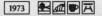

One of the main gateways to Dorset's Jurassic
Coast. Here are spectacular sandstone cliffs
– Burton Cliff glows bright gold in sunlight
– and miles of unspoilt beaches. Hive Beach
is a popular family destination, nearby
Cogden is quieter; both are part of Chesil
Bank, the largest shingle ridge in the world.

Satnav: use DT6 4RF for Burton Bradstock;
DT6 4RL for Cogden. **Parking**: on site.

Dog rating: ❀ **Standard** – Welcome. Dog-free
zone on Hive Beach (1 June to 30 September).

Access:

Find out more: 01297 489481 or
burtonbradstock@nationaltrust.org.uk
nationaltrust.org.uk/burton-bradstock

Cadover Bridge

on Dartmoor, near Shaugh Prior,
Devon 1960

Tranquil moorland by River Plym.
Starting point for walks through ancient
woodland or across open moors and tors.
Note: for satnav use PL7 5EH.

Find out more:
cadoverbridge@nationaltrust.org.uk
nationaltrust.org.uk/cadover-bridge

Castle Drogo

Drewsteignton, near Exeter,
Devon EX6 6PB

1974

**Imposing granite Castle Drogo in Devon, top.
The Library, above, and staircase, right**

High above the ancient woodlands of the
Teign Gorge on the edge of Dartmoor
stands Castle Drogo. Reminiscent of a
medieval fortress, the castle was designed
and built between 1910 and 1930 by the
renowned architect Sir Edwin Lutyens for
the self-made millionaire Julius Drewe.
Inside the imposing granite walls, the
ingenuity of Lutyens' design is revealed
in grand show rooms, functional servants'
spaces and comfortable family rooms,
perfectly suited to the lifestyle of a modern
20th-century family. Outside, hidden

behind immaculate yew hedges, the garden
is a perfect partnership of colourful
seasonal planting with Lutyens' formal
architectural design.

Parking: 400 yards from visitor centre.

Dog rating: 🐾 🐾 **Good** – Welcome
on leads in grounds and Teign Gorge
(assistance dogs only in Castle,
formal garden and café).

Access: 🅿️♿🚻♿♿🔍💻♿♿
♿♿➡️♿

Find out more: 01647 433306 or
castledrogo@nationaltrust.org.uk
nationaltrust.org.uk/castle-drogo

Castle Drogo		M	T	W	T	F	S	S
Castle								
14 Mar–30 Oct	10:30–4:30	M	T	W	T	F	S	S
Garden, visitor centre, café and shop								
19 Feb–13 Mar	11–3	M	T	W	T	F	S	S
14 Mar–30 Oct	10–5	M	T	W	T	F	S	S
4 Nov–31 Dec*	11–3					F	S	S

*Everything closed 24 to 26 December.

Clouds Hill

Bovington, Dorset BH20 7NQ

1937

In this tiny woodsman's cottage you can discover the essentials and the luxuries chosen by T. E. Lawrence after he had abandoned the 'Lawrence of Arabia' persona and remodelled himself as a private in the army at Bovington Camp. Much of the furniture and fittings was designed by Lawrence himself.

Parking: on site.

· **Dog rating**: ❖ **Standard** – Welcome on leads in grounds only.

Access:

Find out more: 01929 405616 or cloudshill@nationaltrust.org.uk
nationaltrust.org.uk/clouds-hill

Clouds Hill		M	T	W	T	F	S	S
2 Mar–30 Oct*	10–4**			W	T	F	S	S

*Also open February half term. **Visit by guided tours only (check before visiting).

Coleton Camp

between Dart Estuary and Brixham, Devon 1981

Great walks along the coast path to Scabbacombe and Man Sands beaches on this rugged stretch of coast. **Note**: naturally uneven coastal paths, steep in places – be aware of cliff edges. For satnav use TQ6 0EQ.

Find out more: 01803 752776 or coletoncamp@nationaltrust.org.uk
nationaltrust.org.uk/brownstone-and-coleton-camp

Coleton Fishacre

Brownstone Road, Kingswear, Devon TQ6 0EQ

1982

This evocative 1920s Arts and Crafts-style house, with its elegant art deco interiors, perfectly encapsulates the spirit of the Jazz Age. The former country home of the D'Oyly Carte family, it has a light, joyful atmosphere with touches of a bygone era. You can also glimpse life 'downstairs' in the servants' rooms. In the RHS-accredited garden, walk down through the valley garden to a coastal viewpoint with inspiring sea views. The paths weave through glades and past tranquil ponds and rare tender plants from New Zealand and South Africa; many exotic plants thrive beneath the tree canopy.

Arts and Crafts Coleton Fishacre in Devon: step back into the 1920s Jazz Age

The Rill Garden at Coleton Fishacre, top, and visitors exploring the house, above

Parking: 20 yards from reception; overflow parking 150 yards.

Dog rating: ❀ ❀ ❀ **Best** – Welcome on short leads in garden and Café Coleton. Tethering rings by house.

Access:

Find out more: 01803 842382 or coletonfishacre@nationaltrust.org.uk
nationaltrust.org.uk/coleton-fishacre

Coleton Fishacre		M	T	W	T	F	S	S
8 Jan–13 Feb	11–3	·	·	·	·	·	S	S
19 Feb–30 Oct	10:30–5	M	T	W	T	F	S	S
5 Nov–18 Dec	11–3	·	·	·	·	·	S	S
27 Dec–31 Dec	11–3	·	T	W	T	F	S	·

Garden, shop and café: winter weekends and 27 to 31 December, open to 4.

Compton Castle

Marldon, Paignton, Devon TQ3 1TA

1951 🏰🏠❀♿🏚🍴

A rare survivor, this medieval fortified manor house has high curtain walls and portcullises. It was once the home of Sir Humphrey Gilbert, part-founder of the New World, and his descendants still live here today. Outside, you can discover roses climbing pergolas, knot and herb gardens and a picnic orchard. **Note**: hall, sub-solar, solar, study, kitchen, scullery, guard room, chapel open.

Parking: all parking must be booked. On grass verges at castle entrance.

Dog rating: ❀ **Standard** – Welcome in the lower orchard on leads. Assistance dogs only in castle and garden.

Access:

Find out more: 01803 661906 or comptoncastle@nationaltrust.org.uk
nationaltrust.org.uk/compton-castle

Compton Castle		M	T	W	T	F	S	S
5 Apr–27 Oct	10:30–3	·	T	W	T	·	·	·

Booking essential.

Compton Castle in Devon: a medieval fortified manor house

Corfe Castle

near Wareham, Dorset

1982

This fairy-tale fortress is an evocative survivor of the English Civil War, partially demolished by the Parliamentarians in 1646. It's a favourite haunt for adults and children alike – all ages are captivated by these romantic ruins with their breathtaking views. There are 1,000 years of the castle's history as a royal palace and fortress to be discovered here. Fallen walls and secret places tell tales of treachery and treason around every corner. Corfe Castle's brooding presence is a backdrop to some of Britain's most beautiful coast and countryside. Corfe Common and Hartland Moor are close by – you can explore them by walking or cycling, discovering rare wild flowers and masses of wildlife along the way. **Note**: steep, uneven slopes; steps; sudden drops throughout castle. All/parts of castle close in high winds.

Corfe Castle in Dorset: this evocative survivor of the English Civil War still sees the occasional sword fight

The romantic ruins of Corfe Castle rise from the early morning mist

Jagged walls stand out against a brooding sky at Corfe Castle

Satnav: use BH20 5DR. **Parking**: 800 yards uphill walk. Purbeck Park car park (½ mile) and West Street in village, neither National Trust (charge including members).

Dog rating: 🐾 🐾 **Good** – Welcome on short leads.

Access: 🅿♿ 🚻 ♿ ♿ 🦽 ♿ ♿

Find out more: 01929 477063 (ticket office) or corfecastle@nationaltrust.org.uk
Corfe, near Wareham, Dorset BH20 5EZ
nationaltrust.org.uk/corfe-castle

Corfe Castle		M	T	W	T	F	S	S
1 Jan–18 Feb	10–4	M	T	W	T	F	S	S
19 Feb–27 May	10–5	M	T	W	T	F	S	S
28 May–5 Jun	10–6	M	T	W	T	F	S	S
6 Jun–22 Jul	10–5*	M	T	W	T	F	S	S
23 Jul–31 Aug	10–6	M	T	W	T	F	S	S
1 Sep–30 Sep	10–5*	M	T	W	T	F	S	S
1 Oct–30 Oct	10–5	M	T	W	T	F	S	S
31 Oct–31 Dec**	10–4	M	T	W	T	F	S	S

Shop and tea-room opening times may vary. *Open 10 to 6, Saturday and Sunday. **Castle, shop and tea-room: closed 25 and 26 December.

East Soar

between Salcombe and Hope Cove,
near Malborough, Devon

 1950

This is a great starting point for exploring
the isolated and rugged coast between
Bolt Head and Bolt Tail. There's so much
history to discover, including remains of
Bronze Age settlements, shipwrecks and
ancient field boundary stones. There is a
one-and-a-half mile marked route to
Overbeck's, overlooking Salcombe.

Satnav: use TQ7 3DR.
Parking: at East Soar car park.

Dog rating: 🐾 **Standard** – Welcome
(must be on a lead near livestock).

Access: [P♿]

Find out more: 01752 346585.
01548 561904 (East Soar Outdoor
Experience) or eastsoar@nationaltrust.org.uk
nationaltrust.org.uk/east-soar

Hikers at East Soar in Devon

Finch Foundry

Sticklepath, Okehampton,
Devon EX20 2NW

1994

This water-powered forge was a 19th-century
family business, located close to the
River Taw to produce a variety of tools
for South-West industries, including farming
and mining. The large machinery and tools
give an idea of working life at the forge.
A delightful cottage garden outside.

Parking: on site (height/width restrictions).

Dog rating: 🐾 **Standard** – Welcome in
all areas (warning, loud noises when
machinery is running).

Access: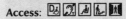

Find out more: 01837 840046 or
finchfoundry@nationaltrust.org.uk
nationaltrust.org.uk/finch-foundry

Finch Foundry	M	T	W	T	F	S	S
30 Mar–30 Oct Tour				W	T	F	S	S

Access guided tour only, at 11, 12, 1 and 2 (places limited,
booking essential). Please arrive 10 minutes before your tour
begins. Open Bank Holiday Mondays.

Fingle Bridge

near Drewsteignton, Devon 1990

Popular spot in Dartmoor's Teign Gorge.
Walkers can explore the footpaths in nearby
Fingle Woods, or climb towards Castle
Drogo. **Note**: uneven terrain. For satnav use
EX6 6PW. Fingle Woods are managed in
partnership with the Woodland Trust.

Find out more:
finglebridge@nationaltrust.org.uk
nationaltrust.org.uk/fingle-bridge

Golden Cap

on the Jurassic Coast, near Bridport, Dorset

 1961

Glowing heather at Golden Cap in Dorset

Spectacular countryside estate on the Jurassic Coast – one of England's natural World Heritage Sites. The great rocky shoulder of Golden Cap is the south coast's highest point, with breathtaking views in all directions. Stonebarrow Hill is a good starting point for discovering the 25 miles of footpaths around the estate.

Satnav: for Stonebarrow use DT6 6RA; Langdon Hill DT6 6EP. **Parking**: at Stonebarrow Hill and Langdon Hill.

Dog rating: 🐾 **Standard** – Welcome.

Find out more: 01297 489481 or goldencap@nationaltrust.org.uk
nationaltrust.org.uk/golden-cap

Greenway

Greenway Road, Galmpton, near Brixham, Devon TQ5 0ES

2000

Here you are given a glimpse into the lives of the famous author Agatha Christie and her family. Their holiday home is set in the 1950s, when Greenway overflowed with friends and family gathered together for holidays and Christmas. The family were great collectors: the house is brimming with their books, archaeology, Tunbridgeware, silver and porcelain. The informal woodland garden drifts down the hillside towards the Dart Estuary and the Boathouse, scene of the crime in *Dead Man's Folly*. Please consider 'green ways' to travel here: ferry (courtesy vehicle available from quay), cycling or walking.
Note: booking essential for parking.

Parking: spaces must be booked – no parking on Greenway Road or Galmpton.

Dog rating: 🐾 🐾 🐾 **Best** – Welcome on short leads in garden and Barn Gallery Café (tethering rings in courtyard).

Relaxed Greenway in Devon, opposite and above: Agatha Christie's holiday home

Access:

Find out more: 01803 842382 (infoline).
01803 882811 (ferry) or
greenway@nationaltrust.org.uk
nationaltrust.org.uk/greenway

Greenway		M	T	W	T	F	S	S
19 Feb–30 Oct	10:30–5	M	T	W	T	F	S	S
5 Nov–18 Dec	11–3*						S	S
27 Dec–31 Dec	11–3*		T	W	T	F	S	

*Garden, shop and café: winter weekends and
27 to 31 December, open to 4.

Hardy Monument

Black Down, near Portesham, Dorset 1938

Memorial to Vice-Admiral Hardy, Flag-Captain of HMS *Victory* at Trafalgar, designed to look like a spyglass. Views over the Channel. **Note**: nearest postcode for satnav is DT2 9HY. There is currently no access to Hardy Monument. Car park open every day all year.

Find out more: 01297 489481 or
hardymonument@nationaltrust.org.uk
nationaltrust.org.uk/hardy-monument

Hardy's Cottage

Higher Bockhampton, near Dorchester, Dorset DT2 8QJ

1948

Unassuming Hardy's Cottage in Dorset

You can find yourself 'far from the madding crowd' as you discover Hardy's rural childhood home, with its quintessential cottage garden, and the birthplace of his literary land of 'Wessex'. **Note**: nearest toilet/café at visitor centre (not National Trust). Bridlepath/woodland paths to cottage uneven and steep.

Parking: 700 yards, pay and display (not National Trust, charge including members). For designated parking, call 01305 262366.

Dog rating: ✿ **Standard** – Welcome on leads in garden only (assistance dogs only in cottage).

Access:

Find out more: 01305 262366 or
hardyscottage@nationaltrust.org.uk
nationaltrust.org.uk/hardys-cottage

Hardy's Cottage		M	T	W	T	F	S	S
1 Mar–30 Oct*	Tour**			T	W	T	F	S	S

*Also open February half term and weekends in
November and December (closed 24 and 25 December).
**Access by guided tour only (check before visiting);
closes dusk if earlier.

Heddon Valley

on Exmoor, near Combe Martin, Devon

| 1963 |

The dramatic West Exmoor coast, favourite landscape of the Romantic poets, offers not only the beautiful Heddon Valley to explore, but also Woody Bay and the Hangman Hills nearby. At the heart of the valley sits the historic Hunter's Inn, a good place to relax after discovering the spectacular coastal, moorland and woodland walks in the area. Nature highlights include one of the UK's last surviving colonies of high brown fritillary butterflies, which can be seen in June and July on the bracken-clad hillsides of Heddon Valley. Look out for the rich diversity of fungi in autumn.

Satnav: use EX31 4PY.
Parking: opposite toilets.

Dog rating: 🐾 🐾 🐾 **Best** – Welcome on leads.

Access:

Find out more: 01598 763402 or heddonvalley@nationaltrust.org.uk
nationaltrust.org.uk/heddon-valley

Heddon Valley		M	T	W	T	F	S	S
Pantry								
19 Feb–27 Feb	10:30–4	M	T	W	T	F	S	S
5 Mar–27 Mar	10:30–4	·	·	·	·	·	S	S
1 Apr–31 Aug	10:30–5	M	T	W	T	F	S	S
1 Sep–31 Oct	10:30–4	M	T	W	T	F	S	S
5 Nov–31 Dec*	10:30–4	·	·	·	·	·	S	S

*Open 19 December to 3 January 2023 (excluding 25 and 26 December), 10:30 to 4.

Two views of Heddon Valley on Devon's dramatic West Exmoor coast

Killerton

Broadclyst, Exeter, Devon EX5 3LE

1944 🏛 🏠 ✿ 🌱 ☕ 📷 🎭 🚶

Would you give away your family home for your political beliefs? Sir Richard Acland did just that with his Killerton Estate in the heart of Devon, when he gave it to the Trust in 1944. Today you'll find a welcoming Georgian house set in 2,600 hectares (6,400 acres) of working farmland, woods, parkland, cottages and orchards. There's plenty of calm space in the glorious garden, beautiful year-round with rhododendrons, magnolias, champion trees and formal lawns. You can explore winding paths, climb an extinct volcano, discover an Iron Age hill fort and take in distant views towards Dartmoor. More family home than grand mansion, the relaxed house holds the National Trust's largest fashion collection, with selected items exhibited.

Satnav: on arrival, follow brown signs to main car park. **Parking**: main car park 280 yards. Additional smaller car parks, including Ashclyst Forest Gate, Ellerhayes Bridge, Danes Wood.

Dog rating: 🐾 🐾 **Good** – Welcome in the parkland and estate (assistance dogs only in garden and chapel grounds).

Access: 🅿 ♿ 🚻 🚽 ♿ 🚹 ♿ ♿ ♿

Killerton in Devon: this welcoming Georgian house holds the National Trust's largest fashion collection

Killerton's garden and grounds are beautiful whatever the season, this picture and below

Find out more: 01392 881345 or
killerton@nationaltrust.org.uk
nationaltrust.org.uk/killerton

Killerton		M	T	W	T	F	S	S
House and Killerton Kitchen								
12 Feb–30 Oct*	11–4	M	T	W	T	F	S	S
26 Nov–31 Dec**	11–3	M	T	W	T	F	S	S
Chapel, garden, Stables coffee shop, shop and plant centre								
1 Jan–11 Feb	10–4	M	T	W	T	F	S	S
12 Feb–30 Oct	10–5	M	T	W	T	F	S	S
31 Oct–31 Dec	10–4	M	T	W	T	F	S	S
Wider parkland								
Open all year†	8–7	M	T	W	T	F	S	S

House: timed tickets at peak times. †Wider parkland: open daily to 7, or dusk if earlier. *Fashion exhibition: open as house. **Christmas opening to 2 January 2023, ground floor only. Everything closes at 2 on 24 December; closed 25 and 26 December.

Killerton Estate: Ashclyst Forest

near Broadclyst, Exeter, Devon 1944

One of the largest woods in East Devon. A haven for butterflies, bluebells and birds. **Note**: for satnav use EX5 3DT.

Find out more: 01392 881345 or
ashclystforest@nationaltrust.org.uk
nationaltrust.org.uk/ashclyst-forest

Killerton Estate: Budlake Old Post Office

Broadclyst, Exeter, Devon EX5 3LW 1944

Visiting this old village post office is like stepping back into the 1950s. **Note**: nearest toilets at Killerton. For opening times please call Killerton on 01392 881345.

Find out more: 01392 881345 or
budlakepostoffice@nationaltrust.org.uk
nationaltrust.org.uk/budlake-old-post-office

Killerton Estate: Clyston Mill

Broadclyst, Exeter, Devon EX5 3EW 1944

A historic working water-powered corn mill in a picturesque setting by the River Clyst. **Note**: nearest toilets in Broadclyst village. For opening times please call Killerton on 01392 881345.

Find out more: 01392 881345 or clystonmill@nationaltrust.org.uk **nationaltrust.org.uk/clyston-mill**

Killerton Estate: Marker's

Broadclyst, Exeter, Devon EX5 3HS 1944

A medieval hall-house with a thatched roof, smoke-blackened timbers, a rare painted screen, garden and cob summerhouse. **Note**: nearest toilets in Broadclyst village. For opening times please call Killerton on 01392 881345.

Find out more: 01392 881345 or markers@nationaltrust.org.uk **nationaltrust.org.uk/markers**

Kingston Lacy

Wimborne Minster, Dorset

1982 🏛️🏠❄️♿️☕️📷🏛️📷🌿

Home to the Bankes family for over 300 years, Kingston Lacy is a monument to the family's exceptional taste and desire to surround themselves with beauty.

The new multi-use trail at Kingston Lacy in Dorset

After the family lost their Corfe Castle stronghold to the Parliamentarians in the Civil War, they moved here and gradually created an astonishing Italian palace in the heart of rural Dorset. Today you can discover an internationally acclaimed art collection, including paintings by Rubens, Velázquez and Titian, exquisite carvings and lavish interiors. There's even more to explore outside, with sweeping lawns, a Japanese Garden, kitchen garden, woodland and parkland walks – look out for the award-winning herd of Red Ruby Devon cattle – and a huge 3,500-hectare (8,500-acre) countryside estate to enjoy. **Note**: some rooms may close at short notice. Low light levels.

Satnav: unreliable, follow B3082 to main entrance. Use BH21 4EL for Eye Bridge; BH21 4EE for Pamphill Green; DT11 9JL for Badbury Rings. **Parking**: on site or at Eye Bridge, Pamphill Green and Badbury Rings. Members pay for parking at Badbury Rings on point-to-point race days.

The dining room at Kingston Lacy

There's more for members here: nationaltrust.org.uk/members-area

Runners on Kingston Lacy's woodland trail, top, and sculpture inside the house, above

Dog rating: ❀ ❀ **Good** – Welcome on leads in parkland, woodlands, wider estate and café (including inside).

Access: 🅿 ♿ 🚻 ♿ ♿ 🎦 📹 ♿ ♿ ➡ ♿

Find out more: 01202 883402 or
kingstonlacy@nationaltrust.org.uk
Wimborne Minster, Dorset BH21 4EA
nationaltrust.org.uk/kingston-lacy

Kingston Lacy		M	T	W	T	F	S	S
House*								
Open all year**	10:30–4	M	T	W	T	F	S	S
Garden and parkland								
1 Jan–20 Feb	9:30–4	M	T	W	T	F	S	S
21 Feb–23 Oct	9:30–5	M	T	W	T	F	S	S
24 Oct–31 Dec**	9:30–4	M	T	W	T	F	S	S

*House: limited availability; some rooms/areas may close
at short notice. Last entry one hour before closing.
**Everything closed 25 December.

Knightshayes

near Tiverton, Devon

[1972] 🔭 🏠 ❀ 🐕 ☕ 🛍 🏠 🅿 🚶

With one of the finest gardens in the South West, Knightshayes is a masterpiece of architectural planting, home to one of the most outstanding botanical collections in the country. Among champion trees, including first introductions to this country, there are hidden glades and pathways to discover far-reaching views. The Gothic Revival house is a rare example of the genius of William Burges, whose opulent designs have inspired extremes of opinion, even among the family who commissioned them. The walled garden combines full productivity with aesthetic appeal and is an excellent example of a restored Victorian kitchen garden. **Note**: access to the house and garden is restricted during spring and winter.

Satnav: can be unreliable. Suggested postcode to enter is EX16 7RH. Alternatively, follow brown signs on nearing Tiverton/Bolham. **Parking**: on site.

Dog rating: ❀ **Standard** – Welcome on leads in parkland and woods; in formal garden, November to February only.

Gothic Revival Knightshayes in Devon

The grounds at Knightshayes

Access: [icons]

Find out more: 01884 254665 or
knightshayes@nationaltrust.org.uk
Bolham, near Tiverton, Devon EX16 7RQ
nationaltrust.org.uk/knightshayes

Knightshayes		M	T	W	T	F	S	S
Garden, café, shop and plant centre								
1 Jan–27 Feb	10–4	M	T	W	T	F	S	S
28 Feb–30 Oct	10–5	M	T	W	T	F	S	S
31 Oct–31 Dec	10–4	M	T	W	T	F	S	S
House (ground floor)								
1 Jan–27 Feb	11–4						S	S
28 Feb–30 Oct	11–4	M	T	W	T	F	S	S
5 Nov–31 Dec	11–4						S	S

Parkland and woods: open daily, 7 to 6:30 (5:30, November to February). House and kitchen garden: open weekends and school holidays, November to February. Everything closed 24 to 26 December.

Little Dartmouth

near Dartmouth, Devon 1970

A gentle coastal landscape west of Dartmouth, with wonderful views, wild flowers and the remains of a Civil War encampment. **Note**: Compass Cottage holiday let – ideal base for exploring Dartmouth and the coast.

Find out more: 01752 346585 or
littledartmouth@nationaltrust.org.uk
nationaltrust.org.uk/little-dartmouth

Lorna Doone Valley

near Lynton, Devon

2020 [icons]

Made famous by R. D. Blackmore in his novel *Lorna Doone*, this mystical valley is a gateway to many inspiring walks. You can extend your time here by staying at Cloud Farm Campsite.

Satnav: use EX35 6NU. **Parking**: on site.

Dog rating: 🐾 🐾 🐾 **Best** – Welcome, including in the tea-room.

Access: [icons]

Find out more: 01598 741172 or
lornadoonevalley@nationaltrust.org.uk
nationaltrust.org.uk/lorna-doone-valley

Lorna Doone Valley		M	T	W	T	F	S	S
Buttery								
5 Mar–27 Mar	10:30–4						S	S
1 Apr–31 Aug	10:30–5	M	T	W	T	F	S	S
1 Sep–31 Oct	10:30–4	M	T	W	T	F	S	S

Loughwood Meeting House

Dalwood, Axminster, Devon EX13 7DU 1969

Atmospheric 17th-century thatched Baptist meeting house dug into the hillside. **Note**: sorry no toilet.

Find out more: 01752 346585 or
loughwood@nationaltrust.org.uk
nationaltrust.org.uk/loughwood-meeting-house

Lundy

Bristol Channel, Devon

Grey seal at Lundy in the
Bristol Channel, Devon

Lundy is a remarkable island in the Bristol
Channel, a place of solitude, stark beauty
and abundant wildlife, much loved by its
regular visitors and residents. A day trip on
the MS *Oldenburg* allows time to explore
the rugged clifftops, discover seabirds and
visit the church, castle and welcoming
tavern. **Note**: National Trust owned; run by
Landmark Trust. *Oldenburg* runs from
Bideford or Ilfracombe.

Satnav: use EX34 9EQ for Ilfracombe;
EX39 2EY for Bideford. **Parking**: at Bideford
and Ilfracombe, not National Trust
(charge including members).

Access:

Find out more: 01271 863636 or
lundy@nationaltrust.org.uk
The Lundy Shore Office, The Quay,
Bideford, Devon EX39 2LY
nationaltrust.org.uk/lundy

Lundy

MS *Oldenburg* sails from Bideford or Ilfracombe up to four
times a week from the end of March until the end of October
carrying both day and staying passengers. A helicopter
service operates from Hartland Point from November to
mid-March, Mondays and Fridays only, for staying visitors.

Lydford Gorge

Lydford, near Tavistock, Devon

This steep-sided river gorge, carved
into the western edge of Dartmoor, has
been drawing visitors in search of the
picturesque waterfall since Victorian times.
Around every corner the River Lyd plunges,
tumbles, swirls and gently meanders
as it travels through the steep-sided,
oak-wooded valley, which is abundant with
wildlife. Walking through the gorge (the
deepest in the South West) is a challenging
and rewarding adventure. Be prepared for
strenuous climbs and rugged ground. Trails
of varying lengths. **Note**: rugged terrain,
vertical drops and climbs. Sturdy footwear
with good grip essential.

Lydford Gorge, Devon: deepest in the South West

Dramatic Lydford Gorge

Satnav: EX20 4BH (Devil's Cauldron entrance); EX20 4BL (Waterfall entrance).
Parking: on site.

Dog rating: 🐾 **Standard** – Welcome on leads.

Access: [icons]

Find out more: 01822 820320 or lydfordgorge@nationaltrust.org.uk
nationaltrust.org.uk/lydford-gorge

Lydford Gorge	M	T	W	T	F	S	S
Lydford Gorge walking trails							
29 Mar–30 Oct 10–4:30*	·	T	W	T	F	S	S
Tea-room							
29 Mar–30 Oct 10:30–4:30*	T	W	T	F	S	S	

*1 to 30 October: close 4. Open Bank Holiday Mondays. Check for November and December openings.

Max Gate

Dorchester, Dorset

1940 [icons]

Max Gate, home to Dorset's most famous author and poet, Thomas Hardy, was designed by the writer himself. Built in 1885, this atmospheric Victorian house is where Hardy wrote some of his most famous novels, including *Tess of the d'Urbervilles* and *Jude the Obscure*, and most of his poetry.

Satnav: enter Max Gate not postcode.
Parking: on roadside in front of the house (50 yards, limited spaces, not National Trust).

Dog rating: 🐾 **Standard** – Welcome on leads in garden only.

Access: [icons]

Max Gate, Dorset: Thomas Hardy's home

Find out more: 01305 262538 or maxgate@nationaltrust.org.uk
Alington Avenue, Dorchester, Dorset DT1 2FN
nationaltrust.org.uk/max-gate

Max Gate		M	T	W	T	F	S	S
1 Mar–30 Oct*	Tour**	·	T	W	T	F	S	S

*Also open February half term and weekends in November and December (excluding 24 and 25 December).
**Please check for details.

Mortehoe

near Ilfracombe, Devon 1909

Gateway to a wild, remote coast with a rich history of wrecking and smuggling. Dramatic walks and abundant wildlife awaits.
Note: use EX34 7DX for village car park and toilets, neither National Trust (charge including members). Town Farmhouse (not National Trust) offers cream teas in summer.

Find out more: 01271 891970 or mortehoe@nationaltrust.org.uk
nationaltrust.org.uk/mortehoe

Overbeck's Garden

Sharpitor, Salcombe, Devon TQ8 8LW

1937 | icons

Tucked away on the cliffs above Salcombe lies this hidden paradise: a subtropical garden, bursting with colour, filled with exotic and rare plants and offering surprises round every corner. The views from the garden over the estuary and coast are truly breathtaking. **Note**: entrance path and grounds are very steep in places.

Satnav: follow brown signs through Salcombe. Large vehicles, including campervans, use TQ7 3DR (1½-mile walk). **Parking**: limited parking. Additional parking at East Soar.

Access: icons

Find out more: 01548 842893 or overbecks@nationaltrust.org.uk **nationaltrust.org.uk/overbecks**

Overbeck's Garden		M	T	W	T	F	S	S
3 Apr–3 Nov	10:30–4	M	T	W	T	.	.	S

Booked visits only. Last entry one hour before closing.

The striking Knot Garden at Overbeck's Garden in Devon

Parke

near Bovey Tracey, Devon

1974 | icons

Parke in Devon: tranquil historic parkland

On the south-eastern edge of Dartmoor sits this historic parkland, rich in wildlife. The Wray Valley cycle trail runs along the old railway line, and paths follow the course of the River Bovey meandering through woodlands and meadows. Look out for the walled garden and historic orchard.

Satnav: use TQ13 9JQ. **Parking**: on site (limited).

Dog rating: 🐾 **Standard** – Welcome under close control.

Access: icons

Find out more: 01647 433306 or parke@nationaltrust.org.uk **nationaltrust.org.uk/parke**

Parke

Home Farm Café (not National Trust) open daily, 10 to 5 (10 to 4, November to March), plus Friday and Saturday evenings (booking essential).

Plymbridge Woods

near Plymouth, Devon

1968

Cycling on the route of the old railway track through Plymbridge Woods in Devon

The wooded valley of the River Plym creates a link from the edge of Plymouth to the heights of Dartmoor. Footpaths lead through woodlands and alongside industrial ruins. There's also a family-friendly cycle path (NCN27) along an old railway line, a wooded mountain-bike trail and a variety of running routes.

Satnav: use PL7 4SR for Plymbridge.
Parking: at Plymbridge.

Dog rating: ❀ Standard – Welcome under close control.

Access: 🅿♿

Find out more: 01752 341377 or plymbridgewoods@nationaltrust.org.uk
nationaltrust.org.uk/plymbridge-woods

Ringstead Bay

on the Jurassic Coast, near Weymouth, Dorset

1949

This quiet, unspoilt stretch of the Jurassic Coast in west Dorset is like the seaside of childhood memories: a perfect sweep of shingle beach with rock pools inviting you to explore, backed by farmland and cliffs covered with flowers and butterflies. The seawater is incredibly clear.

Satnav: use DT2 8NQ for Southdown.
Parking: on the clifftop farmland at Southdown Farm and beach car park (not National Trust).

Dog rating: ❀ Standard – Welcome, including on the South West Coast Path.

Find out more: 01297 489481 or ringsteadbay@nationaltrust.org.uk
nationaltrust.org.uk/ringstead-bay

The sun rises over the shingle beach at unspoilt Ringstead Bay in Dorset

Saltram

near Plymouth, Devon

1957

High above the River Plym, with magnificent views across the estuary, Saltram's rolling landscape parkland now provides wooded walks and open space for rest and play on Plymouth's outskirts.

Saltram was home to the Parker family from 1743, and the house reflects their increasingly prominent lifestyle during the Georgian period. The magnificent decoration and original contents include Robert Adam's Neo-classical Saloon, original Chinese wallpapers, 18th-century oriental, European and English ceramics and a superb country-house library. Outside, the garden's planting offers something of interest all year, and there are also follies and an 18th-century orangery to explore.

Paintings on the staircase at Saltram, Devon: part of the original contents acquired by the Parker family

The magnificent Georgian façade at Saltram, above, and a young visitor, below

Satnav: enter Romilly Gardens, not postcode (look for Saltram sign).
Parking: 50 yards.

Dog rating: 🐾 🐾 **Good** – Welcome in the park (identified on- and off-lead areas).

Access: 🅿 🅳 ♿ 🚻 🍴 📖 ♿ ♿ ♿ ➡ ♿

Find out more: 01752 333500 or
saltram@nationaltrust.org.uk
Plympton, near Plymouth, Devon PL7 1UH
nationaltrust.org.uk/saltram

Saltram		M	T	W	T	F	S	S
House and Chapel Tea-room								
12 Feb–31 Oct	11–4	M			T	F	S	S
25 Nov–31 Dec*	10:30–4	M	T	W	T	F	S	S
Garden, Park Café and shop								
1 Jan–11 Feb	10–4**	M	T	W	T	F	S	S
12 Feb–31 Dec*	10–5**	M	T	W	T	F	S	S
Park								
Open all year	7–7	M	T	W	T	F	S	S

*November and December opening may change.
**Garden: last entry 45 minutes before closing.
Everything closed 25 and 26 December.

Shaugh Bridge

on Dartmoor, near Shaugh Prior,
Devon 1960

Ancient oakwoods and mossy boulders
cloak the Plym Valley; riverside walks pass
the atmospheric Dewerstone Rocks and
industrial ruins. **Note**: for satnav use
PL7 5HD. Watch out for climbers on
the Dewerstone Rocks.

Find out more:
shaughbridge@nationaltrust.org.uk
nationaltrust.org.uk/shaugh-bridge

South Milton Sands

Thurlestone, near Kingsbridge, Devon

1980

Fun at South Milton Sands, Devon

This popular beach – a long sweep of
golden sand and rock pools – edges a
sheltered bay of crystal-clear water and
looks out to the iconic Thurlestone Rock
offshore. The nearby wetland is home to
many bird species and is an ideal place
to spot rare migratory visitors.
Note: toilet (not National Trust).

Buckets and spades at South Milton Sands

Satnav: use TQ7 3JY. **Parking**: car park
behind beach very busy in summer.
Narrow lane from South Milton village
(limited passing places).

Dog rating: ❉ **Standard** – Welcome
on coast path and beach under close
control at all times.

Access: ♿ 🅿♿ 🚶

Find out more: 01752 346585 or
southmiltonsands@nationaltrust.org.uk
nationaltrust.org.uk/south-milton-sands

South Milton Sands

Café (tenant-run): open all year round subject to weather,
call 01548 561144 for details.

Spyway

on the Purbeck coast, Langton Matravers,
near Swanage, Dorset 1982

Gateway to Dancing Ledge and a dramatic
coast of grassy clifftops teeming with
wildlife. Fabulous walking – some
steep slopes. **Note**: sorry no toilet.
For satnav use BH19 3HG.

Find out more: 01929 450002 or
spyway@nationaltrust.org.uk
nationaltrust.org.uk/spyway

Studland Bay

Studland, near Swanage, Dorset

| 1982 | 🏖️🏔️🐾🚫☕🏠⛺🚶 |

This glorious slice of Purbeck coastline is famed for its 4-mile stretch of golden sand, gently shelving bathing waters (forming the Marine Conservation zone), and views of Old Harry Rocks and the Isle of Wight. With four beaches to choose from, Studland is loved by families and watersports fans of all ages, and it includes the most popular naturist beach in Britain. The vast swathe of heathland behind the beach is a haven for native wildlife and features all six British reptiles. Footpaths and bridleways through dunes, woods and wild open landscape encourage you to explore. Wildlife to spot includes deer, insects and birds, as well as numerous wild flowers. Studland was the inspiration for Toytown in Enid Blyton's *Noddy*. **Note**: toilets at Shell Bay, Knoll Beach and Middle Beach; also South Beach (not National Trust).

The coast path to Old Harry, Studland Bay, above, and Agglestone Rock, below

The beach at Studland Bay in Dorset is 4 miles long

Satnav: use BH19 3AQ for Knoll Beach.
Parking: at Shell Bay (9 to 8); South Beach (9 to 11); Knoll Beach and Middle Beach (9 to 8, or dusk if earlier). No overnight parking.

Dog rating: 🐾 **Standard** – Welcome on leads (2 metres maximum) 1 May to 30 September. Under control in winter.

Access: 🅿️♿🚻♿📷♿♿

Find out more: 01929 450500 or studlandbay@nationaltrust.org.uk
nationaltrust.org.uk/studland

Studland Bay		
Shop and café		
Open every day all year*		9:30–4:30**

*Closed 3 March and 25 December. **Open later in summer.

Old Harry Rocks at Studland Bay

Watersmeet

on Exmoor, near Lynmouth, Devon

| 1955 | 🏠 🚐 ⛺ 🏕 ☕ 🚩 |

This area, where the lush valleys of the East Lyn and Hoar Oak Water meet the high open moorland of Kipscombe, is a haven for wildlife and offers excellent walking. At the heart sits Watersmeet House, a 19th-century fishing lodge, which is now a tea garden. **Note**: deep gorge with steep walk down to house.

Satnav: use EX35 6NT. **Parking**: pay and display (not National Trust) on Watersmeet Road; steep walk down to house. Trust car parks nearby at Combe Park and Countisbury. Please call to book designated parking.

Dog rating: 🐾 🐾 **Good** – Welcome on leads.

Access: 🄳🄹 ♿ 🐾

Swimming at Watersmeet

Find out more: 01598 752648 or watersmeet@nationaltrust.org.uk
nationaltrust.org.uk/watersmeet

Watersmeet		M	T	W	T	F	S	S
Tea-room and tea garden								
19 Feb–27 Feb	10:30–4	M	T	W	T	F	S	S
5 Mar–27 Mar	10:30–4	·	·	·	·	·	S	S
1 Apr–31 Aug	10:30–5	M	T	W	T	F	S	S
1 Sep–31 Oct	10:30–4	M	T	W	T	F	S	S
5 Nov–18 Dec	10:30–4	·	·	·	·	·	S	S
19 Dec–31 Dec*	10:30–4	M	T	W	T	F	S	S

*Closed 25 and 26 December.

Watersmeet in Devon: a haven for wildlife and joy for walkers

Wembury

near Plymouth, Devon

The excellent rock pools at Wembury in Devon, below, and racing the waves, above

A great beach, and more: some of the best rock pools in the country, good surfing, masses of wildlife and views of a distinctive island – the Great Mewstone. Starting point for lovely coastal walks to Wembury Point and the Yealm Estuary.

Satnav: use PL9 0HP.
Parking: on site, above beach.

Dog rating: **Standard** – On leads near livestock. Welcome on beach, 1 October to 30 April.

Access: 🅿♿

Find out more: 01752 346585. 01752 862538 (Marine Centre) or wembury@nationaltrust.org.uk
nationaltrust.org.uk/wembury

Wembury
Old Mill Café (tenant-run): for details of seasonal opening telephone 01752 863280.

White Mill

Sturminster Marshall, near Wimborne Minster, Dorset BH21 4BX 1982

This 18th-century corn mill with original wooden machinery is built on a Domesday Book site in a peaceful riverside setting. **Note**: open April to October, weekends and Bank Holidays only.

Find out more: 01258 858051 or whitemill@nationaltrust.org.uk
nationaltrust.org.uk/white-mill

Woolacombe

near Ilfracombe, Devon 1935

A golden beach and huge dunes, amazing surfing, perfect coves for rock-pooling and numerous headland walks with views of Lundy. **Note**: parking not National Trust (charge including members). For satnav use EX34 7BG.

Find out more: 01271 891970 or woolacombe@nationaltrust.org.uk
nationaltrust.org.uk/woolacombe

Visitors in the Botanic Garden
at Lacock, Wiltshire

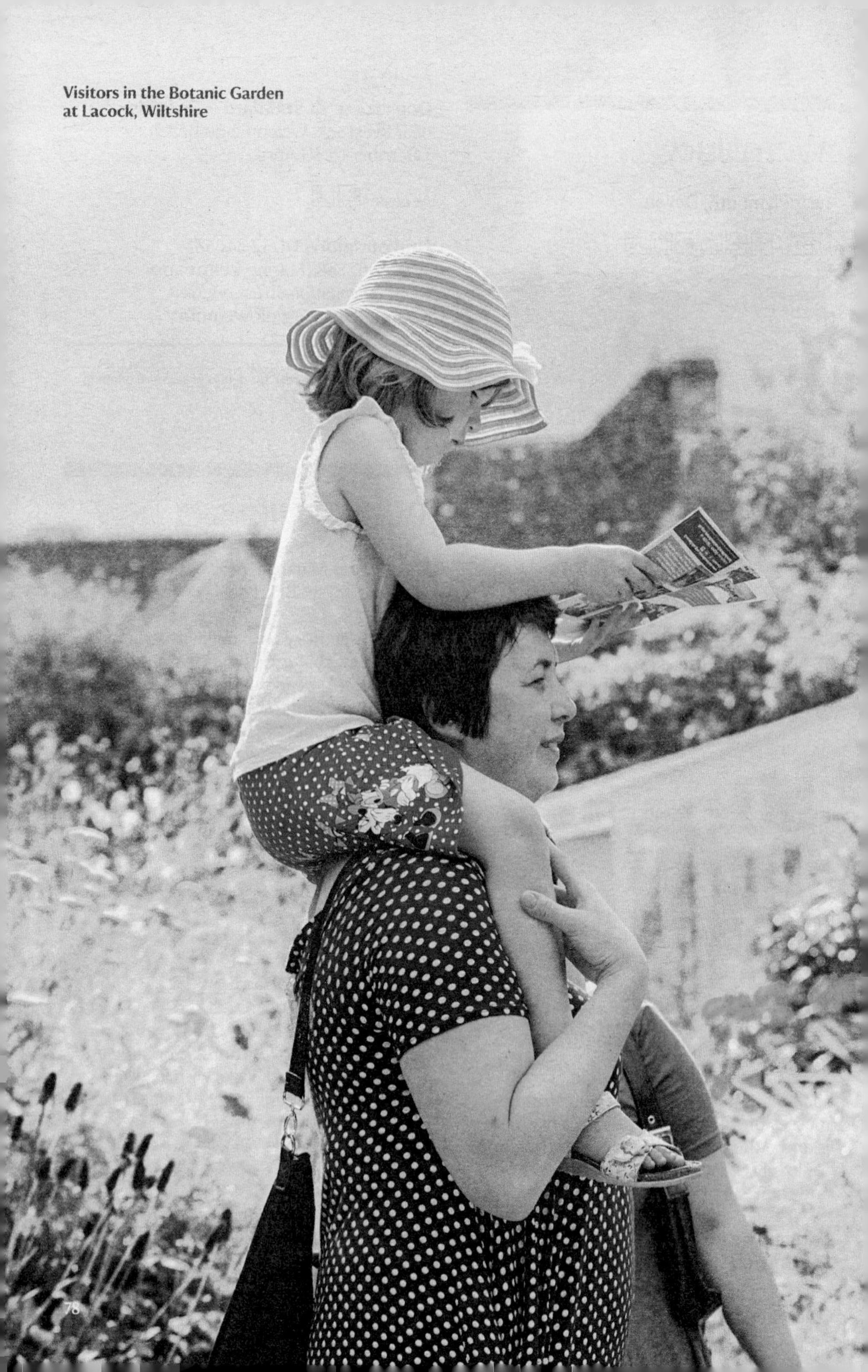

Somerset
and Wiltshire

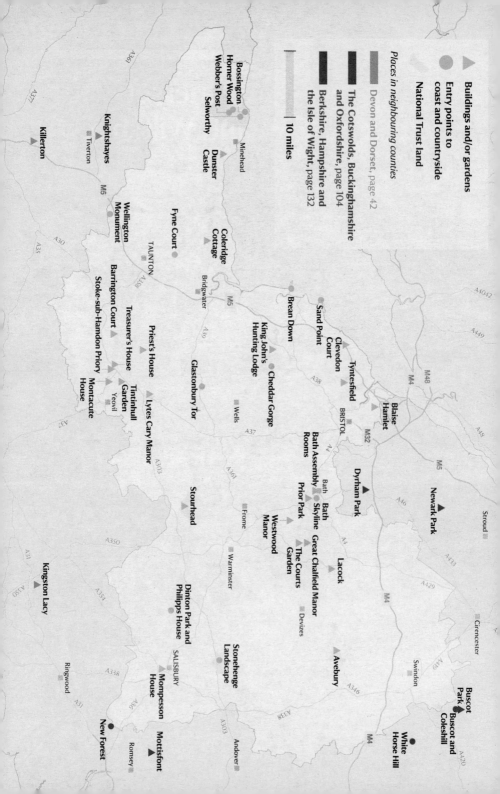

National Trust land

Entry points to
coast and countryside

Buildings and/or gardens

Places in neighbouring counties

Devon and Dorset, page 42

The Cotswolds, Buckinghamshire
and Oxfordshire, page 104

Berkshire, Hampshire and
the Isle of Wight, page 132

10 miles

Bossington
Homer Wood
Webber's Post
Selworthy

Minehead

Dunster
Castle

Killerton

Knightshayes

Tiverton

M5

Wellington
Monument

Fyne Court

Coleridge
Cottage

TAUNTON

Bridgwater

M5

Brean Down

Sand Point

Clevedon
Court

Tyntesfield

Blaise
Hamlet

BRISTOL

M32

M48

M4

M5

Newark Park

Stroud

Barrington Court

Stoke-sub-Hamdon Priory

Treasurer's House

Montacute
House

Yeovil

Priest's House

Tintinhull
Garden

Lytes Cary Manor

King John's
Hunting Lodge

Cheddar Gorge

Glastonbury Tor

Wells

A37

Bath Assembly
Rooms

Bath

Prior Park

Skyline

Bath

Dyrham Park

Lacock

A46

M4

Stourhead

Frome

Westwood
Manor

The Courts
Garden

Great Chalfield Manor

Devizes

Warminster

A350

Cirencester

Swindon

Kingston Lacy

Dinton Park and
Philipps House

SALISBURY

Stonehenge
Landscape

Avebury

Buscot
Park

Buscot
and
Coleshill

White
Horse Hill

Ringwood

Mompesson
House

Mottisfont

New Forest

Romsey

Andover

Avebury

near Marlborough, Wiltshire

[1943] 🏠 🖼 ♣ 🐾 ☕ 🛍 🔒 🎏 🚹

At Avebury you'll find the largest stone circle in the world, comprising an outer stone circle and henge, as well as the remains of two inner circles. The site also partially encompasses a pretty village. The Avebury landscape forms part of the Stonehenge and Avebury World Heritage Site, listed for its exceptional Neolithic and Bronze Age archaeology, and provides an ideal starting point to explore the remakable wider countryside, which contains some globally significant archaeological sites. The renowned archaeologist Alexander Keiller excavated at Avebury in the 1930s, and the museum displays local archaeological finds and tells the story of this prehistoric landscape. Keiller's home, the 15th-century Avebury Manor with its lovely garden, is located near the museum. **Note**: the National Trust owns and manages Avebury Stone Circle (under guardianship of English Heritage).

Long winter shadows are cast by the mysterious prehistoric stone circle at Avebury in Wiltshire

Satnav: use SN8 1RD. **Parking**: 300 yards. Please do not park on village streets.

Dog rating: 🐾 🐾 **Good** – Welcome on leads (assistance dogs only in the manor, garden and cafés).

Access: 🅿️ 🅳 🚻 🔆 🏠 📷 📺 ♿ 🚻
♿ ➡️ 📧

Find out more: 01672 539250 or avebury@nationaltrust.org.uk
National Trust Estate Office, High Street, Avebury, Wiltshire SN8 1RF
nationaltrust.org.uk/avebury

Avebury		M	T	W	T	F	S	S
Stone circle								
Open all year	Dawn–dusk	M	T	W	T	F	S	S
Museum, restaurant and shop*								
Open all year	11–4	M	T	W	T	F	S	S
Manor*								
19 Feb–31 Dec**	11–4				T	F	S	S
Manor garden*								
27 Mar–29 Oct**	11–4	M	T	W	T	F	S	S

*Extended opening in summer (check before visiting). Guided tours available for stone circle and Avebury Manor. **Manor and garden: closed 20 to 22 June; Manor also closed 31 October to 17 November for Christmas preparations. Everything closed: 24 to 26 December.

Avebury Manor, above, offers hands-on experiences, below

Barrington Court

near Ilminster, Somerset

1907

Exploring the garden at Barrington Court in Somerset

Colonel Lyle, whose family firm became part of Tate & Lyle, rescued the partially derelict 16th-century Court House in the 1920s, surrounding it with a productive model estate. A keen collector of architectural salvage, Colonel Lyle filled the house with his collection of panelling, fireplaces and staircases. The walled White Garden, Rose and Iris Garden and Lily Garden were influenced by Gertrude Jekyll, with playing fountains, vibrant colours and intoxicating scents. In constant production since 1921, the original kitchen garden is a working gem. The estate buildings comprise all the elements expected of a comfortable and wealthy 1920s estate. **Note**: major re-roofing conservation project underway. Artisan workshops independently run.

Satnav: misdirects visitors to rear entrance – follow brown signs from Barrington village. **Parking**: 200 yards.

Dog rating: 🐾 **Standard** – Assistance dogs only in formal garden.

Access:

Find out more: 01460 241938 or barringtoncourt@nationaltrust.org.uk
Barrington, near Ilminster, Somerset TA19 0NQ
nationaltrust.org.uk/barrington

Barrington Court		M	T	W	T	F	S	S
Garden, parkland and shop								
4 Mar–30 Oct	10–5*	M	T	W	T	F	S	S
5 Nov–27 Nov	10–3*						S	S
30 Nov–31 Dec**	10–3*			W	T	F	S	S
Café								
4 Mar–30 Oct	10–4:45	M	T	W	T	F	S	S
5 Nov–27 Nov	10–2:45						S	S
30 Nov–31 Dec**	10–2:45			W	T	F	S	S

*Shop: opens 11. **Closed 25 and 26 December.
House: due to building works opening arrangements may vary (please check website before visiting).
Artisan workshops open throughout.

Bath Assembly Rooms

Bennett Street, Bath, Somerset BA1 2QH 1931

The Assembly Rooms were at the heart of fashionable Georgian society. **Note**: limited access during functions. Bath Assembly Rooms is run by Bath and North East Somerset Council. Home to the Fashion Museum – for details call, email or visit fashionmuseum.co.uk.

Find out more: 01225 477789 or bathassemblyrooms@nationaltrust.org.uk
nationaltrust.org.uk/bath-assembly-rooms

Bath Skyline

Bath, Somerset

One of Bath's unique features, leading to its World Heritage Site designation, is its 'green setting' – encircling meadows and wooded hillsides where you can walk and relax with grandstand views over the historic cityscape. There's a 6-mile Bath Skyline waymarked walk, plus shorter routes to follow from the city centre. **Note**: sorry no toilet.

Parking: none on site, nearest city centre, not National Trust (charge including members).

Dog rating: ❀ **Standard** – Welcome under control (on leads in some areas). Cattle grazing April to November.

Access: ➡

Find out more: 01225 833977 or bathskyline@nationaltrust.org.uk
nationaltrust.org.uk/bath-skyline

Blaise Hamlet

Henbury, Bristol BS10 7QY 1943

Delightful hamlet of nine picturesque cottages, designed by John Nash in 1809 for retired Blaise Estate workers. **Note**: access to green only; cottages are lived in and not open. Sorry no toilet.

Find out more: 01275 461900 or blaisehamlet@nationaltrust.org.uk
nationaltrust.org.uk/blaise-hamlet

Bossington

on Exmoor, near Minehead, Somerset

Bossington, Somerset: enjoying the view from Bossington Hill above Porlock Bay

Part of the Holnicote Estate, Bossington is a peaceful coastal hamlet with distinctive thatched cottages. You can race sticks from the footbridge in the woods, look for water voles or wander down to the pebble beach. There's wildlife to spot and far-reaching views to Wales and along the Exmoor coastline. **Note**: accessible facilities in the car park.

Satnav: use TA24 8HF. **Parking**: on site.

Dog rating: ❀ **Standard** – Welcome on leads.

Access: ♿ ♿

Find out more: 01643 862452 or bossington@nationaltrust.org.uk
nationaltrust.org.uk/bossington

Brean Down

near Burnham-on-Sea, Somerset

1954

One of Somerset's most striking coastal landmarks: a dramatic limestone peninsula jutting out into the Bristol Channel. You can relax on the beach at the foot of the down or take a walk along this spectacular 'natural pier' to the fort, which provides a unique insight into Brean's military past. **Note**: steep climbs and cliffs; please stay on main paths. Tide comes in quickly.

Satnav: use TA8 2RS. **Parking**: on site.

Dog rating: ❀ **Standard** – Welcome on leads, but please note that stock may be grazing.

Access: ♿

Find out more: 01278 751874 or breandown@nationaltrust.org.uk
nationaltrust.org.uk/brean-down

The beach at the foot of Brean Down in Somerset

Cheddar Gorge

in the Mendips, near Wells, Somerset

1910

At almost 400 feet deep and 3 miles long, Cheddar is Britain's largest gorge. It was formed during successive ice ages, when glacial meltwater carved into the limestone, creating steep cliffs. The gorge is a haven for wildlife and contains many rare plants and flowers, including the Cheddar pink. **Note**: terrain is steep away from the road. Private caves and car parks (charge including members).

Satnav: use BS27 3QE. **Parking**: car parks on both sides of gorge, not National Trust (charge including members).

Dog rating: ❀ **Standard** – Welcome on leads.

Find out more: 01278 751874 or cheddargorge@nationaltrust.org.uk
nationaltrust.org.uk/cheddar-gorge

Cheddar Gorge in Somerset, above and below, is Britain's largest gorge

Clevedon Court

Tickenham Road, Clevedon,
North Somerset BS21 6QU

1961

Home to Clevedon's lords of the manor
for centuries, Clevedon Court features rare
domestic architecture from the medieval
period and a beautiful terraced garden.
The house was bought by Abraham Elton
in 1709 and is still the well-loved family
home of the Eltons today.

Parking: 50 yards (unsuitable for trailer
or motor caravans). Alternative parking
100 yards east of entrance in cul-de-sac.

Access:

Find out more: 01275 872257 or
clevedoncourt@nationaltrust.org.uk
nationaltrust.org.uk/clevedon

Clevedon Court		M	T	W	T	F	S	S
3 Apr–29 Sep	2–5			**W**	**T**			**S**

Car park: opens 1:15. House: entry by timed ticket (not
bookable). Open Bank Holiday Mondays.

Medieval Clevedon Court in North Somerset

Coleridge Cottage

35 Lime Street, Nether Stowey, Bridgwater,
Somerset TA5 1NQ

1909

**Simple Coleridge Cottage in Somerset
witnessed a genius at work**

Home to Samuel Taylor Coleridge for three
years. This simple house, where he wrote
his best-known poems, was the birthplace
of literary Romanticism. You can immerse
yourself in 18th-century sights and sounds,
and Coleridge's poetry comes to life in the
cottage and wildflower garden.

Parking: in pub car park
(not National Trust).

Access:

Find out more: 01278 732662 or
coleridgecottage@nationaltrust.org.uk
nationaltrust.org.uk/coleridge-cottage

Coleridge Cottage		M	T	W	T	F	S	S
23 Mar–29 Oct	11–5			**W**	**T**	**F**	**S**	
10 Dec–18 Dec	11–5						**S**	**S**

Tea-room and shop: opening arrangements not confirmed
at time of print, please check before visiting.

The Courts Garden

Holt, near Bradford on Avon,
Wiltshire BA14 6RR

| 1943 |  |

This curious English country garden is a
hidden gem. Garden rooms of different
styles, shaped by the vision of past owners
and gardeners, reveal themselves at every
turn. You'll find herbaceous borders,
topiary, a peaceful water garden, statuary,
an arboretum, kitchen garden, naturally
planted spring bulbs and a sunken garden.

Parking: 80 to 100 yards
(not National Trust), follow signs.
No parking on village streets please.

Access: 🦽♿🚪🎵👁️📷♿➡️

Find out more: 01225 782875 or
courtsgarden@nationaltrust.org.uk
nationaltrust.org.uk/courts-garden

The Courts Garden		M	T	W	T	F	S	S
5 Feb–27 Feb	11–4						S	S
28 Feb–30 Oct	10:30–5	M	T		T	F	S	S

Dinton Park and Philipps House

Dinton, Salisbury, Wiltshire SP3 5HH | 1943 |

Tranquil rolling parkland, perfect for walks
and picnics, surrounds a neo-Grecian house
designed by Jeffry Wyatville in 1820.
Note: sorry no toilet. Park open daily
(Philipps House currently closed).

Find out more: 01747 841152 or
dintonpark@nationaltrust.org.uk
nationaltrust.org.uk/dinton-park-and-philipps-house

Dunster Castle and Watermill

Dunster, near Minehead,
Somerset TA24 6SL

| 1976 |  |

Dunster Castle and Watermill in Somerset

Dramatically sited on top of a wooded hill,
a castle has existed here since at least
Norman times. Its impressive medieval
gatehouse and ruined Bastion Tower are a
reminder of its turbulent history. The castle
that you see today, home to the Luttrell
family for over 600 years, became an
elegant country home during the 19th
century and features ornate plaster ceilings
and rare 17th-century leather hangings.
The terraced garden displays varieties
of Mediterranean and subtropical plants,
while the tranquil riverside wooded garden
below, with its natural play area, leads
to the surviving 18th-century working
Watermill. There are panoramic views from
the castle and grounds of the surrounding
Exmoor countryside and over the Bristol
Channel towards Wales.

See how you've helped, and what more you can do: nationaltrust.org.uk/donate

Dunster Castle, opposite, sits high on a steep wooded hill. Discovering the garden, above

Parking: castle 300 yards, Watermill 800 yards (main car park – enter from A39). No separate parking at watermill.

Dog rating: 🐾 🐾 **Good** – Welcome on short leads everywhere (excluding castle).

Access:

Find out more: 01643 823004 (Infoline). 01643 821314 or dunstercastle@nationaltrust.org.uk
nationaltrust.org.uk/dunster

Dunster Castle		M	T	W	T	F	S	S
Castle, Watermill and garden								
1 Jan–20 Mar	10–4*						S	S
21 Feb–27 Feb	10–4*	M	T	W	T	F	S	S
21 Mar–30 Oct	10–5*	M	T	W	T	F	S	S
5 Nov–18 Dec	10–4*						S	S
20 Dec–31 Dec	10–4*	M	T	W	T	F	S	S
Park								
1 Jan–20 Mar	10–5	M	T	W	T	F	S	S
21 Mar–30 Oct	10–6	M	T	W	T	F	S	S
31 Oct–31 Dec	10–5	M	T	W	T	F	S	S

*Castle: closes one hour earlier; garden: last entry one hour before closing. Tea-room and shop: opening arrangements not confirmed at time of print, please check before visiting. Everything closed 24 and 25 December.

Fyne Court

near Bridgwater, Somerset

1967

This is a hidden gem in the Quantock Hills. While the house (former home of amateur scientist Andrew Crosse) no longer stands, the site remains simply beautiful within its woods and meadows. A great place for gentle walks, splashing in streams, building dens and discovering ruins.

Satnav: use TA5 2EQ. **Parking**: on site.

Dog rating: 🐾 🐾 **Good** – Welcome on leads in courtyard and on woodland trails. Please keep under close control on wider site.

Access:

Find out more: 01823 451587 or fynecourt@nationaltrust.org.uk
nationaltrust.org.uk/fyne-court

Fyne Court	
Estate	
Open every day all year	

Tea-room: closed 24 and 25 December. Opening varies according to weather conditions.

Glastonbury Tor

near Glastonbury, Somerset   1933

Iconic tor topped by a 15th-century tower, with spectacular views over the Somerset Levels, Dorset and Wiltshire. **Note**: sorry no toilet.

Find out more: 01278 751874 or glastonburytor@nationaltrust.org.uk
nationaltrust.org.uk/glastonbury-tor

Great Chalfield Manor and Garden

near Melksham, Wiltshire SN12 8NH

1943

Great Chalfield Manor and Garden in Wiltshire

A monkey, soldiers and griffins adorn the rooftops of this moated medieval Manor, looking over the terraces of the romantic garden with topiary houses, rose garden and spring-fed fishpond. All is lovingly looked after by the Floyd family. The Manor has featured in several television dramas, including *Wolf Hall*. **Note**: home to the donor family tenants, who manage it for the National Trust.

Parking: 100 yards, on grass verge outside manor gates.

Access:

Find out more: 01225 782239 or greatchalfieldmanor@nationaltrust.org.uk
nationaltrust.org.uk/great-chalfield

Great Chalfield Manor		M	T	W	T	F	S	S
Manor								
3 Apr–30 Oct	Tour*		T	W	T			S
Garden								
3 Apr–30 Oct	1–5							S
5 Apr–27 Oct	11–5		T	W	T			

*Manor: admission by 45-minute guided tour (places limited, bookable) Tuesday, Wednesday and Thursday at 11, 12, 2, 3 and 4; Sunday at 2, 3 and 4. Group visits welcome Friday and Monday (not Bank Holidays); please contact the tenant on 01225 782239 (charges apply, including members).

Horner Wood

on Exmoor, near Minehead, Somerset

1944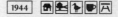

One of the largest and most beautiful ancient oak woods in Britain, Horner Wood is part of the Holnicote Estate. 324 hectares (800 acres) of woodland clothe the lower slopes of surrounding moorland, following river and stream valleys. This National Nature Reserve is home to a rich variety of wildlife. **Note**: toilets in car park.

Satnav: use TA24 8HY. **Parking**: on site.

Dog rating: 🐾 🐾 **Good** – Welcome under close control (wildlife and grazing animals).

Find out more: 01643 862452 or hornerwood@nationaltrust.org.uk
nationaltrust.org.uk/horner-wood

King John's Hunting Lodge

The Square, Axbridge, Somerset BS26 2AP 1968

This early Tudor timber-framed wool merchant's house (dating from around 1500) provides a fascinating insight into local history.
Note: run as a local history museum by Axbridge and District Museum Trust. Open daily, 1 April to 31 October, 1 to 4.

Find out more: 01934 732012 or kingjohns@nationaltrust.org.uk
nationaltrust.org.uk/king-johns-hunting-lodge

Lacock

near Chippenham, Wiltshire

1944 🏛 🏠 ✿ ♨ 🍽 ☕ 🚻 📷 🚶

You can see why Ela of Salisbury chose this spot for her abbey in 1232: nestled alongside the River Avon in a rolling Wiltshire landscape, Lacock invites you to stay. The abbey reveals evidence of a legacy of almost 800 years of past owners with sophisticated taste, who sensitively turned it from a nunnery into an unusual family home, furnished with well-loved mementoes and furniture. Seasonal colour can be discovered in the wooded grounds, Botanic Garden, greenhouse and orchard. The Fox Talbot Museum celebrates William Henry Fox Talbot, who created the first photographic negative and established this as a birthplace of photography. Lacock has a homely feel and the village, with its timber-framed cottages, remains a bustling community. **Note**: abbey winter opening arrangements are limited.

The cloisters at Lacock in Wiltshire are a reminder of a time when this unusual family home was an abbey

Three views of Lacock, above and below: where there is so much to discover

Satnav: may direct down closed road. Set to Hither Way, Lacock, for car park.
Parking: 220 yards. No visitor parking on village streets.

Dog rating: 🐾 🐾 **Good** – 1 September to 31 March welcome on short leads in abbey grounds.

Access:

Find out more: 01249 730459 or lacock@nationaltrust.org.uk
Lacock, near Chippenham, Wiltshire SN15 2LG
nationaltrust.org.uk/lacock

Lacock		M	T	W	T	F	S	S
Abbey Cloister, grounds and Fox Talbot Museum								
2 Jan–27 Feb	11–4			W	T	F	S	S
28 Feb–30 Oct	10–5	M	T	W	T	F	S	S
31 Oct–31 Dec	11–4	M	T	W	T	F	S	S
Abbey rooms (first floor)								
28 Feb–30 Oct	10:30–4:30	M	T	W	T	F	S	S
26 Nov–31 Dec*	11:30–3:30	M	T	W	T	F	S	S

Stables Café and shop: open all year. Courtyard Tea-room: open weekends and school holidays, March to October and Christmas. Last entry 45 minutes before closing. Closed 25, 26 December and 1 January 2023.
*Some rooms open for Christmas.

Download the app to get opening details on your phone – scan the QR code on page 3

Lytes Cary Manor

near Somerton, Somerset TA11 7HU

1949

This intimate medieval manor house was originally home to the Lyte family, who lived here for several generations until the 18th century. After years of neglect, Lytes Cary was lovingly restored in the early 20th century by Sir Walter Jenner and his wife, Lady Flora, and is arranged as it was in their time. A stroll around the Arts and Crafts-inspired garden beside the house reveals garden rooms, divided by high yew hedges, collections of topiary, sensuous herbaceous borders, orchards and manicured lawns. The Manor is surrounded by fertile farmland, wild meadows, woodland and flood plains. **Note**: access to parts of the garden may be restricted to preserve the grass.

Lytes Cary Manor, Somerset, above and below, was lovingly restored in the early 20th century

Parking: 40 yards.

Dog rating: 🐾 🐾 **Good** – Welcome on leads in the courtyard and on estate walks.

Access:

Find out more: 01458 224471 or lytescarymanor@nationaltrust.org.uk
nationaltrust.org.uk/lytes-cary-manor

Lytes Cary Manor		M	T	W	T	F	S	S
19 Feb–27 Mar	10–4*	M	T	W	T	F	S	S
28 Mar–30 Oct	10–5**	M	T	W	T	F	S	S

*House: open 11 to 3:30; tea-room closes 3:45.
**House open 11 to 4:30; tea-room closes 4:45.

Mompesson House

The Close, Salisbury, Wiltshire SP1 2EL

1952 🏠❀✕

Visiting Salisbury's Cathedral Close, you step back into a past world. As you enter Mompesson House, featured in the film *Sense and Sensibility*, the feeling of leaving the modern world behind deepens. The tranquil atmosphere is enhanced by the magnificent plasterwork, graceful oak staircase and fine period furniture, which are the main features of this perfectly proportioned Queen Anne town house. Mompesson House has one of the finest displays of English 18th-century drinking glasses and a collection of stumpwork, a fascinating example of raised embroidery. The garden, with traditional herbaceous borders and pergola, is an oasis of calm in Salisbury.

Step into another world at tranquil Mompesson House in Salisbury, Wiltshire, above and left

Parking: 260 yards in city centre, not National Trust (charge including members).

Access: 🅳♿🦽🖼️♿👁️📷♿

Find out more: 01722 335659 or mompessonhouse@nationaltrust.org.uk
nationaltrust.org.uk/mompesson-house

Mompesson House		M	T	W	T	F	S	S
4 Mar–30 Oct	11–4	M	T	·	·	F	S	S

Montacute House

Montacute, Somerset TA15 6XP

1931 🏠❄✿🦽☕🏚🎭🚶

This architecturally daring Elizabethan mansion was built to flaunt both wealth and power. Today its glittering façade houses a complex interior developed by its owners over 400 years. Montacute House boasts nationally important collections gained from donors' generosity, from 500-year-old tapestries to period portraits on loan from the National Portrait Gallery. Outside, you can walk in Elizabethan footsteps through a formal garden, broken by cloud-pruned hedges and Victorian floral profusion. Wide lawns create open spaces, while avenues of trees lead you out into parkland, bluebell woods and a former motte-and-bailey castle now topped by an 18th-century folly.

Parking: on site.

Dog rating: 🐾 🐾 **Good** – Welcome in garden and café courtyard on short leads (assistance dogs only elsewhere). Dog-friendly walks.

Access: ♿🅿️♿♿♿♿:♿♿➡

Montacute House in Somerset, above and below: a beacon of Elizabethan pomp and style

Find out more: 01935 823289 or montacute@nationaltrust.org.uk
nationaltrust.org.uk/montacute-house

Montacute House		M	T	W	T	F	S	S
House								
1 Jan–27 Feb	11–3	M	T	W	T	F	S	S
28 Feb–30 Oct	11–4:30	M	T	W	T	F	S	S
31 Oct–31 Dec*	11–3	M	T	W	T	F	S	S
Garden, parkland, café and shop								
1 Jan–27 Feb	10–4**	M	T	W	T	F	S	S
28 Feb–30 Oct	10–5**	M	T	W	T	F	S	S
31 Oct–31 Dec*	10–4**	M	T	W	T	F	S	S

*Closed 24 and 25 December. **Café: closes 15 minutes before garden and parkland; shop: opens 11.

Priest's House, Muchelney

Muchelney, Langport, Somerset TA10 0DQ 1911

Medieval hall-house, built in 1308. **Note**: private home. Sorry no toilet. For satnav use TA10 0DQ. Open Sunday and Monday, 10 April to 26 September, 2 to 5.

Find out more: 01935 823289 (Montacute House) or priestshouse@nationaltrust.org.uk
nationaltrust.org.uk/priests-house-muchelney

Prior Park Landscape Garden

Ralph Allen Drive, Bath, Somerset BA2 5AH

[1993] 🍀🦮📷⛸🚶

Perched on a hillside overlooking Bath, this elevated spot was chosen by Ralph Allen to show off his estate to the city. The magical landscape garden that he created captures a moment in time: 1764, the year of Allen's death. There is a lot to discover, including winding paths leading to hidden retreats, dramatic views over Bath and a rare Palladian Bridge. The major restoration project to repair the 18th-century dams is due to finish this year, with replanting to follow. Access to the lakes may be restricted, but you'll have a rare opportunity to see the work in progress. **Note**: steep slopes, steps, uneven paths. House not accessible (not National Trust).

Parking: on site for disabled visitors only (not available during project, please telephone for information). Car parks in city centre, 1 mile (steep, uphill walk), not National Trust (charge including members). Frequent bus services from bus station or City Sightseeing bus (Skyline route) from city centre.

Prior Park Landscape Garden in Bath, Somerset: picnickers, above, and the Palladian Bridge, left

Dog rating: 🐾 **Standard** – Welcome on short leads.

Access: ♿🚻 🚸

Find out more: 01225 833977 or priorpark@nationaltrust.org.uk
nationaltrust.org.uk/prior-park

Prior Park		M	T	W	T	F	S	S
1 Jan–13 Feb	10–4						S	S
19 Feb–30 Oct	10–5*	M	T	W	T	F	S	S
5 Nov–31 Dec**	10–4						S	S

Also open winter Bank Holidays. Last entry one hour before closing. *Closes dusk if earlier. **Closed 25 December. Tea Shed opening times vary.

Sand Point

near Kewstoke, North Somerset [1964]

A natural pier into the Bristol Channel, north of Weston-super-Mare and Brean Down. Perfect for picnics; views across Sand Bay. **Note**: sorry, no toilets. For satnav use BS22 9UD. Steep climbs and cliffs – please stay on main paths. Tide comes in quickly. Overflow car park closed October to March.

Find out more: 01278 751874 or sandpoint@nationaltrust.org.uk
nationaltrust.org.uk/sand-point

Selworthy

on Exmoor, near Minehead, Somerset

1944

Selworthy is a good place to start discovering the wonderfully varied Exmoor landscapes within the 4,856-hectare (12,500-acre) Holnicote Estate. This is a timeless rural landscape of thatched cottages, a medieval church, woodland walks and sweeping views across the vale to Dunkery Beacon, Exmoor's highest point.

Satnav: use TA24 8TP. **Parking**: on site.

Dog rating: 🐾 🐾 **Good** – Welcome under close control.

Find out more: 01643 862452 or selworthy@nationaltrust.org.uk
nationaltrust.org.uk/selworthy

Stoke-sub-Hamdon Priory

North Street, Stoke-sub-Hamdon, Somerset TA14 6QP 1946

Fascinating small complex of buildings, formerly the home of priests serving the Chapel of St Nicholas (now destroyed). **Note**: sorry no toilet. Please respect the privacy of tenants in the main house. Open 10 April to 26 September, Sunday and Monday, 2 to 5.

Find out more: 01935 823289 or stokehamdonpriory@nationaltrust.org.uk
nationaltrust.org.uk/stoke-sub-hamdon-priory

Stonehenge Landscape

near Amesbury, Wiltshire

1927

You can wander freely through thousands of acres of downland within the Stonehenge and Avebury World Heritage Site. The landscape around the famous stones is studded with ancient monuments, such as the Avenue and Cursus, and abounds with wildlife. The visitor centre shuttle stops at Fargo woodland on request. **Note**: English Heritage manages stone circle/facilities. Trust members free (excluding International National Trust or affiliate organisations).

Satnav: use SP3 4DX.
Parking: at visitor centre (English Heritage). Pay and display (free to National Trust members displaying Trust sticker). Booking essential to guarantee a space. Limited parking at Woodhenge.

Dog rating: 🐾 **Standard** – Only in areas where there is no livestock.

Access:

Find out more: 0370 333 1181 (English Heritage). 01672 539920 (National Trust) or stonehenge@nationaltrust.org.uk
nationaltrust.org.uk/stonehenge-landscape

Stonehenge Landscape

English Heritage manages the stone circle and visitor centre (free to National Trust members). Please present your membership card before purchasing tickets or book online via english-heritage.org.uk.

Stourhead

near Mere, Wiltshire BA12 6QD

1946 🏠🏠❄🍽🍴🏪🎒🎯♿

'A living work of art' is how Stourhead was described when it first opened nearly 300 years ago. The world-famous landscape garden surrounds a glistening lake. There are towering trees, exotic rhododendrons, classical temples and a magical grotto to explore. The house at Stourhead was one of the first in the country to showcase Palladian architecture. With a unique Regency library, Chippendale furniture and inspirational paintings, this was a grand family home, shaped by generations of the Hoare family. Outside, views stretch across the countryside, and the lawns are perfect for picnics. Great for walking and wildlife spotting, with 1,072 hectares (2,650 acres) of chalk downs, ancient woods, Iron Age hill forts and farmland to explore.

Stourhead in Wiltshire: discovering the house, below, garden and follies, right and opposite

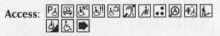

Parking: 400 yards. King Alfred's Tower, 100 yards.

Dog rating: 🐾 🐾 **Good** – Welcome on estate and in garden (on short fixed leads) all year.

Access: 🅿♿♿🚾♿♿♿♿♿♿♿♿ ♿♿➡

Find out more: 01747 841152 or stourhead@nationaltrust.org.uk
nationaltrust.org.uk/stourhead

Stourhead		M	T	W	T	F	S	S
Garden, shop and café								
Open all year	9–4:30*	M	T	W	T	F	S	S
House								
3 Jan–11 Mar**	Tour	M	T	W	T	F	S	S
12 Mar–30 Oct	11–4:30	M	T	W	T	F	S	S
31 Oct–6 Nov	11–3:30	M	T	W	T	F	S	S
25 Nov–23 Dec†	11–3:30	M	T	W	T	F	S	S

*Garden: 28 March to 30 October, closes 5:30; 25 November to 31 December, closes 3:30. Shop: opens 10:30. **House: Monday to Friday, access by tour only (booking essential); Entrance Hall only at weekends. †Selected show rooms only, decorated for Christmas. King Alfred's Tower: contact Stourhead for openings. Everything closed 25 December.

Tintinhull Garden

Farm Street, Tintinhull, Yeovil,
Somerset BA22 8PZ

[1953] 🏵🏠⚔️

The vision of Phyllis Reiss, amateur
gardener, lives on in this small yet
perfectly formed garden, with 'living
rooms' of colour and scent. Created
in the last century around a 17th-century
manor house, it's one of the most
harmonious small gardens in Britain,
featuring secluded lawns, pools and
imaginative borders.

Parking: 150 yards.

Access: 🅿️♿🖼️♨️👣

Find out more: 01458 224471 or
tintinhull@nationaltrust.org.uk
nationaltrust.org.uk/tintinhull

Tintinhull Garden		M	T	W	T	F	S	S
1 Apr–2 Oct	11–4	M	T	.	.	F	S	S

Treasurer's House, Martock

Martock, Somerset TA12 6JL [1971]

Completed in 1293, this medieval
house includes a Great Hall, 15th-century
kitchen and an unusual wall-painting.
Note: private home. Sorry no toilet.
Open 10 April to 26 September,
Sunday and Monday, 2 to 5.

Find out more: 01935 823289
(Montacute House) or
treasurersmartock@nationaltrust.org.uk
nationaltrust.org.uk/treasurers-house-martock

Tyntesfield

Wraxall, Bristol, North Somerset BS48 1PA

[2002] 🏠🏠✖️⚔️♨️🍴🏠🏠🚶‍♂️

**Tyntesfield, North Somerset, this page and
opposite: the height of Victorian Gothic design**

Cocooned in the Somerset countryside,
Tyntesfield is a rare survivor – a near-
complete Victorian Gothic country house
and estate. It was created for the Gibbs
family to celebrate their achievements,
raise their children and share their passions
for family and faith. The richly decorated
house contains over 60,000 of the family's
possessions, some collected by William
Gibbs as he traded in the Hispanic world.
Born in Madrid, William's story is one of
long struggles with debts, of young love,
loss, a close-knit family and the making of
a vast fortune. Today you're welcomed into
this cherished place with its ornate private
chapel, flower-filled terraces, towering
trees, abundant kitchen garden and
views across the working estate to the
Somerset hills.

Tyntesfield		M	T	W	T	F	S	S
House								
1 Jan–20 Feb	11–2:15						S	S
21 Feb–30 Oct	10:30–3:30	M	T	W	T	F	S	S
5 Nov–27 Nov	11–2:15						S	S
1 Dec–31 Dec	11–2:15*	M	T	W	T	F	S	S
Estate								
1 Jan–20 Mar	10–5	M	T	W	T	F	S	S
21 Mar–30 Oct	10–6	M	T	W	T	F	S	S
31 Oct–31 Dec	10–5*	M	T	W	T	F	S	S

*For Christmas opening hours and events, check website. Everything closed 24 and 25 December. Shop closes 30 minutes before estate. Home Farm Café: open 10 to 4. Lower Garden takeaway: open 10:30 to 4:30 in main season. Estate: last entry one hour before closing.

The gardens and chapel at Tyntesfield, above and top

Parking: 50 yards.

Dog rating: 🐾 🐾 **Good** – Welcome on short leads in specified areas (advice available from welcome building).

Access: 🅿♿🚽♿🔊🏛♿📷 🚶♿♿

Find out more: 01275 461900 or tyntesfield@nationaltrust.org.uk **nationaltrust.org.uk/tyntesfield**

Webber's Post

on Exmoor, near Minehead, Somerset | 1944 |

Great spot for views over Horner Wood, short strolls, cycling, picnics and walking up to Dunkery Beacon, Exmoor's highest point. **Note**: sorry no toilet.
For satnav use TA24 8TB.

Find out more: 01643 862452 or webberspost@nationaltrust.org.uk **nationaltrust.org.uk/webbers-post**

Wellington Monument

near Wellington, Somerset

1934

Standing in an informal rural setting on the edge of the Blackdown Hills, Wellington Monument – the world's tallest three-sided obelisk – has recently undergone major repairs and the interior can be viewed on a tour. Enjoy far-reaching views across the Quantock Hills and Exmoor. **Note**: sorry no toilet.

Satnav: use TA21 9PB.
Parking: small car park, ⅓ mile.

Dog rating: 🐾 🐾 **Good** – Welcome under close control.

Access:

Find out more: 01823 451587 or wellingtonmonument@nationaltrust.org.uk
nationaltrust.org.uk/wellington-monument

Wellington Monument
Monument tour times vary, check before visiting.

Wellington Monument in Somerset is the world's tallest three-sided obelisk

Westwood Manor

Westwood, near Bradford on Avon, Wiltshire BA15 2AF

1960

Westwood Manor in Wiltshire: late medieval, Tudor and Jacobean styles all mix harmoniously

Over the centuries, the residents of this small late medieval, Tudor and Jacobean house have modified the building to their own tastes, each leaving a permanent mark. The interiors are rich with decorative plasterwork, fine furniture and beautiful tapestries. Highlights are two rare keyboard instruments: a spinet and a virginal. **Note**: Westwood Manor is a family home, administered by the tenants.

Parking: 90 yards.

Access:

Find out more: 01249 730459 (Lacock) or westwoodmanor@nationaltrust.org.uk
nationaltrust.org.uk/westwood-manor

Westwood Manor			M	T	W	T	F	S	S
3 Apr–28 Sep	2–5				T	W			S

Groups (eight people plus): please email to arrange private tour.

The Cotswolds, Buckinghamshire and Oxfordshire

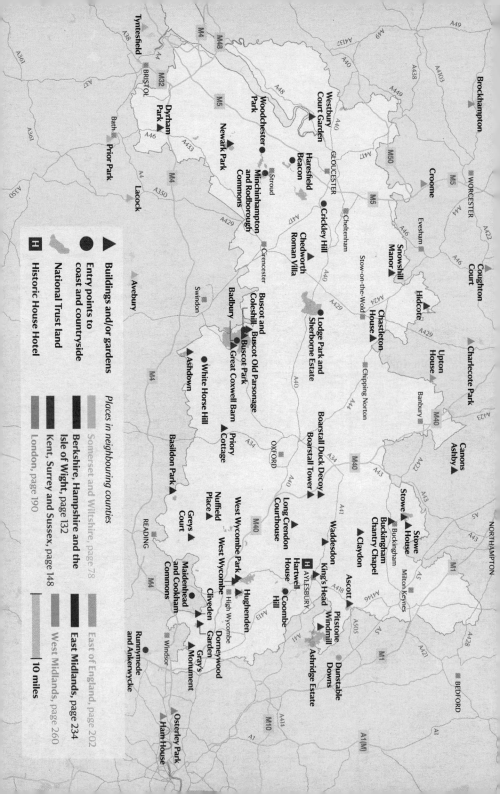

Ascott

Visitors Entrance, Wing, Leighton Buzzard,
Buckinghamshire LU7 0PP

1949 🏚🍀♿☕🏠🍴

Ascott House, an 'Old English'
half-timbered manor, dates back to
the 16th century. It was transformed
by the Rothschilds towards the end
of the 19th century and houses several
exceptional collections. The extensive
gardens are an attractive mix of formal
and natural, with specimen trees, shrubs
and beautiful herbaceous borders.
Note: Ascott is a family home,
administered by the de Rothschild family.

Parking: on site (218 yards).

Access: 🅿♿🏠🔑🚶🏚♿

Find out more: 01296 688242 or
ascott@nationaltrust.org.uk
nationaltrust.org.uk/ascott

Ascott		M	T	W	T	F	S	S
15 Mar–18 Sep	12–5*	·	·	T	W	T	F	S	S

Open Bank Holiday Mondays. *House: opens 2. Tea-room:
open 12 to 4:45. National Gardens Scheme: 2 May and
29 August (adult £6/child £3, charge including members);
house closed. House and garden tickets must be booked
separately online.

**The topiary sundial at
Ascott in Buckinghamshire**

Ashdown

Lambourn, Newbury, Oxfordshire RG17 8RE

1956 🏚🍀♿👨‍👩‍👧🏠🍴

**Ashdown in Oxfordshire was built
for the Queen of Bohemia**

Unique 17th-century chalk-block hunting
lodge, with doll's-house appearance, built
for the Queen of Bohemia by the Earl of
Craven, set in a historic woodland. Come
and learn about this family's intriguing
history, and discover the fine 17th-century
paintings which hang alongside the
staircase. Outstanding rooftop views across
three counties. **Note:** access to roof via
100-step staircase.

Satnav: from B4000 follow local
brown signs. **Parking:** in main estate
car park, 437 yards.

Dog rating: 🐾 **Standard** – Welcome on
leads in woodland only.

Access: ♿🚻🏠🔑🚶

Find out more: 01793 762209 or
ashdown@nationaltrust.org.uk
nationaltrust.org.uk/ashdown

Ashdown		M	T	W	T	F	S	S
House*								
6 Apr–29 Oct	2–5	·	·	W	·	·	S	·
Woodland								
Open all year	Dawn–dusk	M	T	W	T	F	S	S

*House: access by booked tour only (at 2, 3 and 4).

Badbury

Coleshill, near Swindon

2011

Carpets of bluebells light up the woods at Badbury, near Swindon

This former plantation woodland is criss-crossed with easy circular walks, offering stunning views over the Upper Thames Valley. A spread of snowdrops heralds spring, followed by a carpet of bluebells. A copse of military-straight beech trees defines the Iron Age hill fort. **Note**: sorry no toilet.

Satnav: use SN7 7NL.
Parking: at countryside car park.

Dog rating: 🐾 **Standard** – Welcome under close control.

Find out more: 01793 762209 or badbury@nationaltrust.org.uk
nationaltrust.org.uk/badbury

Boarstall Duck Decoy

Boarstall, near Bicester,
Buckinghamshire HP18 9UX 1980

One of the last remaining decoys in the country, a fascinating insight into rural life, with a peaceful woodland walk.

Note: open Sundays, 3 April to 25 September, 11 to 5. Also open Bank Holidays, April to August.

Find out more: 01280 817156 or boarstalldecoy@nationaltrust.org.uk
nationaltrust.org.uk/boarstall-duck-decoy

Boarstall Tower

Boarstall, near Bicester,
Buckinghamshire HP18 9UX 1943

Charming 14th-century moated gatehouse set in beautiful gardens, retaining original fortified appearance. Grade I listed. **Note**: access to upper levels is via a spiral staircase. Approach paths not suitable for wheelchairs. Opening arrangements not confirmed at time of print, please check before visiting.

Find out more: 01280 817156 or boarstalltower@nationaltrust.org.uk
nationaltrust.org.uk/boarstall-tower

Buckingham Chantry Chapel

Market Hill, Buckingham,
Buckinghamshire MK18 1JX 1912

Atmospheric 15th-century chapel, restored by Sir Gilbert Scott in 1875, in the heart of Buckingham. **Note**: opening arrangements not confirmed at time of print, please check before visiting.

Find out more: 01280 817156 or buckinghamchantry@nationaltrust.org.uk
nationaltrust.org.uk/buckingham-chantry-chapel

The Buscot and Coleshill Estates

Coleshill, near Swindon

1956

These countryside estates on the western border of Oxfordshire include the attractive, unspoilt villages of Buscot and Coleshill, each with a thriving tea-room. There are circular walks of differing lengths and a series of footpaths criss-crossing the estates, with breathtaking countryside and wildlife at Buscot Lock and Badbury Hill. **Note**: toilets at the Old Carpenters Yard in Coleshill, outside the estate office and in Buscot.

Satnav: use SN6 7PT. **Parking**: at Buscot car park, Coleshill Old Carpenters Yard and by Coleshill Estate office.

Dog rating: ✿ **Standard** – Welcome on leads near livestock and under close control at all times.

Access:

Find out more: 01793 762209 or buscotandcoleshill@nationaltrust.org.uk
nationaltrust.org.uk/buscot-coleshill-estates

Buscot and Coleshill
Countryside and footpaths open dawn to dusk.

Buscot Old Parsonage

Buscot, Faringdon, Oxfordshire SN7 8DQ 1949

Beautiful early 18th-century house with small walled garden, on the banks of the Thames. **Note**: sorry no toilet. Access by email request.

Find out more: 01793 762209 or buscot@nationaltrust.org.uk
nationaltrust.org.uk/buscot-old-parsonage

Buscot Park

Faringdon, Oxfordshire SN7 8BU

1949

Buscot Park in Oxfordshire

Lord Faringdon's family live in the house, maintain the interior, manage the grounds, gardens and tea-room, and are responsible for the public display of the contents owned by The Faringdon Collection Trust. This unusual arrangement with the National Trust breathes life into the property and gives it an individualistic air.

Parking: on site.

Dog rating: ✿ **Standard** – In paddock (overflow car park) only.

Access:

Find out more: 01367 240932 (Infoline). 01367 240786 or buscotpark@nationaltrust.org.uk
nationaltrust.org.uk/buscot-park

Buscot Park
Opening arrangements not confirmed at time of print, please check before visiting.

Chastleton House

near Moreton-in-Marsh, Oxfordshire

1991

Chastleton House, Oxfordshire, is an intriguing time capsule of 400 years of family life

Within the warm, weathered Cotswold stone walls of this ancient country house lie faded elegant interiors full of myths and memories – a compelling time capsule of 400 years of family life. Discover the secrets they hide, then explore the garden, a sleeping beauty preserved in graceful decline. **Note**: house is challenging for the less able.

Satnav: use GL56 0SP to the Greedy Goose pub, then follow brown signs.
Parking: on site at visitor centre. Limited designated parking (available by request). No roadside parking.

Access:

Find out more: 01608 674355 or chastleton@nationaltrust.org.uk
Chastleton, near Moreton-in-Marsh, Oxfordshire GL56 0SU
nationaltrust.org.uk/chastleton

Chastleton House		M	T	W	T	F	S	S
2 Mar–30 Oct	1–5*			W	T	F	S	S

*House: last entry one hour before closing.

Chedworth Roman Villa

Yanworth, near Cheltenham, Gloucestershire GL54 3LJ

1924

Cradled in a beautiful wooded valley and fed by a natural spring, this high-status Roman villa saw imperial fashions and local spirits living side by side. Nature took over and hid the magnificent mosaics, intricate hypocaust systems, bathhouses and ancient water shrine for more than 1,500 years until Victorian gamekeepers rediscovered the site. The National Trust has, in turn, looked after Chedworth's Roman treasures and Victorian legacy for nearly a century, providing its modern villa guests with new facilities, as well as astonishing archaeology, to enjoy. It remains a hidden place of natural beauty and continual discovery.

The Shooting Lodge at Chedworth Roman Villa, Gloucestershire, below. Living history, above

Parking: on lane at entrance, plus woodland overflow (February to November).

Access: 🅿️ 🅳 ♿ 🚻 📷 🧏 🎧 ♿ ➡️

Find out more: 01242 890256 or chedworth@nationaltrust.org.uk
nationaltrust.org.uk/chedworth

Chedworth Roman Villa		M	T	W	T	F	S	S
14 Feb–27 Mar	10–4	M	T	W	T	F	S	S
28 Mar–30 Oct	10–5	M	T	W	T	F	S	S
31 Oct–27 Nov	10–4	M	T	W	T	F	S	S

Claydon

Middle Claydon, near Buckingham, Buckinghamshire MK18 2EY

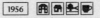 1956 🏠🏠♿☕

The Gothic Room at elegant Georgian Claydon in Buckinghamshire

Nestled in peaceful parkland, Claydon House bears testament to the tenacity and resilience of the Verney family who established the estate in 1620. A simple Georgian exterior hides lavish interiors showcasing every 18th-century style imaginable; Palladian, Neo-classical, chinoiserie and Gothick fantasy. Claydon is an architectural wonder. A house of inspiration. **Note**: Claydon Courtyard (not National Trust).

Parking: on site, limited hard-standing parking.

Dog rating: ❀ **Standard** – Welcome on leads in the courtyard and on public rights of way (assistance dogs only in house).

Access: 🅿️ 🅳 ♿ 🚻 📺 🎧 ♿ ➡️

Find out more: 01296 730349 or claydon@nationaltrust.org.uk
nationaltrust.org.uk/claydon

Claydon		M	T	W	T	F	S	S
House and south lawn*								
6 May–1 Oct	11–3					F	S	

*House: booking advisable. Phoenix Kitchen (not National Trust), open 10 to 5.

Cliveden

near Maidenhead, Buckinghamshire

1942 🏛♣🏊🍴🛍🏠🎑🚶

Satnav: for gardens use Cliveden Road and SL1 8NS; for woodlands use SL6 0HJ.
Parking: on site.

Dog rating: 🐾🐾 **Good** – Welcome under close control in woodlands; other locations on a short lead.

Access: 🅿🚍🚻♿🔢🔄♿🚶♿➡

Find out more: 01628 605069 or cliveden@nationaltrust.org.uk
Cliveden Road, Taplow, Maidenhead, Buckinghamshire SL1 8NS
nationaltrust.org.uk/cliveden

Cliveden	
Garden, shop, café and woodland	
Open every day all year*	9:30–5**

House and chapel: limited opening April to October (call for details). House: admission by timed ticket only.
*Closed 24 and 25 December. **1 January to 18 February and 31 October to 31 December: estate closes 4. Shop: opens 10.

Cliveden in Buckinghamshire and its gardens, this page and opposite, capture the grandeur of a bygone age

A majestic vision set high above the Thames, Cliveden is a proud celebration of status and splendour, where the charms of art and nature join. Six powerful families have embellished and enhanced Cliveden's history over the course of 350 years. Each family added their own extravagant touch, creating a series of distinctive and delightful gardens. You can discover vibrant floral displays at the grand Parterre, satisfying symmetry in the Long Garden, the tranquil intimacy of the Rose Garden and rich autumn colour within the oriental Water Garden. The tree-lined avenue of the Green Drive is the spine of the estate, acting as a gateway to the miles of footpaths that meander through the majestic woodlands and along the riverbank.

The Cotswolds, Buckinghamshire and Oxfordshire

Coombe Hill

Butler's Cross, near Wendover,
Buckinghamshire 1918

Nationally important chalk grassland site
and the highest viewpoint in the Chilterns –
with stunning views over the Aylesbury Vale.
Note: sorry no toilet. For satnav use HP17 0UR.

Find out more: 01494 755573 or
coombehill@nationaltrust.org.uk

Crickley Hill

Birdlip, Gloucestershire GL4 8JY 1935

Sitting high on the Cotswold escarpment
with views towards the Welsh hills, Crickley
Hill overlooks Gloucester and Cheltenham.
Note: car parks, café, toilets and visitor
centre not National Trust. Parking charges
(including members). For satnav use GL4 8JY.

Find out more: 01452 814213 or
crickleyhill@nationaltrust.org.uk
nationaltrust.org.uk/crickley-hill

Dorneywood Garden

Dorneywood, Dorney Wood Road,
Burnham, Buckinghamshire SL1 8PY 1942

Ministerial residence since 1954 with country
garden. Teas. Open selected afternoons.
Note: no photography. Visitor details
recorded for security reasons. Opening
arrangements may change, please check
before visiting (booking essential).

Find out more:
dorneywood@nationaltrust.org.uk
nationaltrust.org.uk/dorneywood

Dyrham Park

Dyrham, near Bath,
South Gloucestershire SN14 8HY

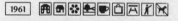

**Ancient parkland surrounds Dyrham Park in
South Gloucestershire: perfect for adventures**

Dyrham Park is a place of exploration.
Outdoor adventurers can savour the
far-reaching views towards the Welsh
hills from the 109 hectares (270 acres)
of ancient parkland. For inspiration and
tranquillity, you can wander round the
ever-changing garden. Sumptuous planting
in the Pool Garden contrasts with the
formality of The Avenue, set against the
peaceful wooded terraces. In the house
you'll be able to get a taste of the
17th century, with a collection of objects
and art belonging to William Blathwayt –
Secretary at War to King William III and
Auditor General of Plantation Revenues.
A newly opened exhibition will explore
Blathwayt's career and the developments
that helped shape modern Britain.

Dyrham Park offers a taste of the 17th century, with intriguing treasures and collections

The Cotswolds, Buckinghamshire and Oxfordshire

Exploring Dyrham Park
inside and out, above and top

Satnav: enter via A46. **Parking**: on site
(just over ½ mile from house).

Access: 🅿️♿🚾♿♿🖼️📷♿♿➡️

Find out more: 0117 937 2501 or
dyrhampark@nationaltrust.org.uk
nationaltrust.org.uk/dyrham-park

Dyrham Park		M	T	W	T	F	S	S
Park, garden, shop and tea-room								
Open all year*	10–4**	M	T	W	T	F	S	S
House								
Open all year*	12–4	M	T	W	T	F	S	S

*Last entry one hour before closing; closed 24 and
25 December. **19 February to 30 October: tea-room
open to 4:30, everything else to 5; shop opens 11.

Gray's Monument

Stoke Poges, Buckinghamshire
SL2 4NZ 1925

This 5-metre-high monument, surrounded
by expansive parkland views, captures
the poet Thomas Gray's long association
with the village. **Note**: sorry no toilet.
For satnav use SL2 4NZ.

Find out more: 01628 605069 (Cliveden)
or graysmonument@nationaltrust.org.uk

Great Coxwell Barn

Great Coxwell, Faringdon,
Oxfordshire SN7 7LZ 1956

Former 13th-century monastic barn, a
favourite of William Morris, who would
regularly bring his guests to wonder at its
structure. **Note**: sorry no toilet; narrow
access lanes leading to property.

Find out more: 01793 762209 or
greatcoxwellbarn@nationaltrust.org.uk
nationaltrust.org.uk/great-coxwell-barn

Greys Court

Rotherfield Greys, Henley-on-Thames,
Oxfordshire RG9 4PG

1969 

Set in the rolling hills of the Chilterns, Greys Court is a picturesque Tudor manor house surrounded by layers of history, intimate walled gardens and glorious wooded parkland. The house is warm and welcoming, unfurling the memories of the Brunner family through the rooms of their comfortable home. Across the perfect lawn, a medieval tower and patchwork of mellow brick buildings conceal an English country garden. Through an ancient arch, seasonal blooms are revealed, from bright bulbs through clematis and wisteria to glorious peonies and roses in the summer. Winter walks in the woodland are a must.

Parking: 220 yards.

Dog rating: ❀ **Standard** – Welcome on leads (excluding house, tea-room and walled gardens). Livestock grazing all year.

Greys Court in Oxfordshire: Lady Brunner's Bedroom, above, and the garden in May, below

Access:

Find out more: 01491 628529 or
greyscourt@nationaltrust.org.uk
nationaltrust.org.uk/greys-court

Greys Court		M	T	W	T	F	S	S
House*								
16 Feb–6 Nov	11–4**	·	·	W	T	F	S	S
26 Nov–31 Dec†	11–3	·	·	W	T	F	S	S
Garden, tea-room and shop								
Open all year†	10–5**	M	T	W	T	F	S	S

*House: last entry one hour before closing. **1 January to 27 March and 31 October to 31 December: site closes at 4, house closes 3; 4 September: everything opens at midday for village fête. †Closed 24 and 25 December.

Haresfield Beacon

near Stroud, Gloucestershire

1931 🏠♿🖼

High on three spurs of the Cotswold escarpment with views towards the Brecon Beacons. Abundant wildlife and a wealth of archaeological features to discover, including a hill fort and cross dyke.

Satnav: use GL6 6PP for Shortwood car park. **Parking**: at Shortwood.

Dog rating: ✿ **Standard** – Welcome on leads.

Find out more: 01452 814213 or haresfieldbeacon@nationaltrust.org.uk **nationaltrust.org.uk/haresfield-beacon**

Hartwell House and Spa

Oxford Road, near Aylesbury, Buckinghamshire HP17 8NR

2008 🏠✿♿🍴

Elegant Grade I-listed stately home, with both Jacobean and Georgian façades, a magnificent Great Hall and elegant drawing rooms. Set in beautifully landscaped grounds, including a ruined Gothick church, lake, bridge and 36 hectares (90 acres) of parkland. One hour from central London. **Note**: access is for hotel guests only, including for luncheon, afternoon tea and dinner. Children over six welcome. Held on a long lease from the Ernest Cook Trust.

Find out more: 01296 747444 or info@hartwell-house.com **hartwell-house.com**

Hidcote

near Chipping Campden, Gloucestershire

1948 ✿🍴🏠🖼🦮

Vivid tulips at Hidcote in Gloucestershire

This world-famous Arts and Crafts-inspired garden is nestled in a north Cotswolds hamlet. Created by the talented horticulturist Major Lawrence Johnston, Hidcote's colourful and intricately designed outdoor spaces are full of surprises, which change in harmony with the seasons. Many of the unusual plants found growing in the garden were collected from Johnston's plant-hunting trips around the world. Wandering along the narrow pathways, you come across secret gardens, unexpected views and plants that burst with colour.

Satnav: follow signs to Mickleton village and then brown signs to Hidcote. **Parking**: 100 yards.

Access: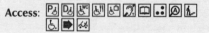

Find out more: 01386 438333 or
hidcote@nationaltrust.org.uk
Hidcote Bartrim, near Chipping Campden,
Gloucestershire GL55 6LR
nationaltrust.org.uk/hidcote

Hidcote		M	T	W	T	F	S	S
Garden, shop and Winthrop's Café								
1 Jan–13 Feb	11–4						S	S
14 Feb–27 Mar	11–4	M	T	W	T	F	S	S
28 Mar–25 Sep	10–5	M	T	W	T	F	S	S
26 Sep–30 Oct	11–4	M	T	W	T	F	S	S
5 Nov–18 Dec	11–4						S	S

Barn café and plant centre: opening hours vary.
Garden: last entry one hour before closing.

Hughenden

High Wycombe, Buckinghamshire HP14 4LA

It's hardly surprising that the
unconventional Victorian Prime Minister
Benjamin Disraeli so loved Hughenden. His
handsome home, set in an unspoiled
Chiltern valley with views of ancient woods
and rolling hills, is full of fascinating
personal memorabilia of this charismatic
colourful statesman. Disraeli's country
retreat later became the headquarters for a
top-secret Second World War operation
codenamed 'Hillside' and put Hughenden
high on Hitler's target list. The Hillside
exhibition and ice-house bunker bring
wartime Britain to life. The estate also
offers a variety of walks in the parkland
and wider countryside, rewarding visitors
with views of the Chiltern Hills.

Parking: on site.

Dog rating: 🐾 🐾 **Good** – Welcome on
short leads in orchard, gardens and shop.
Assistance dogs only in manor.

Access: ⬚⬚⬚⬚⬚⬚⬚⬚⬚⬚⬚
⬚⬚⬚⬚➡

Find out more: 01494 755565 (Infoline).
01494 755573 or
hughenden@nationaltrust.org.uk
nationaltrust.org.uk/hughenden

Hughenden		M	T	W	T	F	S	S
House								
12 Feb–30 Oct	11–5*	M	T	W	T	F	S	S
31 Oct–31 Dec	11–3*	M	T	W	T	F	S	S
Garden								
1 Jan–11 Feb	10–4	M	T	W	T	F	S	S
12 Feb–30 Oct	10–5	M	T	W	T	F	S	S
31 Oct–31 Dec	10–4	M	T	W	T	F	S	S

Everything closed 24 and 25 December.
*House: last entry 45 minutes before closing.

Hughenden, Buckinghamshire, below and left

King's Head

King's Head Passage,
Market Square, Aylesbury,
Buckinghamshire HP20 2RW | 1925 |

Historic public house dating back to 1455, with a pleasant family atmosphere. This is one of England's best-preserved coaching inns. **Note**: Farmers' Bar leased by Chiltern Brewery. Open every day all year, times vary (please check before visiting).

Find out more: 01296 718812 (Farmers' Bar). 01280 817156 (National Trust) or kingshead@nationaltrust.org.uk
nationaltrust.org.uk/kings-head

Lodge Park and Sherborne Park Estate

near Cheltenham, Gloucestershire

| 1987 |

A family explores Lodge Park and Sherborne Park Estate in Gloucestershire

The Sherborne Park Estate is home to a wide array of wildlife. Lodge Park is England's only 17th-century deer-coursing grandstand. Set within a landscape designed by Charles Bridgeman, it was built to satisfy John 'Crump' Dutton's love of gambling and entertaining. There are lovely waymarked walks around the estate. **Note**: no toilets. Lodge Park open on occasional weekends and by booking only.

Satnav: for Lodge Park use GL54 3PP; for Sherborne Estate use GL54 3DT (Ewe Pen Barn) or GL54 3DL (Water Meadows).
Parking: on site for Lodge Park. For Sherborne Estate use either Ewe Pen Barn or Water Meadows car parks.

Dog rating: ❖ **Standard** – Welcome on leads.

Access: [🦽]

Find out more: 01451 844257 or sherborneestate@nationaltrust.org.uk
Aldsworth, near Cheltenham, Gloucestershire GL54 3PP
nationaltrust.org.uk/lodge-park-and-sherborne-estate

Lodge Park and Sherborne Park	
Sherborne Park Estate	
Open every day all year	Dawn–dusk

Lodge Park: for more information email lodgepark@nationaltrust.org.uk or visit website.

Long Crendon Courthouse

Long Crendon, Aylesbury,
Buckinghamshire HP18 9AN | 1900 |

Superb example of a 14th-century courthouse with a wealth of local history – the second building acquired by the National Trust. **Note**: extremely steep stairs. Sorry no toilet. Open April to October, Wednesdays, Saturdays and Sundays, 11 to 5, plus Bank Holidays, April to October.

Find out more: 01280 817156 or longcrendon@nationaltrust.org.uk
nationaltrust.org.uk/long-crendon-courthouse

Minchinhampton and Rodborough Commons

near Stroud, Gloucestershire

 1913

Minchinhampton and Rodborough Commons in Gloucestershire

These historic Cotswold commons, traditionally grazed, are famed for rare flowers and butterflies, prehistoric remains and far-reaching views. Minchinhampton Common contains a nationally important complex of Neolithic and Bronze Age burial mounds, while Rodborough Common's limestone grasslands have abundant wild flowers, including rare pasqueflowers and many varieties of orchid.

Satnav: use GL5 5BJ for Minchinhampton; GL5 5BP for Rodborough (postcodes may be approximate). **Parking**: at reservoir car park on Minchinhampton Common; Rodborough Fort car park on Rodborough Common.

Dog rating: ✿ **Standard** – Welcome on leads.

Find out more: 01452 814213 or minchinhampton@nationaltrust.org.uk
nationaltrust.org.uk/minchinhampton-and-rodborough-commons

Newark Park

Ozleworth, Wotton-under-Edge, Gloucestershire GL12 7PZ

1949

With splendid views from the Cotswold escarpment, Newark Park is a secluded estate with a historic country home at its heart. From Tudor beginnings to dramatic rescue by a 20th-century Texan, the house has many stories. The informal garden and estate offer space to play, contemplate and explore. **Note**: café open-air seating only.

Satnav: only works when approaching from north; if approaching from south follow brown signs from Wotton-under-Edge and A46. **Parking**: 100 yards from house.

Dog rating: ✿ ✿ **Good** – Welcome on leads in garden and estate (be aware of peacocks and grazing livestock).

Access:

Find out more: 01453 842644 or newarkpark@nationaltrust.org.uk
nationaltrust.org.uk/newark-park

Newark Park		M	T	W	T	F	S	S
Garden, estate and tea pavilion*								
1 Jan–6 Feb	10–4						S	S
7 Feb–27 Feb	10–4	M		W	T	F	S	S
28 Feb–30 Oct	10–5	M		W	T	F	S	S
4 Nov–18 Dec	10–4					F	S	S
26 Dec–31 Dec**	10–4	M		W	T	F	S	
House								
5 Feb–30 Oct	11–4	M		W	T	F	S	S
4 Nov–18 Dec	11–4					F	S	S

*Tea pavilion: open 10:30 to 4. **Garden, estate and tea pavilion: also open 3 January.

Nuffield Place

Huntercombe, near Henley-on-Thames,
Oxfordshire RG9 5RY

2011 · 🏠 ✺ 📷 🎍

**Nuffield Place in Oxfordshire remains just
as the owners left it, both inside and out**

Nuffield Place reveals the surprisingly
down-to-earth lives of Lord Nuffield,
founder of the Morris Motor Company,
and his wife. Their home and personal
possessions are just as they left them, the
décor and furnishings intact. This intimate
home exudes the tastes and interests
of its remarkable owner.

Parking: on site.

Dog rating: ✤ **Standard** – Welcome on
leads in the gardens and woodlands.

Access: P♿ ♿WC 🖥 🎍 ♿

Find out more: 01491 641224 or
nuffieldplace@nationaltrust.org.uk
nationaltrust.org.uk/nuffield-place

Nuffield Place

Opening arrangements not confirmed at time of print,
please check before visiting.

Pitstone Windmill

Ivinghoe, Buckinghamshire LU7 9EJ 1937

Believed to be the oldest postmill
in England with stunning views of
the Chilterns. **Note**: sorry no toilet.
Access to windmill 262 yards via
a grassy field track. Steep steps.
Opening arrangements not
confirmed at time of print,
please check before visiting.

Find out more: 01442 851227 or
pitstonemill@nationaltrust.org.uk
nationaltrust.org.uk/pitstone-windmill

Priory Cottage

1 Mill Street, Steventon, Abingdon,
Oxfordshire OX13 6SP 1939

Now converted into two houses, these
former monastic buildings were gifted
to the National Trust by the famous
Ferguson's Gang. **Note**: administered
by tenant. Sorry no toilet. Open by
appointment only, please email.

Find out more: 01793 762209 or
priorycottages@nationaltrust.org.uk
nationaltrust.org.uk/priory-cottage

Snowshill Manor and Garden

Snowshill, near Broadway,
Gloucestershire WR12 7JU

1951 ⌂ ❀ ☕ ⛫ ⛩ 🚶 🐕

Charles Wade was an artist and architect who collected curious and interesting objects that were for him a celebration of colour, craftsmanship and design. With a sense of fun and theatre, he took great pleasure in turning his home into a stage for these varied and sometimes unusual finds. Next to the manor house is the small cottage where Charles Wade lived. Both the manor house and cottage are surrounded by an intimate Arts and Crafts terraced garden where he created 'different courts for different moods'.

Satnav: follow signs from centre of village.
Parking: 500 yards.

Access: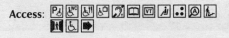

Find out more: 01386 852410 or
snowshillmanor@nationaltrust.org.uk
nationaltrust.org.uk/snowshill-manor

Snowshill Manor		M	T	W	T	F	S	S
Manor								
14 Mar–30 Oct	11:30–4:30	M	T	W	T	F	S	S
5 Nov–27 Nov	11–2:30						S	S
Garden, shop and café								
14 Mar–30 Oct	11–5:30	M	T	W	T	F	S	S
5 Nov–27 Nov	10:30–3:30						S	S

Manor: admission places limited, entry by timed tickets.
Last entry one hour before closing. Charles Wade's cottage opens at 11.

The Nychthemeron Clock, above, and attic, below, at Snowshill Manor and Garden, Gloucestershire

Stowe

Buckingham, Buckinghamshire MK18 5EQ

1989 | 🏠🎴🎣🍺🏠📷🧗

The beauty of Stowe has attracted visitors since 1717. At first glance, the grounds might look like natural, rolling countryside with a river meandering through it, but Stowe was created by human hand. Full of

hidden meaning, classical references and visual trickery, this is an earthly paradise. Picture-perfect views, temples and lakeside walks create a monumental landscape that changes with the seasons. Follow in the footsteps of 18th-century tourists by starting your visit at the New Inn visitor centre. From here it is a half-mile walk down a tree-lined avenue to the garden, where another world awaits. Enjoy the perfect balance of nature, beauty and history as you choose your own route through the historic gardens and parkland beyond.

Parking: 800 metres.

Dog rating: 🐾 🐾 **Good** – Welcome on leads (downloadable dog trail available). Tie-up points and water provided.

Access: ♿🚻🧑‍🦽🔄♿⬆♿

Stowe in Buckinghamshire: the Palladian Bridge, below, and Pebble Alcove, above

The arch of the cascade frames a view of the Eleven Acre Lake at Stowe

Find out more: 01280 817156 or stowe@nationaltrust.org.uk
nationaltrust.org.uk/stowe

Stowe	
Open every day all year*	10–5**

Gardens and café: open 9 at weekends.
*Closed 24 and 25 December. **1 January to 6 February and 31 October to 31 December: closes 4.

Stowe House

Buckingham, Buckinghamshire
MK18 5EH 1997

Stunning 18th-century house in the heart of Stowe's gardens. You can explore the restored state rooms and discover fascinating history. **Note**: operated by the Stowe House Preservation Trust. For satnav use MK18 5EQ. Opening arrangements not confirmed at time of print, please check before visiting.

Find out more: 01280 818002 or stowehouse@nationaltrust.org.uk

Waddesdon

Waddesdon, near Aylesbury,
Buckinghamshire HP18 0JH

Dog rating: 🐾 🐾 **Good** – Welcome outdoors on short leads (except parterre, aviary and woodland playground).

Access: [icons]

Find out more: 01296 820414 or enquiries@waddesdon.org.uk
nationaltrust.org.uk/waddesdon

Waddesdon		M	T	W	T	F	S	S
Winter Light, gardens, aviary, playground, food-to-go, shop								
6 Jan–23 Jan	2–9	·	·	·	T	F	S	S
Gardens, aviary, playground, gallery, shop, food-to-go*								
12 Feb–27 Feb	10–4	·	·	W	T	F	S	S
2 Mar–30 Oct	10–5	·	·	W	T	F	S	S
House**								
23 Mar–30 Oct	11–4	·	·	W	T	F	S	S
Christmas Fair and Winter Light								
12 Nov–23 Dec	12–7	·	·	W	T	F	S	S
Christmas Winter Light								
27 Dec–31 Dec	2–9	·	T	W	T	F	S	·

*Grounds: also open 21/22 February, 18/19 April, 2 and 30/31 May, 30 August, 25/26 October. **House: entry by timed ticket (advance online booking advised), recommended entry before 2:30; open Bank Holidays 18 April, 2 May and 29 August. Special ticketed events 2, 3 and 4 September and 12 November to 2 January 2023. Everything closed 31 October to 11 November and 24 to 26 December. Check at waddesdon.org.uk for house and restaurant opening details.

Waddesdon in Buckinghamshire:
the north front of the French-style château

Waddesdon is a Rothschild house and gardens managed by the Rothschild Foundation. Baron Ferdinand started building the manor in 1874 to display his outstanding collection of art treasures and entertain fashionable society. His choice of a French-style château surprises many visitors. The highest quality 18th-century French decorative arts are displayed alongside magnificent English portraits and Dutch Old Master paintings in 40 elegant interiors. Outside is one of the finest Victorian gardens in Britain, famous for its parterre and ornate working aviary, and enhanced with classical and contemporary sculpture. Today, the manor continues its tradition of entertainment and hospitality, with events celebrating food and wine. Changing exhibitions help visitors find out more about Waddesdon's history, collections and gardens.

Parking: ¾ mile, frequent shuttle bus (tickets available online or on bus). Also Premium parking £20, book online (charge including members). Electric vehicle charging points in both car parks.

Enjoying a sunny picnic on the lawn at Waddesdon, this picture, and the Grey Drawing Room, opposite

West Wycombe Park

West Wycombe, Buckinghamshire HP14 3AJ

1943

Alongside this historic village lies an exquisite Palladian villa. This lavish home and serene landscape garden reflect the wealth and personality of its creator, the infamous Sir Francis Dashwood, founder of the Hellfire Club. Still home to the Dashwood family and their fine collection, it remains a busy, private estate. **Note**: opened in partnership with the Dashwood family. The Hellfire Caves and café are privately owned.

Parking: on site.

Access:

Find out more: 01494 755571 (Infoline). 01494 513569 or westwycombe@nationaltrust.org.uk
nationaltrust.org.uk/west-wycombe-park

West Wycombe Park		M	T	W	T	F	S	S
House								
1 Jun–31 Aug	2–5*	M	T	W	T			S
Garden								
3 Apr–31 Aug	2–5	M	T	W	T			S

*House: entry Monday to Thursday by guided tour (timed tickets). Free flow on Sundays and Bank Holidays.

The Palladian villa at West Wycombe Park in Buckinghamshire, this picture, and looking up at the hill from the park, above

West Wycombe Village and Hill

West Wycombe, Buckinghamshire HP14 3AJ

This historic village, above, with its many buildings of architectural interest, was an important coaching stop between London and Oxford. West Wycombe Hill offers commanding views over West Wycombe Park and the surrounding countryside. On top of the hill is St Lawrence Church with its famous golden ball. **Note**: church and mausoleum not National Trust.

Parking: roadside parking in village and on West Wycombe Hill.

Dog rating: 🐾 🐾 **Good** – Welcome on West Wycombe Hill and in village.

Find out more: 01494 755571 (Infoline). 01494 513569 or westwycombe@nationaltrust.org.uk **nationaltrust.org.uk/west-wycombe-park-village-and-hill**

Westbury Court Garden

Westbury-on-Severn, Gloucestershire GL14 1PD

Originally laid out between 1696 and 1705, this is the only restored Dutch water garden in the country. There are canals, clipped hedges, working 17th-century vegetable plots and many old varieties of fruit trees.

Parking: car park (spaces limited) 300 yards from main road.

Dog rating: 🐾 **Standard** – Welcome on short leads at all times.

Access:

Find out more: 01452 760461 or westburycourt@nationaltrust.org.uk **nationaltrust.org.uk/westbury-court-garden**

Westbury Court Garden		M	T	W	T	F	S	S
2 Mar–30 Oct	11–5	·	·	**W**	**T**	**F**	**S**	**S**

Open Bank Holidays.

The Summer House at Westbury Court Garden in Gloucestershire

White Horse Hill

Uffington, Oxfordshire

1979

The White Horse at Uffington is part of an ancient landscape, steeped in history and mythology. It's the oldest chalk figure in the country, dated to the late Bronze Age about 3,000 years ago. Its linear form dominates the landscape, yet no one knows how it was made. The walls of an Iron Age hill fort are visible on the hilltop, the highest point in Oxfordshire. You can also look down on a valley known as The Manger and a natural outcrop known as Dragon Hill, where

White Horse Hill in Oxfordshire, this picture, and discovering the ancient landscape, above

**Scouring the chalk figure, above, at
White Horse Hill, and the White Horse, top**

St George was said to have fought and
slain the dragon. **Note**: archaeological
monuments under English Heritage
guardianship. Sorry no toilet.

Satnav: use SN7 7QJ. **Parking**: on site.

Dog rating: ❧ **Standard** – Welcome
on leads at all times (stock grazing
and nesting birds).

Access: 🅿♿

Find out more: 01793 762209 or
whitehorsehill@nationaltrust.org.uk
nationaltrust.org.uk/white-horse-hill

Woodchester Park

Nympsfield, near Stroud, Gloucestershire

 1994

This tranquil wooded valley contains
a 'lost landscape': remains of an 18th- and
19th-century landscape park with a chain of
five lakes. The restoration of this landscape
is an ongoing project. Waymarked trails
(steep in places) lead through picturesque
scenery, passing an unfinished Victorian
mansion. **Note**: toilet not always available.
Mansion managed by Woodchester
Mansion Trust (not National Trust).

Satnav: nearest GL10 3TS, then follow
signs. **Parking**: accessible from Nympsfield
road, 300 yards from junction with B4066.

Dog rating: ❧ **Standard** – Welcome
on leads.

Find out more: 01452 814213 or
woodchesterpark@nationaltrust.org.uk
nationaltrust.org.uk/woodchester

**Woodchester Park in Gloucestershire:
one of the many walks**

A family exploring the parkland in autumn at Basildon Park, Berkshire

Berkshire, Hampshire and the Isle of Wight

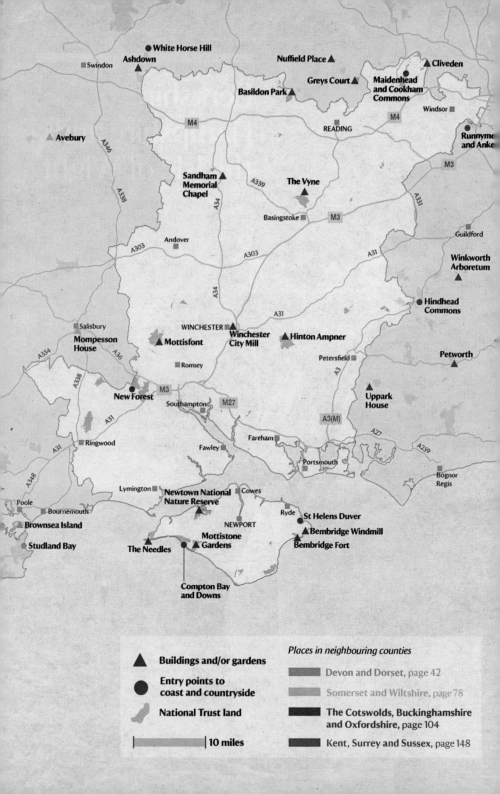

White Horse Hill

Swindon

Ashdown

Nuffield Place

Cliveden

Greys Court

Maidenhead
and Cookham
Commons

Basildon Park

Windsor

M4

M4

READING

Runnyme
and Anke

Avebury

A346

A338

Sandham
Memorial
Chapel

A339

The Vyne

M3

M3

A34

Basingstoke

M3

Guildford

Andover

A303

A303

A34

A31

Winkworth
Arboretum

A31

A354

Salisbury

Mompesson
House

A36

WINCHESTER

Mottisfont

Winchester
City Mill

A31

Hinton Ampner

Hindhead
Commons

Petworth

A338

Romsey

Petersfield

A3

Uppark
House

New Forest

M3

Southampton

M27

A31

Ringwood

Fawley

M27

Fareham

A3(M)

Portsmouth

A27

A259

Bognor
Regis

Poole

Bournemouth

Lymington

Newtown National
Nature Reserve

Cowes

Ryde

St Helens Duver

A348

Brownsea Island

Studland Bay

The Needles

Mottistone
Gardens

NEWPORT

Bembridge Windmill

Bembridge Fort

Compton Bay
and Downs

▲ Buildings and/or gardens

● Entry points to
coast and countryside

National Trust land

|_____| 10 miles

Places in neighbouring counties

Devon and Dorset, page 42

Somerset and Wiltshire, page 78

The Cotswolds, Buckinghamshire
and Oxfordshire, page 104

Kent, Surrey and Sussex, page 148

Basildon Park

near Reading, Berkshire

1978

Sitting elegantly in 162 hectares (400 acres) of historic parkland and gardens, this 18th-century mansion was saved from destruction by Lord and Lady Iliffe in the 1950s when it was derequisitioned after the Second World War. In a true labour of love, the Iliffes spent nearly 50 years renovating and returning the house to its former glory, acquiring a collection of fine furnishings and carefully selected Old Masters. The wooded parkland showcases glorious seasonal colour all year round, while the landscape has been restored to offer wonderful views, peaceful trails and picnic places. **Note**: entrance to main show rooms of mansion on first floor – 21 steps from ground level.

Basildon Park, Berkshire, sits in wooded parkland, below. The Octagon Drawing Room, above

Satnav: not reliable, please follow brown signs. **Parking**: 400 yards.

Dog rating: ✿ **Standard** – Welcome on leads in grounds (cattle in parkland all year). Assistance dogs only in house.

Access:

Exploring the fine interiors at Basildon Park

Find out more: 01491 672382 or
basildonpark@nationaltrust.org.uk
Lower Basildon, near Reading,
Berkshire RG8 9NR
nationaltrust.org.uk/basildon-park

Basildon Park		M	T	W	T	F	S	S
House								
14 Feb–6 Nov	11–5*	M	T	W	T	F	S	S
16 Nov–31 Dec**	11–4	M	T	W	T	F	S	S
Garden, parkland, tea-room and shop								
Open all year**	10–5*	M	T	W	T	F	S	S

*1 January to 27 March and 31 October to 31 December,
everything closes 4. **Closed 24 and 25 December.
Last entry to site one hour before closing.

Bembridge Fort

Bembridge Down, near Bembridge,
Isle of Wight PO36 8QY 1967

In a commanding position on Bembridge
Down, this unrestored Victorian fort is
part of the area's rich military history.
Note: sorry no toilet. Not suitable for
children under 10. Access by guided tour
only (booking essential).

Find out more: 01983 741020 or
bembridgefort@nationaltrust.org.uk
c/o Longstone Farmhouse, Strawberry
Lane, Mottistone, Isle of Wight PO30 4EA
nationaltrust.org.uk/bembridge-fort

Bembridge Windmill

Bembridge, Isle of Wight

1961

Built more than 300 years ago, the Isle
of Wight's only surviving windmill is one of
the island's most iconic buildings. The sails
last turned in 1913, but inside most of its
original machinery is still intact. Climb
to the top and follow the milling process
down four floors. **Note**: steep steps
inside the Windmill.

Satnav: do not use, follow brown signs.
Parking: free (not National Trust),
100 yards in lay-by.

Dog rating: **Standard** – Welcome in
grounds on leads. Assistance dogs only
on ground floor of Windmill.

Access:

Find out more: 01983 873945 or
bembridgemill@nationaltrust.org.uk
High Street/Mill Road, Bembridge,
Isle of Wight PO35 5SQ
nationaltrust.org.uk/bembridge-windmill

Bembridge Windmill		M	T	W	T	F	S	S
12 Apr–2 Oct	10:30–5		T		T			S

Bembridge Windmill on the Isle of Wight

Compton Bay and Downs

Compton, Isle of Wight

 🏊⛰🏕

Beach at Compton Bay and Downs, Isle of Wight

With sandy beaches and colourful cliffs, Compton Bay is considered one of the best beaches on the island. It's also a prime site for fossil-hunting – look out for dinosaur foot casts. The clifftops and downs are rich in wildlife and easy-to-access walks, with views as far as Dorset. **Note**: steep steps down to the beach.

Satnav: use PO30 4HB. **Parking**: on site.

Dog rating: 🐾 🐾 **Good** – Welcome on beach between Hanover Point and Brook Chine all year.

Access: ♿WC

Find out more: 01983 741020 or comptonbay@nationaltrust.org.uk **nationaltrust.org.uk/compton-bay-and-downs**

Hinton Ampner

near Alresford, Hampshire

1986 🏛🏚❄🦌♿☕🏠🎭🏃

Hinton Ampner is the fulfilment of one man's vision. After a catastrophic fire in 1960, Ralph Dutton rebuilt his home in the light and airy Georgian style he loved. A passionate collector, he filled the sunny rooms with ceramics and art. Outside, Dutton designed a series of tranquil garden rooms, each with their own distinctive planting still apparent today. Geometric topiary, exotic-coloured dahlias and borders of repeat-flowering roses lead onto terraces with panoramic views across the South Downs. Extensive lawns, a park with ancient oaks and beech woodland provide plenty of space to stroll, play, relax and picnic.

Lovingly rebuilt after a catastrophic fire in 1960, Hinton Ampner in Hampshire is the fulfilment of one man's vision

The tranquil and extensive gardens at Hinton Ampner

Satnav: use SO24 0NH – takes you to Hinton Arms pub, 21 yards west of main entrance. **Parking**: on site.

Dog rating: ❀ **Standard** – Welcome on short leads in the grounds. Assistance dogs only in some areas.

Access: [access icons]

Find out more: 01962 771305 or hintonampner@nationaltrust.org.uk near Alresford, Hampshire SO24 0LA **nationaltrust.org.uk/hinton-ampner**

Hinton Ampner								
House								
18 Jan–25 Mar	11–3		T	W	T	F		
29 Mar–28 Oct	11–4		T	W	T	F		
1 Nov–11 Nov	11–3		T	W	T	F		
29 Nov–30 Dec*	11–3		T	W	T	F		
Estate, garden, shop and café								
1 Jan–27 Mar**	10–4†	M	T	W	T	F	S	S
28 Mar–30 Oct	10–5†	M	T	W	T	F	S	S
31 Oct–31 Dec*	10–4†	M	T	W	T	F	S	S

*Everything closed 25 and 26 December.
**Shop: closed 4 to 30 January. †Shop: opens 11.

Maidenhead and Cookham Commons

near Maidenhead, Berkshire

1934

This chain of ancient commons offers footpaths through broadleaf woodlands, chalk downland, marshes dotted with orchids and hay meadows buzzing with insects in summer. These rich habitats are great for spotting wildlife throughout the year – you might see emperor dragonflies, marbled white butterflies, redwings, skylarks and fieldfares.

Satnav: use SL6 9SB for Cookham Moor car park. **Parking**: eight car parks (height restrictions at Henley Road and Pinkneys Drive car parks).

Dog rating: ❀ **Standard** – Welcome under close control (grazing livestock and ground-nesting birds).

Find out more: 01628 605069 or maidenheadandcookham@nationaltrust.org.uk **nationaltrust.org.uk/maidenhead-and-cookham-commons**

Ancient Maidenhead and Cookham Commons in Berkshire are rich in wildlife all year

Mottisfont

near Romsey, Hampshire

1957

Ancient trees, babbling brooks and rolling lawns frame this 18th-century house with a medieval priory at its heart. Maud Russell made Mottisfont her home in the 1930s, bringing artists here to relax and create works inspired by Mottisfont's past, including an extraordinary drawing room painted by Rex Whistler. Those artistic traditions are continued today with a permanent 20th-century art collection and major exhibitions in the top-floor gallery. Outside, carpets of spring bulbs, walled gardens, rich autumn leaves and a colourful winter garden create a feast for the senses all year. The world-famous collection of old-fashioned roses flowers once a year in June and there are spaces to run, jump and play, and always something for families to do.

**Exploring a walled garden
at Mottisfont in Hampshire**

Satnav: use SO51 0LN. **Parking**: on site.

Dog rating: 🐾 🐾 **Good** – Welcome on short leads outside, excluding rose gardens, formal lawns and play areas.

Access: 🅿️♿🚾♿🚻♿👁️📷🚶♿👥➡️

Find out more: 01794 340757 or mottisfont@nationaltrust.org.uk near Romsey, Hampshire SO51 0LP
nationaltrust.org.uk/mottisfont

Mottisfont stands proudly fronted by rolling lawns, above. The Winter Garden, below

Mottisfont	
Open every day all year*	10–5**

*Closed 24 and 25 December. House: closed 10 to 23 January, 29 May to 5 July and 7 to 24 November. Gallery: closed between exhibitions. **House and gallery: open 11 to 4:40; 1 to 31 January and 1 November to 31 December, closes 4. Garden: some extended opening hours in June.

Mottistone Gardens and Estate

Mottistone, near Brighstone,
Isle of Wight PO30 4ED

1965 ❀ 🐾 ♿ ☕ 🏠 🚻 🚹

Set in a sheltered valley, these 20th-century gardens are filled with shrub-lined banks, hidden pathways and colourful borders. They surround an ancient manor house (not open) and have a Mediterranean-style planting scheme, taking advantage of the southerly location, including drought-tolerant plants and an olive grove. Other features include a monocot border, an organic kitchen garden and a tea garden alongside The Shack, a cabin retreat designed as their summer drawing office by architects John Seely (2nd Lord Mottistone) and Paul Paget. A network of footpaths crosses the adjoining Mottistone Estate, taking walkers high onto the downs via the historic Longstone.

Parking: 50 yards.

Dog rating: 🐾 **Standard** – Welcome on leads in the gardens, under close control around livestock on the estate.

Access: 🅿️ 🐕 ♿ 🚻 🧗 📖 🏛️ 🌳 🔍 🐾 🚹 ➡️

Find out more: 01983 741302 or
mottistonegardens@nationaltrust.org.uk
nationaltrust.org.uk/mottistone-estate

Mottistone Gardens		M	T	W	T	F	S	S
5 Mar–30 Oct	10:30–5	**M**	**T**	**W**	**T**	**F**	**S**	**S**
Estate: open every day all year.								

Colourful herbaceous borders at Mottistone Gardens and Estate on the Isle of Wight, above and below

The Needles Batteries and Headland

West High Down, Alum Bay, Isle of Wight PO39 0JH

| 1975 |

Walking from Freshwater Bay to The Needles Headland along Tennyson Down, there are views as far as Dorset. At the end, high above The Needles amid acres of countryside, is the Needles Old Battery. This Victorian fortification, built in 1862, was used throughout both world wars. The Parade Ground has two original guns, and the military history is brought to life with displays, models and a series of vivid cartoons. An underground tunnel leads to a searchlight emplacement, with dramatic views over The Needles rocks at the tip of the island. The New Battery, further up the headland, was once a secret rocket-testing site used during the Cold War. **Note**: steep paths and uneven surfaces. Spiral staircase to tunnel. Toilet at Old Battery only.

Parking: no parking on site (limited designated parking by arrangement). Nearest at Alum Bay, ¾ mile, not National Trust (chargeable, with 20 per cent reduction for National Trust members). Freshwater Bay, 3½ miles (not National Trust), or Highdown (196:SZ325856), 2 miles.

Dog rating: 🐾 **Standard** – Welcome on leads (assistance dogs only in upstairs tea-room; all dogs welcome downstairs).

Access: 🅿️♿🚻📷📺♿📷♿🚻♿

Find out more: 01983 754772 or needles@nationaltrust.org.uk
nationaltrust.org.uk/the-needles-old-battery-and-new-battery

The Needles		M	T	W	T	F	S	S
Old Battery*								
5 Mar–30 Oct	10:30–5	M	T	W	T	F	S	S
New Battery*								
16 Apr–1 Oct	10:30–4	·	·	·	·	·	S	·
Old Battery tea-room**								
8 Jan–6 Feb	11–3	·	·	·	·	·	S	S
12 Feb–20 Feb	11–3	M	T	W	T	F	S	S
5 Mar–30 Oct	10:30–5	M	T	W	T	F	S	S
5 Nov–18 Dec	11–3	·	·	·	·	·	S	S
26 Dec–31 Dec	11–3	M	T	W	T	F	S	·

*Needles Batteries: close in high winds.
**Old Battery tea-room: also open 1 to 3 January, plus 26 and 27 February; 11 to 3.

The Needles Batteries, below, and Headland, left, on the Isle of Wight, offer history and drama

Looking down over The Needles rocks
at the tip of the island

New Forest Commons and Foxbury

near East Wellow, Hampshire

 1928 🦽🚶

Woodland, grassland, heathland, bogs and mires make up the unique landscape of the New Forest Commons, a wilderness that's teeming with wildlife. The National Trust looks after commons at the following places: Bramshaw, Foxbury, Hale Purlieu, Hightown, as well as Rockford and Ibsley. Foxbury, a gateway to the New Forest, is a 150-hectare (370-acre) area of heathland restoration. Wide open spaces, gentle hillsides and hidden ponds are there to be discovered in this recovering landscape. This is a fragile conservation site for wildlife and access is only allowed for special seasonal events.

Satnav: follow the Omega signs; for Foxbury use SO51 6AQ; Bramshaw Commons SO51 6AQ; Hale Purlieu SP6 2QZ; Hightown Common BH24 3HH; Rockford and Ibsley Commons BH24 3NA. **Parking**: for Foxbury at Half Moon car park on Blackhill Road.

Dog rating: 🐾 **Standard** – Welcome on leads or under close control March to July (due to nesting birds).

New Forest Commons and Foxbury, Hampshire: bug hunting, above, and wild ponies, below left

Find out more: 01425 650035 or newforest@nationaltrust.org.uk **nationaltrust.org.uk/new-forest-northern-commons**

New Forest

For your safety we would not advise access to the New Forest between dusk and dawn. Foxbury is accessible for special seasonal events only.

Newtown National Nature Reserve and Old Town Hall

Newtown, near Shalfleet, Isle of Wight PO30 4PA

1933 🏠🐾🦽⛰️🐴🧺🚶

On the water's edge, Newtown is home to a tranquil harbour, wildflower meadows and ancient woodland with rare butterflies and red squirrels. The only National Nature Reserve on the island, Newtown has been cared for by the National Trust since 1963. Tucked away in a tiny hamlet adjoining the National Nature Reserve is the small and quirky 17th-century Old Town Hall, the only remaining evidence of Newtown's former importance. This historic building was the second to be bought and donated to the National Trust by Ferguson's Gang who were battling against the sprawling development of England in the 1930s. **Note**: nearest toilet in the car park by the visitor point.

Parking: on site.

Dog rating: ✿ **Standard** – Welcome on leads on National Nature Reserve (assistance dogs only in Old Town Hall on ground floor).

Access: 🚻♿🏠📷🚼👓📷♿

Find out more: 01983 531785 (Old Town Hall). 01983 531622 (visitor point) or newtown@nationaltrust.org.uk
nationaltrust.org.uk/newtown-national-nature-reserve

Newtown		M	T	W	T	F	S	S
Nature Reserve								
Open all year		M	T	W	T	F	S	S
Bird hide								
5 Mar–30 Oct	10:30–4	M	T	W	T	F	S	S

Old Town Hall: open 30 April/1 May, 4/5 June, 11/12 June, 9/10 July, 6/7 August, 10/11 and 17/18 September, 10:30 to 5.

Newtown National Nature Reserve on the Isle of Wight

St Helens Duver

near St Helens, Isle of Wight

1928 ⚓

Enjoying the beach at St Helens Duver on the Isle of Wight

Once a Victorian golf course with royal patronage, St Helens Duver has sandy beaches, hidden rock pools, undulating sand dunes and coastal woods to explore. It's also a fascinating place to look for wildlife, from burrowing digger wasps to wasp spiders and waterbirds over the harbour. **Note**: sorry no toilet.

Satnav: use PO33 1XY. **Parking**: on site.

Dog rating: ✿ **Standard** – Welcome under close control.

Find out more: 01983 741020 or sthelensduver@nationaltrust.org.uk
nationaltrust.org.uk/st-helens-duver

Sandham Memorial Chapel

Harts Lane, Burghclere, near Newbury,
Hampshire RG20 9JT

1947

Sandham Memorial Chapel, Hampshire, contains epic paintings by Stanley Spencer

Nestled in a quiet village, the Chapel hides an unexpected treasure – an epic series of paintings by the acclaimed artist Stanley Spencer, depicting scenes inspired by his experiences in the First World War. The orchard is perfect for picnics and the garden of reflection provides a peaceful space for contemplation.

Parking: opposite Chapel entrance (designated parking at rear).

Dog rating: ✿ **Standard** – Welcome on leads in grounds only.

Access:

Find out more: 01635 278394 or sandham@nationaltrust.org.uk
nationaltrust.org.uk/sandham

Sandham Memorial Chapel

Opening arrangements not confirmed at time of print, please check before visiting.

The Vyne

Sherborne St John,
near Basingstoke, Hampshire

1956

The Vyne has opened more rooms than ever before, including an exhibition space revealing stories covering 500 years of history. Visitors can discover the story of a brother and sister who became intertwined with The Vyne's survival: one the unexpected heir to the grand Tudor mansion; the other adopted as a companion. Outside, acres of wildlife-rich gardens and woods create a wonderful space for relaxation and exploration, while the play space gives children freedom to let their imagination take them on an adventure. Sweeping lawns offer lakeside picnicking, and a short stroll reveals a bird hide overlooking water meadows.

Satnav: not reliable, follow brown signs.
Parking: on site, limited in winter (October to April) due to ground conditions.

Dog rating: 🐾 **Standard** – Welcome on short leads in woodland and gardens.

Access:

Find out more: 01256 883858 or thevyne@nationaltrust.org.uk
Vyne Road, Sherborne St John, near Basingstoke, Hampshire RG24 9HL
nationaltrust.org.uk/vyne

The Vyne		M	T	W	T	F	S	S
1 Jan–6 Feb	10–4*						S	S
7 Feb–30 Oct	10–5*	M	T	W	T	F	S	S
31 Oct–31 Dec**	10–4*	M	T	W	T	F	S	S

*House: opens 11 to 3; shop: opens 10:30. Last entry one hour before closing. **Only open weekends in November. Closed 24 and 25 December.

The Vyne in Hampshire sits beside a stately lake, below, edged by wildlife-rich water meadows

Winchester City Mill

Bridge Street, Winchester, Hampshire SO23 9BH

The restored Winchester City Mill, Hampshire

This restored watermill – probably the oldest working watermill in the UK – has stood at the heart of the city of Winchester for a millennium. As the official Gateway to the South Downs National Park, it is an integral part of any visit to the South Downs.

Parking: none on site. Use Chesil Street car park or Park and Ride, neither National Trust (charge including members).

Access: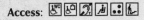

Find out more: 01962 870057 or winchestercitymill@nationaltrust.org.uk
nationaltrust.org.uk/winchester-city-mill

Winchester City Mill

Opening arrangements not confirmed at time of print, please check before visiting.

The Staircase Hall at
Hatchlands Park, Surrey

Kent, Surrey
and Sussex

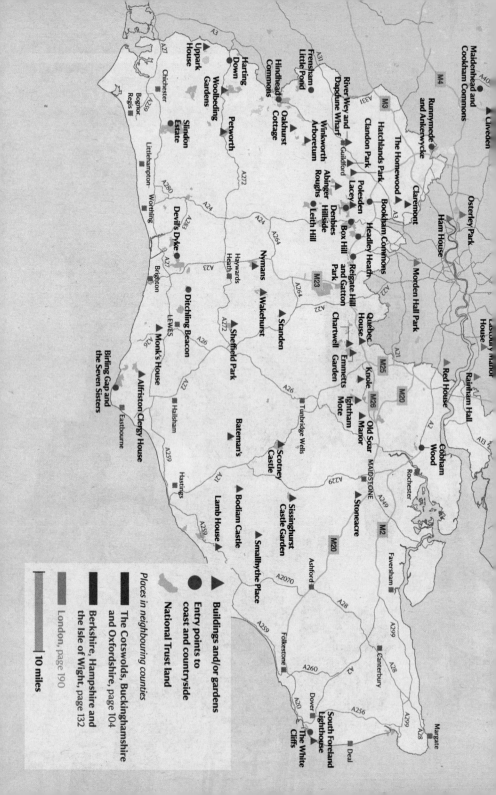

Abinger Roughs and Netley Park

White Downs Lane, Abinger Hammer,
Surrey RH5 6QS 1940

Hidden woods, flower-filled grasslands,
natural play and picnic benches make this
the perfect spot for young nature explorers
and families. **Note**: sorry no toilet.

Find out more: 01306 640062 (rangers) or
abingerroughs@nationaltrust.org.uk
nationaltrust.org.uk/abinger-roughs-and-netley-park

Alfriston Clergy House

The Tye, Alfriston, Polegate,
East Sussex BN26 5TL

1896

This rare 14th-century Wealden 'hall-house',
above, was the first building to be acquired
by the National Trust, in 1896. The
thatched, timber-framed house is in
an idyllic setting, with views across the
River Cuckmere, and is surrounded by
a tranquil cottage garden full of wildlife.
Note: nearest toilet in village car park.

Parking: 500 yards in village car parks
(not National Trust).

Dog rating: ❀ **Standard** – On fixed
short leads in the garden (assistance
dogs only in house).

Access: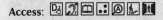

Find out more: 01323 871961 or
alfriston@nationaltrust.org.uk
nationaltrust.org.uk/alfriston

Alfriston Clergy House

Opening arrangements not confirmed at time of print,
please check before visiting.

Bateman's

Bateman's Lane, Burwash,
East Sussex TN19 7DS

1940

The lily pond in September
at Bateman's, East Sussex

Bateman's remains today as Kipling
described it in 1902: 'A grey stone lichened
house – with oak staircase all untouched
and unfaked… It is a good and peaceable
place, standing in terraced lawns nigh to
a walled garden of old red brick and two
fat-headed old oast houses with red brick

Bateman's contains many of Kipling's belongings, exactly as he left them

stomachs and an aged silver-grey dovecot [sic] on top.' Many of Kipling's belongings remain as he left them. Paths wind past Kipling's 1928 Rolls-Royce, through manicured lawns and a wildflower meadow. A 17th-century working watermill stands beside the River Dudwell.

Parking: 30 yards.

Dog rating: 🐾 🐾 **Good** – Welcome on short leads in the garden and on the estate (seasonal cattle grazing).

Access: 🅿️♿🚻♿♿🔄♿♿♿
♿♿➡️

Find out more: 01435 882302 or batemans@nationaltrust.org.uk
nationaltrust.org.uk/batemans

Bateman's	M	T	W	T	F	S	S
House and Park Mill							
1 Jan–13 Feb* 11–3:30	M	T	W	T	F	S	S
14 Feb–30 Oct 11–5	M	T	W	T	F	S	S
31 Oct–31 Dec 11–3:30	M	T	W	T	F	S	S
Garden, shop and tea-room							
Open all year 10–5**	M	T	W	T	F	S	S

*House: 3 January to 11 February, weekday entry by guided tour only. **1 January to 13 February and 31 October to 31 December: close at 4. Closed 24 and 25 December.

Birling Gap and the Seven Sisters

near Eastbourne, East Sussex

1931

For drama, nothing beats the point where the sheer chalk cliffs of the South Downs meet the sea, below. One of the south coast's longest undeveloped stretches, the Seven Sisters are truly iconic. If you venture down the steps onto the beach, you can discover fascinating rock pools and the intricate wave-cut platform. The café and shop are a delightful place to start or end your peaceful downland walk. **Note**: unstable cliff edge, stay away from edge and from cliff base.

Birling Gap and the Seven Sisters, East Sussex: the sheer cliffs, top and opposite, and beach, above

Satnav: use BN20 0AB.
Parking: at Birling Gap.

Dog rating: ✿ **Standard** – Welcome in café, shop and on beach. Always on leads near livestock.

Access: 🅿♿🚻♿♿♿♿

Find out more: 01323 423197 or birlinggap@nationaltrust.org.uk
nationaltrust.org.uk/birling-gap

Birling Gap and the Seven Sisters	M	T	W	T	F	S	S
Café and shop							
1 Jan–23 Jul*	10–5**	M	T	W	T	F	S	S
24 Jul–4 Sep	9:30–5:30**	M	T	W	T	F	S	S
5 Sep–31 Dec	10–5**	M	T	W	T	F	S	S

*1 January to 13 February, close 4. **Weekends only, 18 April to 23 July, close 5:30; 5 September to 2 October, close 5:30; 31 October to 31 December, close 4.
Closed 24 and 25 December; 26 December, 11 to 4.

Bodiam Castle

Bodiam, near Robertsbridge,
East Sussex TN32 5UA

1926 🏠🏡♿🍴☕🛍🚻📷✗

The romantic ruins of Bodiam Castle, East Sussex

Reminiscent of fairy-tales, this romantic ancient ruin rises up from a misty moat where you can spot fish, ducks and geese. Bodiam Castle is the archetypal castle; a symbol of status with historical defensive features, including the 600-year-old portcullis, murder holes and gun loops. You can picnic on the grass and admire the golden sandstone walls, or climb the spiral staircases and walk along the battlements for panoramic views across the Sussex countryside. Discover historic graffiti inside the castle or listen to nationally significant bats chattering in the tower rooms in spring or early summer. **Note**: popular with schools. Main toilets in car park. Portaloos at top of site (main season).

Parking: 510 yards from reception to castle.

Dog rating: 🐾 🐾 **Good** – Welcome in grounds on leads (assistance dogs only in castle).

Access: [access icons]

Find out more: 01580 830196 or bodiamcastle@nationaltrust.org.uk
nationaltrust.org.uk/bodiam-castle

Bodiam Castle		M	T	W	T	F	S	S
Castle								
1 Jan–13 Feb	10–3			W			S	S
14 Feb–27 Mar	10–4	M	T	W	T	F	S	S
28 Mar–30 Oct	10–5	M	T	W	T	F	S	S
31 Oct–31 Dec	10–3	M	T	W	T	F	S	S
Grounds, shop and tea-room								
Open all year	10–5*	M	T	W	T	F	S	S

*1 January to 13 February and 31 October to 31 December: close at 4. Castle View Café seasonal opening. Closed 24 and 25 December.

Trying out the stocks, above, and the medieval moated Bodiam Castle, below

Bookham Commons

near Great Bookham, Surrey

 [1923] [icons]

Wintry walk at Bookham Commons in Surrey

Enchanting ancient oak woodland, grassland plains and tranquil ponds. Listen out for tuneful nightingales and warblers in the spring and in summer look for insects hovering over the ponds. If you're lucky, you may also spot the beautiful, but elusive, purple emperor butterfly.
Note: sorry no toilet.

Satnav: use KT23 3LT.
Parking: at Tunnel, Mark Oak Gate and Hundred Pound Bridge car parks.

Dog rating: 🐾 **Standard** – Welcome, on leads near livestock. Under close control during nesting season (March to October).

Access:

Find out more: 01306 640062 or bookhamcommons@nationaltrust.org.uk
nationaltrust.org.uk/bookham-commons

Box Hill

Tadworth, Surrey

| 1914 |

A great place for family adventures: delving into the ancient woodland, exploring the natural play trail, finding the tower or discovering the River Mole at the Stepping Stones. On a clear day you can see for miles from the top of Box Hill, so if you're hiking up along one of the many footpaths, the stunning views are well worth it. Box Hill and Westhumble and Dorking railway stations are within easy reach.
Note: to protect wildlife habitats, BBQs are not allowed.

Satnav: use KT20 7LB (doesn't work for all satnavs). **Parking**: off the Box Hill Zig Zag Road (short walk to café and viewpoint).

Dog rating: ❀ **Standard** – Welcome under close control where livestock are grazing (assistance dogs only in café).

Looking over the wooden footbridge at Box Hill

Access:

Find out more: 01306 888793 or boxhill@nationaltrust.org.uk
nationaltrust.org.uk/box-hill

Box Hill	
Café and Servery	
Open every day all year*	10–4**

*Closed 24 and 25 December; open 9 at weekends.
**1 March to 30 September: close 5.

Enjoying the view from Salomons Memorial viewpoint at Box Hill, Surrey

Chartwell

Mapleton Road, Westerham, Kent TN16 1PS

1946

Chartwell was the family home of
Sir Winston Churchill, the place that
brought him comfort and inspiration.
Filled with treasures and personal
belongings from every aspect of his life, this
intimate house invites you into the private
world of one of Britain's greatest leaders.
Follow in the footsteps of one of the many
frequent guests who are recorded in the
visitor book. His studio contains the largest
collection of Churchill's paintings and offers
an insight into Churchill the painter. The
garden reflects Churchill's love of landscape
and nature, including the lakes he created.
There are lots of fun things to do in our
woodland area: a tree house, Donkey Jack's
caravan, swings, a bomb crater and much
more to explore. **Note**: steep slopes;
challenging for less able.

Parking: on site.

Dog rating: ❀ ❀ **Good** – Welcome on
short leads in the garden and off lead in
the wider estate.

Access:

Find out more: 01732 868381 or
chartwell@nationaltrust.org.uk
nationaltrust.org.uk/chartwell

Chartwell		M	T	W	T	F	S	S
House								
1 Mar–31 Oct	11:30–5*	M	T	W	T	F	S	S
5 Nov–31 Dec	11:30–4**	.	.	.	.	.	S	S
Garden, estate, shop and café								
Open all year	10–5†	M	T	W	T	F	S	S

House: entry by timed ticket (available from visitor centre).
*Last entry 3:50. **Last entry 2:50. †1 to 31 January and
1 November to 31 December: close 4. Exhibition: opens
as house (access with house ticket). Closed 24 and
25 December.

**Chartwell, Kent, above and below, offered
inspiration and a retreat for Winston Churchill**

Enjoying the garden at Chartwell

Clandon Park

near Guildford, Surrey

1956

The aftermath of the fire at Clandon Park, Surrey

A major project is under way at Clandon following a devastating fire in 2015. We continue to work hard to provide access to parts of the house and garden while work continues, providing a unique opportunity to follow our progress. **Note**: apart from marked public footpaths, the neighbouring parkland is private with no public access.

Satnav: follow brown signs to the entrance on the A247. **Parking**: 250 yards.

Access:

Find out more: 01483 222482 or
clandonpark@nationaltrust.org.uk
West Clandon, near Guildford,
Surrey GU4 7RQ
nationaltrust.org.uk/clandon-park

Clandon Park		M	T	W	T	F	S	S
House*								
1 May–28 Aug	11–4	·	·	·	·	·	S	S
Garden**								
1 Apr–30 Oct	11–4	M	T	W	T	F	S	S

*House: entry by guided tour only (booking essential).
**Toilet: closed.

Claremont Landscape Garden

near Esher, Surrey

1949

Immerse yourself in this green oasis – just the place for a family adventure. Spot daffodils in spring and golden leaves in the autumn. Summer affords endless opportunities for picnics and for the children to explore the play area and build dens in Badger's Basecamp. One of the earliest 18th-century landscape gardens featuring a signature grass amphitheatre, Claremont combines the innovative work of designers Vanbrugh, Bridgeman, Kent and 'Capability' Brown. Once a sanctuary for British, French and Belgian royalty, you can walk in the steps of Queen Victoria, Princess Charlotte and Prince Leopold.

Satnav: unreliable; instead follow brown signs from Cobham and Esher.
Parking: main car park at entrance. Space limited at busy times – please use car park in West End Lane opposite.

Looking down on the the lake at Claremont Landscape Garden, Surrey

The Belvedere at Claremont Landscape Garden

Dog rating: 🐾 🐾 🐾 **Best** – Welcome in garden and café all year.

Access: 🅿️ ♿ 🚻 ♿ 🐕 📷 🅰️ ➡️

Find out more: 01372 467806 or claremont@nationaltrust.org.uk Portsmouth Road, near Esher, Surrey KT10 9JG **nationaltrust.org.uk/claremont-landscape-garden**

Claremont Garden	
Open every day all year*	10–5**

Café: closes 30 minutes earlier than garden. *Closed 24 and 25 December. **1 November to 28 February, garden closes 4.

Cobham Wood and Mausoleum

near Cobham, Kent [2014]

Sitting proud in historic woodland pasture, the 18th-century Darnley Mausoleum commands impressive views across the North Kent downs. **Note**: for satnav use DA12 3HX. Access to mausoleum on foot only, two miles from Shorne Wood Country Park (not National Trust). Mausoleum open on limited days each year, please check before visiting.

Find out more: 01732 810378 or cobham@nationaltrust.org.uk **nationaltrust.org.uk/cobham**

Denbies Hillside

near Dorking, Surrey

[1963] 🏊 🎋

Snow covers the dramatic chalk escarpment of Denbies Hillside in Surrey

Denbies Hillside is a dramatic chalk escarpment with panoramic views of the Surrey countryside. It's a great place to walk, picnic and watch wildlife – you may even spot chalk downland species, such as the Adonis blue and chalkhill blue butterflies.

Satnav: use RH5 6SR.
Parking: at Denbies Hillside.

Dog rating: 🐾 **Standard** – Welcome (on short leads near livestock).

Access: ♿ 🐕

Find out more: 01306 640062 or denbieshillside@nationaltrust.org.uk **nationaltrust.org.uk/denbies-hillside**

Devil's Dyke

near Brighton, West Sussex

1995

At nearly a mile long, the Dyke Valley is the longest, deepest and widest 'dry valley' in the UK. Legend has it that the Devil dug this chasm to drown the parishioners of the Weald. On the other hand, scientists believe it was formed naturally just over 10,000 years ago during the last ice age. The walls of the Iron Age hill fort can be seen when you walk around the hill, and there is a carpet of flowers and a myriad of colourful insects to discover in the valley.

Satnav: use BN1 8YJ. **Parking:** on site.

Dog rating: 🐾 Standard – Welcome (on leads near livestock).

Access:

Find out more: 01273 857712 or southdownseast@nationaltrust.org.uk
nationaltrust.org.uk/devils-dyke

Devil's Dyke in West Sussex, below, was formed during the last ice age. Edburton Escarpment, above

Ditchling Beacon

near Ditchling, East Sussex

Three views of Ditchling Beacon near Brighton. As the highest point in East Sussex, there are far-reaching views in all directions

Dog rating: 🐾 **Standard** – Welcome on leads at all times.

Access: [P&]

Find out more: 01323 423197 or southdownseast@nationaltrust.org.uk
nationaltrust.org.uk/ditchling-beacon

Just 7 miles north of Brighton, at 248 metres above sea level, Ditchling Beacon is the highest point in East Sussex and offers panoramic views from the summit. To the south visitors can see the sea, while to the north you can look across the Weald or east–west across the Downs. The site also has the remains of an Iron Age hill fort. Situated on the South Downs Way, it makes an excellent place to start a walk heading west towards Devil's Dyke or east towards Black Cap and Lewes.

Satnav: use BN6 8XG.
Parking: small car park off Ditchling Road – very busy at weekends.

Emmetts Garden

Ide Hill, Sevenoaks, Kent TN14 6BA

1965 ❀ ♣ ☕ 🏠 ⛺ 🚶

Emmetts is a rare, stunning Edwardian garden known for its beautiful bluebells and spring colour. Summer brings the romantic rose garden, followed by vibrant autumn foliage, and more than 1,000 newly planted winter bulbs – there is something to see all year, as well as wonderful views across the Weald of Kent that can be enjoyed from the garden and on the countryside walks. Emmetts is a garden to enjoy with friends and family, a place where you can let off steam, play games, picnic in the meadow or simply sit back and relax.

Parking: 100 yards.

Dog rating: ❀ ❀ **Good** – Welcome on short leads in gardens and off lead in the wider countryside.

Access: 🅿️ 🚃 ♿ 🔍 🦮 🪑 📷 ♿ ➡️ 🚲

Find out more: 01732 868381 or emmetts@nationaltrust.org.uk
nationaltrust.org.uk/emmetts

Emmetts Garden	
Open every day all year*	10–5**

*Closed 24 and 25 December. **1 to 31 January and 1 November to 31 December: closes 4.

Beautiful all year, Emmetts Garden in Kent, above and below, offers new delights each season

Frensham Little Pond

Priory Lane, Frensham, Surrey GU10 3BT

| 1974 |

Originally created in the 11th century to supply the Bishop of Winchester with fish, the pond and surrounding area is now a sanctuary for wildlife. The heathland is a colourful mosaic of purple heathers, fragrant bright-yellow gorse and rich green bracken with many footpaths to explore. **Note**: to protect the wildlife habitats, swimming, inflatables and BBQs are not allowed.

Parking: on site.

Dog rating: 🐾 **Standard** – Welcome under close control during bird-nesting season (March to October). On leads around café.

Access:

Find out more: 01428 681050 (rangers). 01252 790530 (café) or frensham@nationaltrust.org.uk
nationaltrust.org.uk/frensham-little-pond

Frensham Little Pond	
Café	
Open every day all year*	10–3**

*Closed 24 and 25 December. **1 April to 30 September, closes 4.

Harting Down

near South Harting, West Sussex | 1994 |

Enjoy a walk through a tapestry of downland with scattered scrub and woodland, rich in wildlife and steeped in history. **Note**: nearest toilets at South Harting or Uppark.

Find out more: 01730 816638 or southdownswest@nationaltrust.org.uk
nationaltrust.org.uk/harting-down

Hatchlands Park

East Clandon, Guildford, Surrey GU4 7RT

| 1945 |

The parkland at Hatchlands Park, Surrey, is the perfect place to relax and explore

With open fields grazed by sheep and cattle, ancient woodland and wildflower meadows, the parkland is perfect for relaxation and exploration. The natural adventure area, with its tree house and bug burrow, is perfect for families to get even closer to nature. Nestled in the parkland is a Georgian country house, built for naval hero Admiral Boscawen and his wife, Fanny. Now home to tenant Alec Cobbe, it contains his collection of Old Master paintings and the Cobbe Collection – Europe's largest array of keyboard instruments, including some which inspired world-famous composers such as J. C. Bach and Elgar. **Note**: only six ground-floor rooms open.

Inside the Georgian house at Hatchlands Park

Satnav: follow brown signs to main car park entrance on A246. **Parking**: 300 yards.

Dog rating: 🐾 🐾 **Good** – Welcome under close control in the parkland and designated areas. Dog-friendly Coach House Café.

Access: 🅿️♿🚻♿🐕♿🔦📷😊🔲♿♿➡️♿

Find out more: 01483 222482 or hatchlands@nationaltrust.org.uk
nationaltrust.org.uk/hatchlands

Hatchlands Park		M	T	W	T	F	S	S
House, meadow and parterre								
6 Mar–31 Oct	12–4	M	T	W	T	F		S
1 Dec–30 Dec*	12–3	M	T	W	T	F		S
Park walks and café								
Open all year*	10–5**	M	T	W	T	F	S	S

*Closed 24 and 25 December. **1 to 31 January and 1 November to 31 December: close 4.

Headley Heath

near Headley, Surrey 1946

Wonderful mosaic of heath, chalk downland and mixed woodland, with a wide network of tracks to explore. **Note**: cattle grazing. For satnav use KT18 6NN.

Find out more: 01306 885502 or headleyheath@nationaltrust.org.uk
nationaltrust.org.uk/headley-heath

Hindhead Commons and the Devil's Punch Bowl

near Hindhead, Surrey

1906 🏊🍴🎪

Exploring Hindhead Commons and the Devil's Punch Bowl, Surrey, above and below

Spectacular views from Hindhead Commons and uninterrupted walks to the Devil's Punch Bowl make this an unforgettable place to relax and take in some of the best countryside in the South East. Since the opening of the A3 tunnel, paths and bridleways have been reconnected and natural contours restored. Peace and calm now reign and the glorious landscape, with its carpets of purple heather in the summer and grazing Highland cattle, is there to enjoy.

Satnav: use GU26 6AB.
Parking: off the London Road.

Dog rating: 🐾 **Standard** – Welcome under close control during bird-nesting season (1 March to 30 September); assistance dogs only in café.

Access: 🅿♿🚻♿🍴🎨♿🐕➡

Hindhead Commons and the Devil's Punch Bowl

Find out more: 01428 681050 (rangers). 01428 608771 (café) or hindhead@nationaltrust.org.uk
nationaltrust.org.uk/hindhead-and-devils-punchbowl

Hindhead Commons	
Café	
Open every day all year*	10–4**

*Closed 24 and 25 December. **1 January to 28 February, closes 3; 1 July to 30 September, closes 5.

The Homewood

Portsmouth Road, Esher, Surrey KT10 9JL 1999

Patrick Gwynne's extraordinary early 20th-century family home is a masterpiece of Modernist design in the midst of a picturesque garden. **Note**: administered on behalf of the National Trust by tenant. Nearest toilets and café at Claremont. Open April to October (dates not confirmed at time of print, please check before visiting). Access by guided tour only, booking essential.

Find out more: 01372 467806 (Claremont Landscape Garden) or thehomewood@nationaltrust.org.uk
c/o Claremont Landscape Garden, Portsmouth Road, Esher, Surrey KT10 9JG
nationaltrust.org.uk/homewood

Ightham Mote

Mote Road, Ivy Hatch, near Sevenoaks,
Kent TN15 0NT

1985

**The west front of Ightham Mote in Kent:
a perfectly preserved medieval manor house**

Hidden away in a secluded Kent valley,
this perfectly preserved medieval moated
manor house is just over 700 years old.
Close to water and a wealth of natural
resources, Ightham Mote's location is both
historic and unique. The architecture and
decoration reflect the development of
the English country house, while its past
owners provide the many stories about this
once-cherished family home, evoking a
deep sense of history. In the tranquil
gardens there are streams and lakes fed by
natural springs, an orchard, flower borders
and a cutting garden. The wider estate
offers walks with secret glades and
countryside views. **Note**: very steep slope
from visitor reception – passenger buggy
or lower drop-off available.

Satnav: use TN15 0NU. **Parking**: 100 yards.

Dog rating: ❀ **Standard** – Welcome on
wider estate and café patio. On leads in
garden (November to February).

Access:

Find out more: 01732 810378 or
ighthammote@nationaltrust.org.uk
Mote Road, Ivy Hatch, near Sevenoaks,
Kent TN15 0NT
nationaltrust.org.uk/ightham-mote

Ightham Mote	
Open every day all year*	10–4**

*Selected rooms dressed for Christmas. **1 March to 31
October, closes 5. Closed 24 and 25 December. Estate open
all year.

Touring the garden at Ightham Mote

Knole

Sevenoaks, Kent

1946

Knole offers a vast estate where you can follow in the footsteps of past tourists who have visited Knole's sumptuous show rooms for 400 years. The recently conserved rooms showcase one of the finest collections of Royal Stuart furniture and textiles, and feature paintings by renowned artists. Spend the day and take in panoramic views from the top of the Gatehouse Tower, where you can also discover the life and loves of a former resident. See the scale and magnificence of this 600-year-old estate by exploring the grand courtyards or wandering through Kent's last medieval deer park.

Satnav: use TN13 1HX and follow brown signs to Sevenoaks High Street (entrance opposite St Nicholas Church). **Parking**: 60 yards.

Dog rating: 🐾 🐾 **Good** – Welcome in parkland and courtyards on leads (assistance dogs only in café, shop, bookshop, tower and show rooms).

Access:

Find out more: 01732 462100 or knole@nationaltrust.org.uk Sevenoaks, Kent TN15 0RP **nationaltrust.org.uk/knole**

Knole			M	T	W	T	F	S	S
Show rooms									
14 Feb–23 Dec*	11–4		M	T	W	T	F	S	S
Gatehouse Tower									
Open all year	11–4		M	T	W	T	F	S	S
Brewhouse Café, courtyards and shop									
Open all year	10–5**		M	T	W	T	F	S	S
Royal Oak Foundation Conservation Studio									
5 Jan–31 Dec	11–4				W	T	F	S	

Closed 24 and 25 December. *Some rooms closed November and December **January, November and December: close 4.

Knole in Kent catches the setting sun, above, and inside the house, left and below

Lamb House

West Street, Rye, East Sussex TN31 7ES

1950   ⌂ ❖ ✕

Lamb House in East Sussex was home to both Henry James and E. F. Benson

Georgian home of writers Henry James and E. F. Benson, who described the property in the *Mapp and Lucia* stories. There is a peaceful walled garden, full of colour, designed by Alfred Parsons, as well as a vegetable patch – unusual in the heart of Rye. **Note**: restricted access for buggies and wheelchairs.

Parking: no on-site parking. Nearest car parks in Rye, not National Trust (charge including members).

Access: ⚅ ♿

Find out more: 01797 222909 or lambhouse@nationaltrust.org.uk
nationaltrust.org.uk/lamb-house

Lamb House		M	T	W	T	F	S	S
28 Feb–6 Nov	11–5*	M	T	·	·	F	S	S
28 Nov–18 Dec	11–4*	M	T	·	·	F	S	S

*Last entry 45 minutes before closing.

Leith Hill

near Coldharbour, Dorking, Surrey

1923   ⌂ ⌂ ♿ ☕ ⌷

One of the highest points in south-east England, offering unbeatable views north to London and south to the sea. Once you've climbed the tower, you'll be higher than The Shard in London. The house, Leith Hill Place, was gifted by composer Ralph Vaughan Williams, and used for a time as a school boarding house. You can enjoy walks on the hill, where every season is a riot of colour – starting with the spring bluebells at Frank's Wood, followed by the early summer colour at the Rhododendron Wood and then the stunning autumnal displays of golds and reds. **Note**: sorry no toilet; steep spiral stairs to top of tower.

Leith Hill in Surrey offers unbeatable views from its summit

Satnav: for Rhododendron Wood and Starveall Corner use RH5 6LU (height restriction barrier); for Windy Gap RH5 6LX; for Landslip RH5 6HG. **Parking:** at Rhododendron Wood for Leith Hill Place. For tower, park at Starveall Corner (not National Trust), ¾ mile (level); Windy Gap car park, ¼ mile (steep steps); Landslip car park, ¾ mile (steep gradient).

Dog rating: 🐾 🐾 **Good** – Welcome in Leith Hill Place; on leads on heathland (April to July).

Access: 🔲 📶 🐾

Find out more: 01306 712711 (Leith Hill countryside). 01306 711685 (Leith Hill Place and tower) or leithhill@nationaltrust.org.uk
nationaltrust.org.uk/leith-hill

Leith Hill

Tower and house: opening arrangements not confirmed at time of print, please check before visiting.

Monk's House

near Lewes, East Sussex

1980   🏠 ❀ 🖼

This small 16th-century weatherboarded cottage in the village of Rodmell was the country retreat of novelist Virginia Woolf and husband Leonard and a meeting place for the Bloomsbury Group. The garden features the room where she created her best-known works and includes cottage garden borders, an orchard, allotments and ponds. **Note:** no access to Rodmell from A26.

Satnav: do not use – wrongly indicates access over railway crossing. **Parking:** 100 yards (2-metre height restriction barrier).

Dog rating: 🐾 **Standard** – Welcome on leads in garden.

Access: 🅿️ 📶 🐾 🚶

Find out more: 01273 474760 or monkshouse@nationaltrust.org.uk
Rodmell, near Lewes, East Sussex BN7 3HF
nationaltrust.org.uk/monks-house

Monk's House

Opening arrangements not confirmed at time of print, please check before visiting.

Virginia Woolf's retreat, Monk's House, East Sussex

Nymans

Handcross, near Haywards Heath,
West Sussex RH17 6EB

1954 | 🏛️ 🏚️ ✿ 🎣 ☕ 🏠 🎞️ 🚶

This garden for all seasons, with rare and
unusual plant collections, is set around a
romantic house and partial ruins. The
comfortable, yet elegant, house reflects the
personalities and stories of the talented
Messel family. In spring see blossoms, bulbs
and a stunning collection of subtly
fragranced magnolias. The Rose Garden,
inspired by Maud Messel's 1920s design,
is scented by hints of old-fashioned roses.
Dramatic shows of vibrant native tree
colour in autumn precede winter's
structural form, with pockets of perfumed
daphne throughout the garden. Discover
hidden corners through stone archways,
and walk along tree-lined avenues
surrounded by the lush countryside of the
Sussex Weald. The adjoining woodland,
with lake and bird hides, has plenty of
opportunities to spot wildlife.

**Wide herbaceous borders and yew topiary frame
a classical fountain at Nymans in West Sussex**

View into the walled garden at Nymans, top, and hunting for Easter eggs, above

Parking: on site.

Dog rating: 🐾 **Standard** – Welcome in garden at set times during year (assistance dogs only in house).

Access: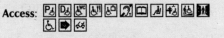

Find out more: 01444 405250 or nymans@nationaltrust.org.uk
nationaltrust.org.uk/nymans

Nymans		M	T	W	T	F	S	S
Garden, café and shop								
Open all year	10–5*	M	T	W	T	F	S	S
House								
Open all year**	11–4	M	T	W	T	F	S	S
Woodland								
Open all year	7–8	M	T	W	T	F	S	S

*Garden: June and July, open to 8:30 on Fridays. Closed 24 and 25 December; café and shop: 1 to 31 January and 30 October to 31 December: close 4. **House: closed 4 to 21 January, 25 April to 31 July and 31 October to 18 November. New Riding House Café opens this year.

Oakhurst Cottage

Hambledon, near Godalming, Surrey GU8 4HF 1952

Timber-framed cottage offering a rare insight into domestic life in the mid-19th century, with a traditional garden to explore. **Note**: nearest toilets and visitor facilities at Winkworth Arboretum. Open 1 April to 29 October, 2 to 5, Wednesday, Thursday, Saturday and Sunday. Access by guided tour only (approximately one hour), booking essential.

Find out more: 01483 208936 (Winkworth Arboretum) or oakhurstcottage@nationaltrust.org.uk
nationaltrust.org.uk/oakhurst-cottage

Old Soar Manor

Plaxtol, Borough Green, Kent TN15 0QX 1947

Dating from 1290, the remaining rooms of this knight's house offer a glimpse back to the time of Edward I. **Note**: sorry no toilet. Narrow lanes. Open daily (excluding Friday), 2 April to 29 September, 9 to 5.

Find out more: 01732 810378 or oldsoarmanor@nationaltrust.org.uk
nationaltrust.org.uk/old-soar-manor

Petworth

Petworth, West Sussex

1947 🏠♿🚻🍴🎁📷🚶

Inspired by the Baroque palaces of Europe, Petworth House is an extraordinary and surprising ancestral seat created by one family over 900 years. The 17th-century building you see today comprises grand state rooms which form the centrepiece of your visit. Designed to display the taste, lifestyle and artistic patronage of generations, the state rooms offer an infinity of paintings and sculpture, including major works by Van Dyck, Turner, Reynolds and Gainsborough. This remarkable collection reflects a family's journey of survival and success through the Tudor Reformation, Gunpowder Plot and the Napoleonic Wars. **Note**: selected rooms may be closed over the winter for conservation.

Petworth, West Sussex, both pages, houses an extraordinary art collection within an extensive 'Capability' Brown landscape and deer park

Satnav: use GU28 9LR.
Parking: on A283, 700 yards. Separate car park for Petworth deer park.

Dog rating: 🐾🐾 **Good** – Welcome under close control in Petworth Park; on leads in Pleasure Garden.

Access: 🅿️♿🚻♿📷🚷🚶♿📷♿♿

Find out more: 01798 342207 or petworth@nationaltrust.org.uk
Petworth, West Sussex GU28 0AE
nationaltrust.org.uk/petworth

Petworth		M	T	W	T	F	S	S
House								
Open all year	10:30–4:30*	M	T	W	T	F	S	S
Pleasure Ground, shop and café								
Open all year	10–5**	M	T	W	T	F	S	S
Deer park								
Open all year	8–8†	M	T	W	T	F	S	S

*Servants' Quarters and select state rooms open all year; 1 to 31 January and 31 October to 31 December, close 3:30.
**1 to 31 January and 1 November to 31 December, close 4. †Closes 6 in winter. Car park gates lock automatically. Closed 24 and 25 December.

Kent, Surrey and Sussex

Polesden Lacey

near Dorking, Surrey

1942

Weekend retreat of Edwardian socialite, Margaret Greville, Polesden Lacey is her lasting legacy to the hospitality and luxury she offered her influential guests. The breathtaking views of the Surrey Hills from the South Lawn invite you to explore the estate, following walking trails that take in ancient woodlands and wildlife habitats – home to rare birds and butterflies. Stroll through the pleasure grounds and colourful formal garden, including the fragrant walled Rose Garden in summer and the picturesque Graham Stuart Thomas-designed garden in winter. Inside the house, you are transported back to her lavish parties as luxury and glamour oozes from every room, with stunning pieces of maiolica, fine French furniture and Dutch Master paintings.

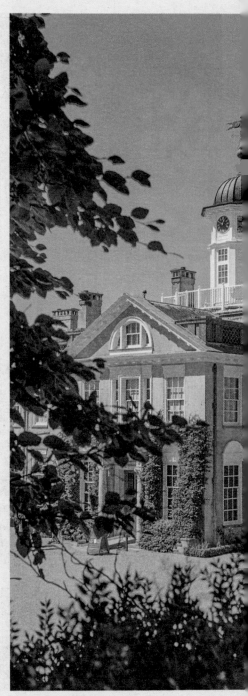

Satnav: use KT23 4PZ. **Parking**: 200 yards.

Dog rating: 🐾 🐾 🐾 **Best** – Welcome on leads in parts of the gardens and on the wider estate.

Access: [icons]

Find out more: 01372 452048 or
polesdenlacey@nationaltrust.org.uk
Great Bookham, near Dorking,
Surrey RH5 6BD
nationaltrust.org.uk/polesden-lacey

Polesden Lacey		M	T	W	T	F	S	S
Gardens, estate, shop and café								
Open all year*	10–5**	M	T	W	T	F	S	S
House†								
1 Jan–27 Feb	11–3:30	.	.	.	.	.	S	S
14 Feb–20 Feb	11–3:30	M	T	W	T	F	S	S
1 Mar–30 Oct	11–4:30††	M	T	W	T	F	S	S
5 Nov–27 Nov	11–3:30	.	.	.	.	.	S	S
1 Dec–31 Dec*	11–3:30	M	T	W	T	F	S	S

*Closed 24 December and 25 December; house also closed 24 to 30 December. **Shop: opens 11; café closes 15 minutes earlier; gardens and estate: close at 4 in winter. †House: access by guided tour or freeflow. ††House: March to October, last entry one hour before closing.

Far left, the luxurious Picture Corridor runs all around the central courtyard at Polesden Lacey, Surrey. Below and left, the gardens are delightful all year

Quebec House

Quebec Square, Westerham, Kent TN16 1TD

| 1918 |

Quebec House in Kent retains its original charm

The childhood home of General James Wolfe, Quebec House retains much of its original charm. A recreated Georgian schoolroom, hands-on collection and objects belonging to Wolfe are used to learn about Georgian family life. An exhibition in the Coach House explores Wolfe's victory at the Battle of Quebec in 1759.

Parking: 80 yards in main town car park on A25 (not National Trust).

Dog rating: ❀ **Standard** – Welcome on short leads in the garden.

Access:

Find out more: 01732 868381 or quebechouse@nationaltrust.org.uk
nationaltrust.org.uk/quebec-house

Quebec House		M	T	W	T	F	S	S
2 Mar–28 Oct	11–4*	·	·	W	T	F	·	·
5 Mar–30 Oct	11–4**	·	·	·	·	·	S	S

*House: Wednesday to Friday, entry by guided tour only.
**Last entry one hour before closing; exhibition open as house.

Reigate Hill and Gatton Park

near Reigate, Surrey

| 1912 |

Reigate Hill commands sweeping views across the Weald to the South Downs. It's a great spot for walking, family picnics, flying a kite and watching wildlife. A short walk away is the 19th-century Reigate Fort. The complex is open every day and the fort buildings open for special events. To the east of Reigate Hill is Surrey Hill's hidden gem, Gatton Park, designed by Lancelot 'Capability' Brown. **Note**: areas of Gatton Park opened monthly by the Gatton Trust.

Satnav: use RH2 0HX.
Parking: at Wray Lane or Margery Wood car park when Wray Lane is full (KT20 7EJ).

Dog rating: ❀ **Standard** – Welcome under close control at all times.

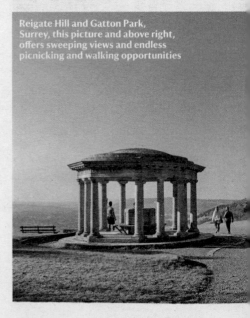

Reigate Hill and Gatton Park, Surrey, this picture and above right, offers sweeping views and endless picnicking and walking opportunities

Access: ⬛⬛

Find out more: 01342 843225 or
reigate@nationaltrust.org.uk
nationaltrust.org.uk/reigate-hill-and-gatton-park

Reigate Hill and Gatton Park
Reigate Fort buildings open by special arrangement.

River Wey and Godalming Navigations and Dapdune Wharf

Navigations Office and Dapdune Wharf,
Wharf Road, Guildford, Surrey GU1 4RR

| 1964 | 🏠🔌🍴🏚🌳🚶 |

A hidden haven where you can relax and unwind on a boat trip, explore a restored barge, or enjoy scenic walks and water sports. Dapdune Wharf in Guildford brings to life stories of the historic waterway, along 20 miles of waterside towpath. A great place for children to have fun. **Note**: boat trip charges, mooring and fishing fees apply to members.

Parking: at Dapdune Wharf.

Dog rating: 🐾 **Standard** – On leads at Dapdune Wharf and lock areas; elsewhere under control.

Access: 🅿️🚾♿🔵🎧♿♿

Find out more: 01483 561389 or
riverwey@nationaltrust.org.uk
nationaltrust.org.uk/riverwey

River Wey and Dapdune Wharf		M	T	W	T	F	S	S
Dapdune Wharf								
26 Mar–6 Nov*	11–5**	M	·	·	T	F	S	S

*Open daily during local school half term and summer holidays. **30 October to 6 November: closes 4. River trips from Dapdune Wharf, 11 to 4 (conditions permitting). Access to towpath during daylight all year.

Runnymede and Ankerwycke

Egham, near Old Windsor, Surrey

1931

Seen by many as the birthplace of modern democracy, this picturesque landscape beside the Thames was witness to King John's sealing of the Magna Carta more than 800 years ago. Within easy reach of the M25, there is so much to enjoy here – ancient woodlands, countryside walks and picnics by the river. Along with Lutyens's Fairhaven Lodges, Runnymede is home to memorials for the Magna Carta, John F. Kennedy and Commonwealth Air Forces, making it the perfect place to reflect.
Note: mooring and fishing (during fishing season) available for additional fee (including members).

Satnav: use TW20 0AE and follow brown 'Runnymede Memorials' signs. **Parking**: either side of A308 (seasonal opening).

Runnymede and Ankerwycke in Surrey, above and below: the birthplace of modern democracy

Dog rating: ✿ **Standard** – Welcome on site and in the Magna Carta Tea-room. On leads near livestock.

Access: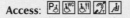

Find out more: 01784 432891 or runnymede@nationaltrust.org.uk
nationaltrust.org.uk/runnymede

Runnymede and Ankerwycke
Memorials car park: open daily, 9 to 5 (January and December, closes 4; 1 April to 30 September, closes 7). Riverside car park: open daily, 1 April to 30 September, 10 to 7. Car parks and facilities closed 24 and 25 December.

Scotney Castle

Lamberhurst, Tunbridge Wells,
Kent TN3 8JN

1970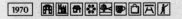

The ruins of the moated 14th-century
Old Castle at Scotney Castle, Kent

Parking: 130 yards (limited), overflow
parking 440 yards.

Dog rating: 🐾 🐾 **Good** – Welcome on
short leads in the garden and on the estate.

Access:

Find out more: 01892 893820 (Infoline) or
scotneycastle@nationaltrust.org.uk
nationaltrust.org.uk/scotney-castle

Scotney Castle		M	T	W	T	F	S	S
House								
1 Mar–31 Dec*	11–4		M	T	W	T	F	S	S
Garden, estate, shop and tea-room								
Open all year**	10–5†		M	T	W	T	F	S	S

*House: closed 1 to 27 November (inclusive); entry by
timed ticket or guided tour. **Closed 24 to 26 December.
†1 January to 11 February and 31 October to 31 December,
site closes at 4.

**The Victorian new house at Scotney Castle,
below, and examining the moat, bottom**

The medieval moated Old Scotney Castle
lies in a peaceful wooded valley. In the
19th century its owner, Edward Hussey III,
set about building a new house, partially
demolishing the Old Castle to create a
romantic folly, the centrepiece of his
picturesque landscape. From the
terraces of the new house, sweeps of
rhododendrons and azaleas cascade down
the slope in summer, followed by highlights
of autumn leaf colour, mirrored in the
moat. In the house three generations
have made their mark, adding possessions
and character to the homely Victorian
mansion which enjoys far-reaching views
out across the estate.

Sheffield Park and Garden

Sheffield Park, Uckfield,
East Sussex TN22 3QX

1954

Originating in the 18th century and developed by each subsequent owner, this garden of colour, perfume and sound excites your senses as you enjoy winding paths, majestic trees, ponds and dappled glades. Falls, cascades and bridges are integral to the garden design. Planting is reflected in ponds so clear that the eye is tricked into thinking up is down. Bold and grand planting has a sculptural form in winter. Spring and summer bring vibrant blooms, fragrant arbours and splashes of colour. Autumn is a blazing kaleidoscope of greens, flame-reds, burnt oranges and bright yellows, planted for their combined display. The encircling park and woodland provide opportunities for further adventure where nature thrives in riverside meadows and woods.

Satnav: look out for brown signs on approach. **Parking**: on site (overflow car park 600 yards, in use when dry); very busy during May and October.

Dog rating: 🐾 🐾 **Good** – Welcome in garden and parkland on short leads; off lead at East Park only.

Access: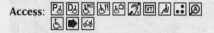

Find out more: 01825 790231 or sheffieldpark@nationaltrust.org.uk
nationaltrust.org.uk/sheffield-park-and-garden

Sheffield Park	
Open every day all year*	10–5**

*Closed 24 and 25 December. **1 to 31 January and 7 November to 31 December: garden, shop and café close at 4.

Vibrant seasonal colour at Sheffield Park and Garden, East Sussex, above and below

Early morning mist rises from Pillbox Pond at Sheffield Park and Garden

Sissinghurst Castle Garden

Biddenden Road, near Cranbrook,
Kent TN17 2AB

 1967

Sissinghurst Castle Garden sits within the ruin of a great Elizabethan house surrounded by the rich Kentish landscape of woods, streams and farmland. The famous garden, with its fairy-tale tower, is the result of the creativity of the formal design of Harold Nicolson and the lavish planting of Vita Sackville-West. The colour schemes, intimacy of the different garden 'rooms' and rich herbaceous borders are the epitome of an English garden. The wider estate, which includes a vegetable garden, lakes and rich variety of wildlife, is waiting to be explored, while our regular exhibitions tell Sissinghurst's stories and show how history and landscape have combined to shape this special place. See the architectural beauty of the garden in winter. **Note**: limited access for buggies and wheelchairs. Sorry no food, drink or buggies in the garden.

The turreted gatehouse, below, rises above Sissinghurst Castle Garden, Kent. The Lime Walk, above

Sissinghurst Castle Garden: the Cottage Garden

Parking: 315 yards.

Dog rating: 🐾 **Standard** – Welcome on leads on estate (assistance dogs only in garden and vegetable garden).

Access: [icons]

Find out more: 01580 710700 or sissinghurst@nationaltrust.org.uk
nationaltrust.org.uk/sissinghurst

Sissinghurst Castle Garden		M	T	W	T	F	S	S
Garden								
1 Jan–27 Mar	11–4*	M	T	W	T	F	S	S
28 Mar–6 Nov	11–5:30*	M	T	W	T	F	S	S
7 Nov–31 Dec	11–4*	M	T	W	T	F	S	S
South Cottage								
1 Jan–31 May	Tour**	M	T	W	T	F	S	S
9 Jul–31 Dec	Tour**	M	T	W	T	F	S	S
Estate, shop and The Granary restaurant								
Open all year	10–5:30†	M	T	W	T	F	S	S

*Last entry 45 minutes before closing. **Tours Monday to Friday, freeflow at weekends. †Shop and restaurant: 1 January to 27 March and 7 November to 31 December, close at 4. Everything closed 24 and 25 December.

Slindon Estate

near Arundel, West Sussex

1950 [icons]

Slindon Estate is a patchwork of woodland, downland, farmland and parkland, with an unspoilt Sussex village at its centre. Historic features cover the landscape, such as Stane Street, the Roman road from Chichester to London. Slindon has a rich and wonderfully varied wildlife with bats, badgers, butterflies and downland flowers.
Note: sorry no toilet.

Satnav: use BN18 0QY for Park Lane; BN18 0SP Duke's Road; RH20 1PH Bignor Hill. **Parking**: at Park Lane (height barrier), Duke's Road (height barrier) and Bignor Hill.

Dog rating: 🐾 **Standard** – Welcome under close control.

Find out more: 01243 814730 or southdownscentral@nationaltrust.org.uk
nationaltrust.org.uk/slindon-estate

View from the Slindon Estate, West Sussex

Smallhythe Place

Smallhythe, Tenterden, Kent TN30 7NG

1939

Surrounded by the rolling Kent countryside, the corridors of this early 16th-century cottage resonate with the vibrant spirit of its theatrical former owner, Victorian actress Ellen Terry. Bursting with memorabilia from her life-long career on stage, visitors can see unique theatrical artefacts and visit the Barn Theatre.

Parking: 50 yards (not National Trust).

Dog rating: ❀ Standard – Welcome on leads in grounds.

Access:

Find out more: 01580 762334 or smallhytheplace@nationaltrust.org.uk
nationaltrust.org.uk/smallhythe-place

Smallhythe Place	M	T	W	T	F	S	S
2 Mar–6 Nov* 11–5**			W	T	F	S	S

*Open Bank Holidays. **Last entry 45 minutes before closing.

Ellen Terry's special Smallhythe Place in Kent

South Foreland Lighthouse

The Front, St Margaret's Bay, Dover, Kent

1989

This historic landmark, above, dramatically situated on The White Cliffs of Dover, guided ships past the infamous Goodwin Sands and has a fascinating story to tell. It was the first lighthouse powered by electricity and the site of the first international radio transmission.
Note: access to lighthouse by road is not permitted.

Parking: no on-site parking, nearest at White Cliffs (2 miles), or St Margaret's village car park (1 mile).

Dog rating: ❀ Standard – Welcome on leads in grounds. Please be aware of cliff edges.

Access:

Find out more: 01304 853281 or southforeland@nationaltrust.org.uk
Langdon Cliffs, Dover, Kent CT16 1HJ
nationaltrust.org.uk/south-foreland-lighthouse

South Foreland Lighthouse		M	T	W	T	F	S	S
Lighthouse*								
1 Apr–30 Oct	11–5:30**	M				F	S	S
Tea-room†								
1 Apr–30 Oct	11–5††	M				F	S	S

*Significant conservation work may affect opening.
**Last tour at 5. †Takeaway kiosk may replace tea-room occasionally. ††30 October, closes at 3.

Standen House and Garden

West Hoathly Road, East Grinstead, West Sussex RH19 4NE

1973 🏛️❄️♣️⚡️☕️📷️🏠️🎭️🚶️

James and Margaret Beale chose an idyllic location to build their rural retreat, nestled in the Sussex countryside with views across the High Weald. Designed by Philip Webb, the house is one of the finest examples of Arts and Crafts workmanship with Morris & Co. interiors and decorative art of the period. The 5-hectare (12-acre) hillside garden established by Mrs Beale is restored to its 1920s glory. Each garden room offers something for every season, from colourful spring bulbs to autumn shades. On the wider estate, footpaths lead into the woodlands and the High Weald Area of Outstanding Natural Beauty.

Parking: 200 yards (steep hill).

Dog rating: 🐾 🐾 **Good** – Welcome on short leads in formal garden, woodland estate and Potting Shed.

Standen House and Garden in West Sussex

A sunny spot at Standen House and Garden

Access: 🅿️♿️🚾️♿️🔊️📷️🖼️🚪️🐕️♿️➡️

Find out more: 01342 323029 or standen@nationaltrust.org.uk
nationaltrust.org.uk/standen-house-and-garden

Standen House		M	T	W	T	F	S	S
House*								
1 Jan–27 Feb	11–3:30	·	·	·	·	·	S	S
28 Feb–29 Oct	11–4:30	M	T	W	T	F	S	S
30 Oct–20 Nov	11–3:30	·	·	·	·	·	S	S
21 Nov–31 Dec	11–3:30	M	T	W	T	F	S	S
Garden, café and shop*								
Open all year	10–5†	M	T	W	T	F	S	S

*House: open Bank Holidays; 5 February to 28 October, closes 4:30. 21 to 25 February: open daily. **Shop: opens 11; café and shop: check closing times before visiting.
†January, November and December: close 4.
Closed 24 and 25 December.

Stoneacre

Otham, Maidstone, Kent ME15 8RS 1928

Medieval farmhouse sitting within a hidden horticultural haven, orchard, meadows and woodland. Home to famous designer and critic Aymer Vallance.
Note: open weekends and Bank Holidays, 19 March to 30 October, 11 to 5.

Find out more: 01580 710701 or stoneacre@nationaltrust.org.uk
nationaltrust.org.uk/stoneacre

Uppark House and Garden

South Harting, Petersfield,
West Sussex GU31 5QR

| 1954 | 🏠🏠✿☕🚻🏛🚶 |

High on its vantage point on the South Downs ridge, Uppark has views as far south as the Solent. Outside, the intimate garden is being gradually restored to its historical design, with plenty of space in the adjacent meadow to play and relax. Filled with purchases from the Grand Tour, Uppark's Georgian interiors illustrate the comfort of life 'upstairs' in contrast to the 'downstairs' world of its servants. Highlights include one of the best examples of an 18th-century British doll's house in the country.
Note: due to conservation work, access to some areas may be limited.

Parking: 300 yards.

Dog rating: 🐾 🐾 **Good** – Welcome on short leads in grounds.

Access: 🅿♿🚾♿👓🎦🖼♿∴🔍♿↕ 🚶♿➡

Find out more: 01730 825415 or
uppark@nationaltrust.org.uk
nationaltrust.org.uk/uppark

Uppark House		M	T	W	T	F	S	S
House								
Open all year*	10:30–3				T	F	S	S
Garden and café								
Open all year*	10–4	M	T	W	T	F	S	S

*Everything closed 4 to 30 January, 31 October to 18 November, plus 25 and 26 December.

The garden, above, and Staircase Hall, below, at Uppark House and Garden, West Sussex

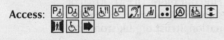

Wakehurst

Ardingly, Haywards Heath,
West Sussex RH17 6TN

1964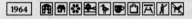

Spring blossoms at Wakehurst in West Sussex

Wakehurst, Kew's wild botanic garden
in Sussex, has more than 202 hectares
(500 acres) of beautiful ornamental
gardens, woodlands and a nature
reserve. Internationally significant for
the collections, scientific research and
plant conservation, you can also visit
Kew's unique Millennium Seed Bank, where
science and horticulture work side by side.
Note: funded and managed by the Royal
Botanic Gardens, Kew. **Parking charges
apply (including members)**.

Parking: 50 yards.

Access:

Find out more: 01444 894066 or
wakehurst@kew.org
nationaltrust.org.uk/wakehurst

Wakehurst		M	T	W	T	F	S	S
1 Mar–31 Oct	10–6*	M	T	W	T	F	S	S
1 Nov–31 Dec**	10–4:30*	M	T	W	T	F	S	S

*Millennium Seed Bank closes one hour earlier. Shop and
catering: closing times may vary. UK National Trust members
free (reciprocal agreements between the Trust and other
parties not applicable). **Closed 24 and 25 December.

The White Cliffs of Dover

Langdon Cliffs, Dover, Kent

1968

There can be no doubt that The White Cliffs
of Dover are one of this country's most
spectacular natural features and have been
a symbol of hope for generations. You can
appreciate their beauty through the
seasons by taking one of the country's most
dramatic clifftop walks, which offer
unrivalled views of the English Channel
while savouring the rare flora and fauna
found only on this chalk grassland. Fan Bay
Deep Shelter, a labyrinth of forgotten
Second World War tunnels, is a reminder of
the fascinating military history of The White
Cliffs. **Note**: nearest toilets at White Cliffs.
Age restrictions apply at Fan Bay.

The truly iconic and spectacular coastline
at The White Cliffs of Dover, Kent

Fan Bay Deep Shelter, above, lies hidden beneath The White Cliffs of Dover, top

Satnav: use CT15 5NA.
Parking: on site, limited (please check before visiting Sundays and Bank Holidays, April to October).

Dog rating: ❀ **Standard** – Welcome on leads. Please be aware of livestock and cliff edges.

Access: 🅿♿🚻♿📷♿♿♿➡

Find out more: 01304 202756 or whitecliffs@nationaltrust.org.uk
nationaltrust.org.uk/white-cliffs

The White Cliffs	
Visitor Centre, shop and kiosk	
Open every day all year*	10–5**

*Closed 24 and 25 December.
**1 January to 13 February and 31 October to 31 December: close at 4. Fan Bay Deep Shelter: opening arrangements not confirmed at time of print, please check before visiting.

Winkworth Arboretum

Hascombe Road, Godalming, Surrey GU8 4AD

1952   ❀🐾🍴🏕🏃

The National Trust's only arboretum was born from one man's vision and passion. Dr Wilfrid Fox used the wooded valley and its lakes as a canvas for 'painting a picture' with trees. His legacy is an award-winning collection of more than 1,000 varieties of trees and shrubs set in the picturesque hills of Surrey. Famous for vibrant autumnal foliage, delicate snowdrops in winter, carpets of bluebells in spring and colourful summer meadows. Visit all year for beautiful scenery, dog walks, picnics and events for all ages. **Note**: some steep slopes; banks of lake and wetlands only partially fenced.

Parking: 100 yards.

Winkworth Arboretum in Surrey, above and below, is the National Trust's only arboretum

Dog rating: 🐾 🐾 **Good** – Welcome on leads.

Access: [icons]

Find out more: 01483 208477 or winkwortharboretum@nationaltrust.org.uk
nationaltrust.org.uk/winkworth

Winkworth Arboretum	
Open every day all year*	10–5**

*Closed 24 and 25 December. **1 January to 31 March and 1 November to 31 December: closes 4. Tea-room closes 30 minutes before Arboretum. Last entry 90 minutes before closing. Car-park gates locked at closing time.

Woolbeding Gardens

Midhurst, West Sussex GU29 9RR

| 1957 | [icons] |

Ever-changing Woolbeding Gardens, West Sussex

Bordering the River Rother, Woolbeding Gardens is a horticultural haven where modern yet romantic planting meets sophisticated colour palettes. Elegant garden rooms and meticulous borders merge with a wooded landscape that conceals dramatic architectural follies. Ever-changing, from the seasons to the planting, every moment offers something new and picturesque. **Note**: access by park-and-ride minibus from Midhurst only (booking essential). Glasshouse opening in the summer.

Parking: none available. Access by park-and-ride minibus from Midhurst (booking essential).

Access: [icons]

Find out more: 0344 249 1895 or woolbedinggardens@nationaltrust.org.uk
nationaltrust.org.uk/woolbeding-gardens

Woolbeding Gardens		M	T	W	T	F	S	S
27 Apr–30 Sep*	10:30–4:30	·	·	W	T	F	·	·

Access by park-and-ride minibus only from Midhurst (booking essential, check website for details); follow instructions on booking ticket to minibus.
*Closed 1, 2 and 3 June.

Morden Hall Park,
South London

London

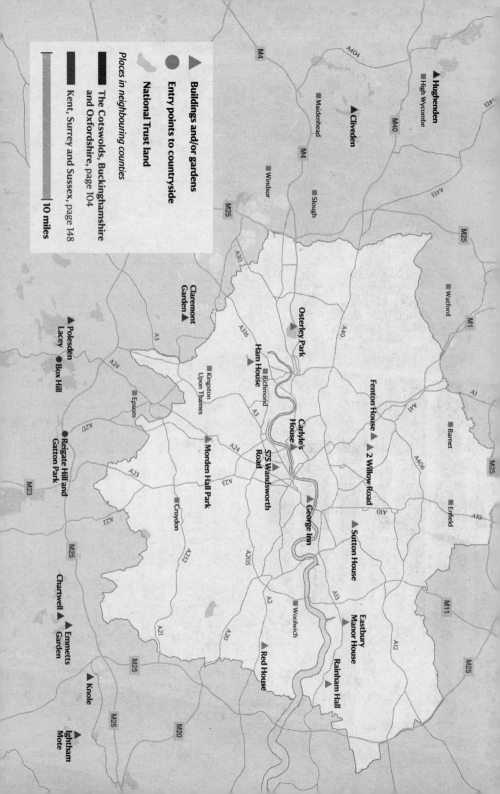

Carlyle's House

24 Cheyne Row, Chelsea,
London SW3 5HL 1936

This home of Victorian writer Thomas
Carlyle was visited by many literary giants,
such as John Ruskin and Charles Dickens.
Note: opening arrangements not
confirmed at time of print, please
check before visiting.

Find out more: 020 7352 7087 or
carlyleshouse@nationaltrust.org.uk
nationaltrust.org.uk/carlyles-house

Note: managed by London Borough of
Barking and Dagenham. Some rooms are
closed occasionally for functions.

Parking: on site, pay and display.

Dog rating: ❧ **Standard** – Welcome on
leads in grounds only.

Access: ♿ 🚾 ♿ ♿ ♿ 🔊 ♿ ✦ ♿ ♿

Find out more: 020 8227 2942 or
eastburymanor@nationaltrust.org.uk
nationaltrust.org.uk/eastbury-manor-house

Eastbury Manor House		M	T	W	T	F	S	S
1 Apr–11 Dec	10–4*	·	·	·	·	**F**	**S**	**S**

*Closes 2 on Fridays.

Eastbury Manor House

Eastbury Square, Barking IG11 9SN

1918 🏠 ❧ ♨ 🛍 📷 🏞 🔧

**Autumn colours in the garden at
Eastbury Manor House in Barking**

Little altered since it was built circa 1573,
this Grade I-listed Elizabethan gentry
house features soaring chimneys, early
17th-century wall-paintings and an original
prospect tower staircase. Outside there is
a cobbled courtyard and peaceful walled
garden with bee boles to explore.

Fenton House and Garden

Hampstead Grove, Hampstead,
London NW3 6SP

1952 🏠 ❧ 🏞 🗡

**Sitting high up in Hampstead, Fenton House
and Garden dates from 1686**

Fenton House is filled with world-class collections of fine and decorative arts

This 1686 house, with views across London from Hampstead's Holly Hill, is filled with world-class collections of ceramics, paintings, textiles and musical instruments. The ever-changing horticultural gem that is the garden includes an orchard, kitchen garden, rose garden, terraces and lawns, and never fails to delight.

Parking: none on site.

Access: 🏠 🚻 ⬛ 🔍 ♿ 🚶

Find out more: 020 7435 3471 or fentonhouse@nationaltrust.org.uk
nationaltrust.org.uk/fenton-house

Fenton House

Opening arrangements not confirmed at time of print, please check before visiting.

George Inn

The George Inn Yard, 77 Borough High Street, Southwark, London SE1 1NH 1937

This public house, dating from the 17th century, is London's last remaining galleried inn. **Note**: leased to a private company. Open every day all year (excluding 25 and 26 December), 11 to 11.

Find out more: 020 7407 2056 or georgeinn@nationaltrust.org.uk
nationaltrust.org.uk/george-inn

Ham House and Garden

Ham Street, Ham, Richmond TW10 7RS

1948 🏠 ✿ ☕ 🏠 🧺 👟

Beautifully situated on the banks of the River Thames, Ham is truly one of London's treasures. You can step back in time, walking on the original marble floors while admiring the lavish furnishings, cabinets and artwork collected by the Duke and Duchess of Lauderdale and enjoyed by Charles II during his visits here. The re-imagining of the 17th-century garden is quite wonderful. Containing a large walled kitchen garden, lavender parterre, woodland wilderness garden, two wildflower meadows and boasting an annual display of spring bulbs, the garden's creation was designed to impress.

Satnav: takes you to stables on nearby Ham Street, carry straight on past these to car park. Parking: none on site, nearest 380 yards (not National Trust) and on street.

Dog rating: 🐾 🐾 Good – Welcome on short leads in garden.

Access: [access icons]

Find out more: 020 8940 1950 or hamhouse@nationaltrust.org.uk
nationaltrust.org.uk/ham-house

Ham House and Garden in Richmond, this page and opposite, is one of London's treasures with impressive gardens

Ham House		M	T	W	T	F	S	S
House								
28 Feb–31 Dec	12–4*	M	T	W	T	F	S	S
Garden and orangery café								
Open all year	10–5*	M	T	W	T	F	S	S
Shop								
Open all year	10–5*			W	T	F	S	S

*Closes at least an hour earlier in winter, depending on light levels. Everything closed 24 and 25 December.

Morden Hall Park

Morden Hall Road, Morden,
London SM4 5JD

1941 🏠🌼🎫🐦🍵🛍️📷🏞️

Step into this 50-hectare (125-acre) oasis
and you'll soon forget you're in South
London. Once a private country estate, the
grounds were gifted to the National Trust
to become a park for all people, and it's
been a local treasure ever since. Peaceful
tree-lined riverside paths lead to wide
open meadows and a collection of historic
buildings which hint at an industrial past.
The 1920s rose garden is a delight for
the senses, while a stroll on the wetland
boardwalk gives a glimpse into the world
of waterbirds. Visit the National Trust's only
garden centre (peat free) where our expert
team will be on hand to help, or drop by
The Stableyard second-hand bookshop.

Morden Hall Park, left, is a haven in bustling
South London. The garden centre, above

Parking: limited, 25 yards (next to
garden centre).

Dog rating: 🐾 🐾 🐾 **Best** – Welcome
in park and Stableyard café, on leads
around buildings, rose garden,
playground and boardwalk.

Access: ♿🅿️🚻♿🍴🔵📷🛗♿🚹♿➡️

Find out more: 020 8545 6850 or
mordenhallpark@nationaltrust.org.uk
nationaltrust.org.uk/morden-hall-park

Morden Hall Park		M	T	W	T	F	S	S
Meadows and wetlands								
Open all year		M	T	W	T	F	S	S
Rose Garden and Potting Shed café								
Open all year	9–5*	M	T	W	T	F	S	S
Garden centre								
Open all year**	10–4	M	T	W	T	F	S	S
Stableyard café								
Open all year	10–2:30	M	T	W	T	F	S	S

*Potting Shed café: closes 4. **Closed 1 January and
Easter Sunday. Car park: locked 5 daily (last entry 4).
Everything (excluding meadows and wetlands) closed
25 and 26 December.

Morden Hall Park, once a private estate, is now a park for everyone

Osterley Park and House

Isleworth, London

1949

A suburban palace caught between town and country, Osterley Park and House is one of the last surviving country estates in London. Past fields and grazing cattle, and just around the lake, the magnificent house awaits, presented as it would have been when it was redesigned by Robert Adam in the late 18th century for the Child family. A place for welcoming friends and clients, fashioned for show and entertaining, the lavish state apartments tell the story of a party palace. Returned family portraits and furniture now add a personal touch to grand rooms. Elegant pleasure gardens and hundreds of acres of parkland are perfect for whiling away a peaceful afternoon.

Satnav: enter Jersey Road and TW7 4RD.
Parking: 400 yards.

Dog rating: 🐾 🐾 **Good** – Welcome on leads, with a designated off-lead area (excluding house and, between March and October, the gardens).

Osterley Park and House in Isleworth, this page and opposite, offers grand interiors and vast stretches of parkland to explore

Access: 🅿️ 🅓 🚌 ♿ 🔊 📷 ♿ ⠿ 🔍 ♿
♿ ➡️ ♿

Find out more: 020 8232 5050 or
osterley@nationaltrust.org.uk
Jersey Road, Isleworth, London TW7 4RB
nationaltrust.org.uk/osterley-park

Osterley Park		M	T	W	T	F	S	S
House and shop*								
Open all year**	11–4†		·	W	T	F	S	S
Garden, park and café								
Open all year**	10–5††	M	T	W	T	F	S	S

*House: November and December, open 11 to 3:30 (selected
rooms only); closed occasionally for filming. **1 January to
13 February and 31 October to 31 December: close 4; closed
24 and 25 December. †Shop: closes at 5; November and
December opening may vary. ††Park: opens at 9.

Rainham Hall

The Broadway, Rainham,
London RM13 9YN

 1949

Rainham Hall, in London's far-eastern fringe, is surrounded by gardens and wild marshland

Built in 1729 for an enterprising merchant, Rainham Hall lies at the heart of Rainham village on the far-eastern fringe of London. Surrounded by wild marshland and thriving industry, this hidden piece of London's history has been home to nearly 50 different inhabitants, including a scientist-vicar and a *Vogue* photographer.

Parking: 300 yards (not National Trust).

Dog rating: ✿ **Standard** – Welcome on short leads in garden.

Access: ⬛⬛⬛

Find out more: 01708 525579 or
rainhamhall@nationaltrust.org.uk
nationaltrust.org.uk/rainham

Rainham Hall		M	T	W	T	F	S	S
3 Feb–31 Dec*	11–4				**T**	**F**	**S**	

*Closed 25 December. Entry by guided tour (approximately one hour), booking recommended.

Red House

Red House, Bexleyheath, London

2003 ⬛⬛⬛⬛⬛

The only house commissioned, created and lived in by William Morris, founder of the Arts and Crafts movement, Red House is a building of extraordinary architectural and social significance. Discover original pre-Raphaelite wall-paintings and Morris's first decorative schemes.

Satnav: use DA6 8HL – Danson Park car park. **Parking**: at Danson Park, just over ½ mile. Charge at weekends and Bank Holidays (including members).

Access: ⬛⬛⬛⬛⬛⬛

Find out more: 020 8303 6359 or
redhouse@nationaltrust.org.uk
Red House Lane, Bexleyheath,
London DA6 8JF
nationaltrust.org.uk/red-house

Red House		M	T	W	T	F	S	S
3 Mar–29 Oct	Tour				**T**	**F**	**S**	

Entry by guided tour (approximately one hour), booking essential.

Red House in Bexleyheath: this William Morris gem is an Arts and Crafts masterpiece

Sutton House and Breaker's Yard

2 and 4 Homerton High Street, Hackney, London E9 6JQ

1938 ⊞ ⌂ ❖ ⊼ ⌿ ✕

Journey through 500 years to discover the hidden delights of the oldest house in Hackney, from a seat of Tudor power to an 80s punk squat. Today it continues to act as a lively cultural and social centre for the community, and a venue for weddings and private events.

Parking: none on site and very limited nearby, not National Trust (charge including members).

Access: ⊞ ⌨ ⊿ ▢ ♿ ⋮ ⊙ ♿ ♿

Find out more: 020 8986 2264 or suttonhouse@nationaltrust.org.uk
nationaltrust.org.uk/sutton-house

Sutton House		M	T	W	T	F	S	S
2 Feb–18 Dec	Tour	·	·	**W**	·	**F**	·	**S**

Entry by guided tour, 11 and 2, plus 3:30 on Sundays (approximately one hour), booking recommended.

575 Wandsworth Road

575 Wandsworth Road, Lambeth, London SW8 3JD 2010

Khadambi Asalache turned this modest Grade II-listed Georgian terraced house into a work of art with hand-carved fretwork. **Note**: sorry no toilet or café. Please wear or bring socks as no outdoor shoes are allowed in the house. Open Thursday, 3 March to 27 October, 11 to 3; entry by guided tour (approximately one hour), booking essential, spaces limited.

Find out more: 0344 249 1895 (bookings) or 575wandsworthroad@nationaltrust.org.uk
nationaltrust.org.uk/575-wandsworth-road

2 Willow Road

Hampstead, London NW3 1TH

1994 ⊞ ⌿ ✕ 🐾

This late 1930s house, above, an architect's vision of the future, paints a vivid picture of the creative and social circles of Ernö and Ursula Goldfinger. Today you can explore the original intimate and evocative interiors, innovative designs, intriguing personal possessions and impressive 20th-century art collection. **Note**: sorry no toilet.

Parking: very limited, metered on-street parking nearby (not National Trust).

Access: ▢ ⊞ ▢ ⊿ ⋮ ⊙ ♿ ⌿

Find out more: 020 7435 6166 or 2willowroad@nationaltrust.org.uk
nationaltrust.org.uk/2-willow-road

2 Willow Road

Opening arrangements not confirmed at time of print, please check before visiting.

East of England

The Lifeboat House
at Blakeney National
Nature Reserve, Norfolk

Tattershall Castle ▲

Belton ▲ House

Woolsthorpe ▲ Manor

▲ Lyveden

A1(M)

PETERBOROUGH

Ramsey Abbey ▲ Gatehouse

Peckover ▲ House

Houghton Mill ▲

Wicken Fen ▲

Newmarket

CAMBRIDGE

Willington Dovecote and Stables ■

Anglesey ▲ Abbey

BEDFORD

Wimpole ▲ Estate

Sundon Hills Country Park ●

Ascott ▲

Pitstone ▲ Windmill

Ashridge ● Estate

Coombe ■ Hill

Whipsnade Tree Cathedral ▲

Sharpenhoe ●

Totternhoe Knolls ●

Luton ■

Dunstable ▲ Downs

Shaw's ▲ Corner

HERTFORD

Morven ● Park

A1(M)

M25

M11

M25

Eastbury ▲ Manor House

Rainham Hall ▲

King's Lynn

Swaffham ■

Oxburgh ▲ Hall

Brancaster Estate ●

Blakeney ●

Morston Quay ●

Sheringham Park ●

West Runton and Beeston Regis Heath ●

Cromer ▲

Felbrigg Hall ▲

Blickling Estate ▲

Horsey Windpump ▲

NORWICH

Great Yarmouth

Elizabethan House Museum ▲

Darrow ● Wood

Dunwich Heath ●

Bury St Edmunds

Theatre Royal ▲

Ickworth ▲

Lavenham ▲ Guildhall

Melford Hall ▲

Kyson ● Hill

Sutton ● Hoo

IPSWICH

Orford Ness ●

Pin Mill ●

Flatford ▲

Paycocke's ▲ House

Colchester ■

Bourne Mill ▲

Grange ▲ Barn

Copt Hall ● Marshes

Northey ● Island

CHELMSFORD

Hatfield ▲ Forest

Danbury Commons and Blakes Wood ●

Rayleigh Mount ●

Anglesey Abbey, Gardens and Lode Mill

Quy Road, Lode, Cambridge,
Cambridgeshire CB25 9EJ

1966

This welcoming and elegant house, gardens and working watermill have something to offer in every season. The nationally celebrated 50-hectare (124-acre) gardens, with sweeping avenues, wildflower meadows, classical statuary and flower borders, offer reflective space, captivating views, vibrant colours and delicious scents throughout the year. Families can play, explore and discover nature in the wider woodland. The house showcases Lord Fairhaven's extensive and unique collection,

Anglesey Abbey, Gardens and Lode Mill, Cambridgeshire: the elegant house evokes a golden age

The Long Gallery at Anglesey Abbey, this picture, and Lode Mill, top right

Check opening dates and times before you set out: nationaltrust.org.uk

including seasonal highlights bringing its story to life, and one of the most significant 20th-century libraries in the National Trust. The historic watermill, on beautiful Quy Water, provides a unique insight into a critical part of East Anglian life.

Parking: 50 yards (2-metre height restrictions in some areas of car park).

Access:

Find out more: 01223 810080 or angleseyabbey@nationaltrust.org.uk
nationaltrust.org.uk/angleseyabbey

Anglesey Abbey		M	T	W	T	F	S	S
Garden								
1 Jan–31 Jan	9:30–4*	M	T	W	T	F	S	S
1 Feb–31 Mar	9:30–5*	M	T	W	T	F	S	S
1 Apr–31 Oct	9:30–5:30*	M	T	W	T	F	S	S
1 Nov–31 Dec	9:30–4*	M	T	W	T	F	S	S
House								
1 Mar–31 Jul	11–3*	M	T	W	T	F	S	S
1 Aug–31 Aug	Tour	M	T	W	T	F	S	S
1 Sep–31 Oct	11–3*	M	T	W	T	F	S	S
1 Dec–31 Dec	11–3*	M	T	W	T	F	S	S
Lode Mill								
1 Jan–30 Jan	11:30–2:30**		T	W	T	F	S	S
1 Feb–30 Oct	11:30–3:30**		T	W	T	F	S	S
1 Nov–31 Dec	11:30–2:30**		T	W	T	F	S	S

House: open 1 and 2 January, 11 to 3 (last entrance at 2). Lode Mill open Bank Holiday Mondays. *Garden and house: last entry one hour before closing. **Mill: last entry 15 minutes before closing. Everything closed 24, 25 and 26 December.

The well-stocked bookcases in the Library at Anglesey Abbey are made of elm wood

Ashridge Estate

near Berkhamsted, Hertfordshire

1926

For centuries everyone from pilgrims to picnickers have been exploring the ancient forests and chalk grasslands of Ashridge Estate. Come and discover for yourself its rich wildlife, diverse habitats and varied history. From the scent of the bluebells in spring, glorious birdsong and spectacular views in summer, the rutting fallow deer in autumn and crisp walks on swathes of open common in winter, Ashridge has a landscape for every season. Experience the Wildwood Den natural play area for children and climb the Bridgewater Monument for fantastic views. Waymarked trails and mobility tracks are available from the visitor centre. **Note**: toilets available only when café open.

Satnav: use HP4 1LT for the visitor centre and Bridgewater Monument. **Parking**: at visitor centre, Ivinghoe Beacon and many other parts of estate.

Dog rating: ❧ ❧ **Good** – Under close control at all times for the safety of wildlife and visitors.

Access:

Find out more: 01442 851227 or ashridge@nationaltrust.org.uk **nationaltrust.org.uk/ashridge**

Ashridge Estate		M	T	W	T	F	S	S
Estate								
Open all year	Dawn–dusk	M	T	W	T	F	S	S
Visitor centre, shop and café								
Open all year	9–4*	M	T	W	T	F	S	S

*Visitor centre and shop: March to October, open daily, 10 to 5; November to February, open daily, 10 to 4.

Bluebells in spring at Ashridge Estate in Hertfordshire. Above, picnickers enjoy a sunny day

Blakeney National Nature Reserve

near Morston, Norfolk

1912 🏠🐾🖼️🛶🌳💷🍵🏺🏛️

At the heart of the Norfolk Coast Area of Outstanding Natural Beauty, internationally important Blakeney National Nature Reserve boasts wide open spaces and uninterrupted views. Blakeney Point, a 4-mile shingle spit, is home to a vast array of resident and migratory wildlife, including summer-breeding terns and winter-breeding grey seals.
Note: nearest toilets at Morston Quay and Blakeney Quay (not National Trust).

Satnav: use NR25 7BH for Morston Quay or NR25 7NE for Blakeney Quay.
Parking: at Morston Quay, Blakeney Quay and Green Way Stiffkey Saltmarshes.

Dog rating: 🐾 **Standard** – Welcome under close control. Seasonal restriction applies at Blakeney Point, 1 April to 15 August.

Access: 🚻♿🏬🅿️♿♿

Find out more: 01263 740241 or blakeneypoint@nationaltrust.org.uk
nationaltrust.org.uk/blakeney

Blakeney National Nature Reserve, Norfolk: the Lifeboat House on Blakeney Point

Blickling Estate

Blickling, Aylsham, Norfolk NR11 6NF

1940 🏠🏠❋♿💷🏺🏛️🚶

Fun in the woods on Blickling Estate, Norfolk

You'll never forget your first sight of Blickling, as the breathtaking Jacobean mansion comes into view, flanked by ancient yew hedging and encircled by its historic park. This 1,933-hectare (4,600-acre) gift to the nation was bequeathed by its visionary owner, Lord Lothian, whose role was pivotal in creating the 1937 Act of Parliament that allowed whole estates to be left to the National Trust without incurring death duties. Your support is helping to tackle crucial conservation work needed to protect the most significant library held by the National Trust and the mansion that houses it.

Blickling Estate: the Jacobean mansion in autumn, this picture, and the formal Parterre Garden, below

Parking: 400 yards.

Dog rating: 🐾 🐾 🐾 **Best** – Welcome under close control in park, Muddy Boots café and outside the Farmyard café (assistance dogs only elsewhere).

Access: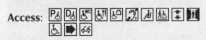

Find out more: 01263 738030 or blickling@nationaltrust.org.uk
nationaltrust.org.uk/blickling

Bourne Mill

Bourne Road, Colchester, Essex CO2 8RT

1936

Bourne Mill in Essex was originally built for banquets

Built for banquets and converted into a mill in the 17th century, Bourne Mill still has a working waterwheel. The surrounding pond, wetlands and woods are home to a variety of wildlife, including birds, bats, waterfowl and many insects, which provide endless nature discoveries.

Parking: Blue Badge parking on site only, or on street nearby.

Dog rating: ❀ **Standard** – Welcome on leads.

Access: ⬚⬚⬚⬚⬚⬚⬚

Find out more: 01206 549799 or bournemill@nationaltrust.org.uk
nationaltrust.org.uk/bourne-mill

Blickling Estate		M	T	W	T	F	S	S
House								
12 Feb–1 Apr	11–3	M	T	W	T	F	S	S
2 Apr–30 Oct	12–4	M	T	W	T	F	S	S
31 Oct–18 Dec	11–3	M	T	W	T	F	S	S
Garden, shops and cafés								
1 Jan–1 Apr	10–4	M	T	W	T	F	S	S
2 Apr–30 Oct	10–5	M	T	W	T	F	S	S
31 Oct–31 Dec	10–4	M	T	W	T	F	S	S
Park								
Open all year	Dawn–dusk	M	T	W	T	F	S	S

Winter Lights (November and December): opening hours subject to change. Everything closed 24 and 25 December.

Bourne Mill		M	T	W	T	F	S	S
2 Apr–9 Apr	11–3:30	·	·	·	·	·	S	·
15 Apr–18 Apr	11–3:30	M	·	·	·	F	S	S
28 May–4 Jun	11–3:30	·	·	·	·	·	S	·
23 Jul–27 Aug	11–3:30	·	·	·	·	·	S	·

Brancaster Estate

near Brancaster, Norfolk

1923

The sandy beach at Brancaster Estate, Norfolk, stretches for miles

The Brancaster Estate comprises the beautiful endless sandy Brancaster Beach, perfect for summer sandcastles and winter walks, the intriguing Branodunum Roman Fort site and the traditional fishing harbour of Brancaster Staithe. The area is rich in wildlife and offers a memorable visit regardless of the time of year. **Note**: beach car park (not National Trust). Toilets at beach and harbour.

Satnav: use PE31 8AX (Beach Road); PE31 8BW (Brancaster Staithe).
Parking: Beach Road, Brancaster (not National Trust), charge including members. Limited parking at Harbour Way, Brancaster Staithe. Both subject to tidal flooding.

Dog rating: 🐾 🐾 **Good** – Welcome under close control. Small seasonal restrictions/dog-free zone on beach, May to September.

Access: [WC] [&]

Find out more: 01263 740241 or brancaster@nationaltrust.org.uk
nationaltrust.org.uk/brancaster-estate

Copt Hall Marshes

near Little Wigborough, Essex 1989

Working farm on the remote and beautiful Blackwater Estuary – a fantastic birdwatching spot, important for overwintering species and farmland wildlife. **Note**: sorry no toilet. For satnav use CO5 7RD. St Nicholas Church not National Trust. Please keep to marked trails. Dogs on leads welcome under control. Car park open 8 to 6, April to October, and 9 to 4, November to March.

Find out more: copthall@nationaltrust.org.uk
nationaltrust.org.uk/copt-hall-marshes

Danbury Commons and Blakes Wood

near Danbury, Essex 1953

Varied countryside, ranging from the lowland heath of Danbury Common to ancient woodland with stunning spring flowers at Blakes Wood. **Note**: sorry no toilet. For satnav for Danbury Commons use CM3 4JH; for Blakes Wood CM3 4AU. Car parks close dusk (may vary).

Find out more: 01245 227662 or danbury@nationaltrust.org.uk
nationaltrust.org.uk/danbury-commons-and-blakes-wood

Darrow Wood

near Harleston, Norfolk 1990

Darrow Wood is a small hedge-enclosed, lightly wooded pasture field containing well preserved earthworks from a compact motte-and-bailey castle. **Note**: sorry no toilet. For satnav use IP20 0AY, Darrow Green Road. Cattle graze in spring/summer on the wooded pasture – look out for signs. Very limited parking on side of road.

Find out more: 01728 648020 (Dunwich Heath) or darrowwood@nationaltrust.org.uk
nationaltrust.org.uk/darrow-wood

Dunstable Downs and the Whipsnade Estate

near Dunstable, Bedfordshire

1928 🏠🏊🐾🖤🗑️🏠🏯

Look down on a landscape sculpted over time. Stand on top of Dunstable Downs to enjoy the far reaching views across the Aylesbury Vale. Bring a picnic and fly a kite or sit back and watch the gliders soar across the hills. Dunstable Downs are a rich habitat for plants and wildlife, including

orchids, butterflies, glow worms, birds and much more. Within the Chilterns Area of Outstanding Natural Beauty, Dunstable Downs is the highest point in Bedfordshire. Follow one of the waymarked trails or walk along the ancient droveways to join the Icknield Way. **Note**: Chilterns Gateway Centre is owned by Central Bedfordshire Council and managed by the National Trust.

Dunstable Downs and the Whipsnade Estate, Bedfordshire, above and left: perfect for kite-flying

Satnav: use LU6 2GY. **Parking**: at Dunstable Downs, off B4541, and Bison Hill off the B4540.

Dog rating: 🐾 🐾 **Good** – Welcome on leads in car parks, in the centre and around livestock.

Access: ♿🚻🛗🅿️♿♿➡️

Find out more: 01582 500920 or dunstabledowns@nationaltrust.org.uk
nationaltrust.org.uk/dunstable

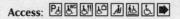

Dunstable Downs

Café: open daily, 10 to 5, 9 March to October weekends (hot food served up to 60 minutes before Centre closes). Centre: closes 5. Main car park: closes 5 (cars can exit any time). Café: closed 24 and 25 December.

Dunwich Heath and Beach

Coastguard Cottages, Minsmere Road, Dunwich, Suffolk IP17 3DJ

1968 | ♿🏖🐕🍴⛺

Two views of Dunwich Heath and Beach in Suffolk: a walkers' paradise

Dunwich Heath has been in the care of the National Trust for more than 50 years. A precious landscape on the Suffolk coast, Dunwich Heath offers a true sense of being at one with nature. Located in the middle of an Area of Outstanding Natural Beauty, there is an abundance of wildlife, including rare birds such as the Dartford warbler and the mysterious nightjar, as well as herds of red deer. The network of footpaths allows you to immerse yourself in nature and explore different habitats, including heather heath, gorse tracks, open grassland, woodland, shingle beach and sandy cliffs.

Satnav: use IP17 3DJ. **Parking:** on site.

Dog rating: 🐾 🐾 🐾 **Best** – Welcome on leads March to September. 'Woof' walk and beach unrestricted. Toys, bowls and treats available.

Access: 🅿♿🚻♿🐕🎫📷♿🚪♿

Find out more: 01728 648501 or dunwichheath@nationaltrust.org.uk
nationaltrust.org.uk/dunwich-heath

Dunwich Heath		M	T	W	T	F	S	S
Café								
1 Jan–20 Feb	10–3						S	S
21 Feb–27 Feb	10–3	M	T	W	T	F	S	S
28 Feb–31 Mar	10–4	M	T	W	T	F	S	S
1 Apr–30 Sep	10–5	M	T	W	T	F	S	S
1 Oct–30 Oct	10–4	M	T	W	T	F	S	S
5 Nov–18 Dec	10–3						S	S
26 Dec–31 Dec	10–3	M	T	W	T	F	S	

Car park opening times vary, please check before visiting.

Elizabethan House Museum

4 South Quay, Great Yarmouth, Norfolk NR30 2QH | 1943

A 16th-century quayside home, set out to reflect day-to-day domestic life from Tudor to Victorian times. **Note:** managed by Norfolk Museums Service. Open 1 April to 31 October (for times check before visiting).

Find out more: 01493 855746 or elizabethanhouse@nationaltrust.org.uk
nationaltrust.org.uk/elizabethan-house-museum

Felbrigg Hall, Gardens and Estate

Felbrigg, near Cromer, Norfolk

1969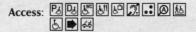

Felbrigg Hall, Gardens and Estate in Norfolk

Atmospheric Felbrigg is a place of tranquillity. The Hall, below, which still contains its original and extensive collection, reflects the people who shaped it. A home to many generations, it has more than 400 years of family stories to be discovered. Set in extensive parkland, with a working walled garden and dove-house, orangery, lake, ancient woodland and miles of estate walks, all framed by big Norfolk skies, Felbrigg is the perfect place to escape and relax at any time of year.

Satnav: use NR11 8PP.
Parking: on site. Electric vehicle charging point in main car park.

Dog rating: 🐾 🐾 **Good** – Welcome under close control in the parkland. On leads during bird-breeding season and around livestock.

Access: [icons]

Find out more: 01263 837444 or felbrigg@nationaltrust.org.uk
Felbrigg, near Cromer, Norfolk NR11 8PR
nationaltrust.org.uk/felbrigg

Felbrigg Hall		M	T	W	T	F	S	S
House								
8 Jan–13 Mar	12–3	.	.	.	.	.	S	S
14 Mar–30 Oct	12–4	M	T	W	.	.	S	S
5 Nov–18 Dec	12–3	.	.	.	.	.	S	S
Gardens								
8 Jan–13 Mar	10:30–3:30	.	.	.	.	.	S	S
14 Mar–30 Oct	10:30–4:30	M	T	W	T	F	S	S
5 Nov–18 Dec	10:30–3:30	.	.	.	.	.	S	S
Shop and tea-room								
1 Jan–13 Mar	10–3:30	M	T	W	T	F	S	S
14 Mar–30 Oct	10–4:30	M	T	W	T	F	S	S
31 Oct–31 Dec*	10–3:30	M	T	W	T	F	S	S
Parkland								
Open all year	Dawn–dusk	M	T	W	T	F	S	S

House and gardens: last entry one hour before closing. House open daily during school holidays, except at Christmas. *Shop and tea-room closed 24 to 26 December.

The River Stour at Flatford, Suffolk, runs through a landscape which inspired John Constable so many years ago

Flatford

East Bergholt, Suffolk CO7 6UL

| 1943 |

Flatford lies at the heart of the Dedham Vale Area of Outstanding Natural Beauty. This charming hamlet was the inspiration for some of John Constable's most famous paintings, including *The Hay Wain*, *Boat Building* and *Flatford Mill*. The exhibition gives you an insight into Constable's life and career while Bridge Cottage tells the story of the people who lived and worked at Flatford. You can explore the beautiful countryside on one of the circular walks or follow riverside paths to the nearby villages of Dedham and East Bergholt. A visit to Flatford is a chance to walk in Constable's footsteps. **Note**: no public access inside Flatford Mill, Valley Farm and Willy Lott's House.

Parking: 100 yards.

Dog rating: ❖ **Standard** – Welcome, but please keep dogs on leads near livestock.

Access:

Find out more: 01206 297201 or flatford@nationaltrust.org.uk **nationaltrust.org.uk/flatford**

Flatford		M	T	W	T	F	S	S
Tea-room								
1 Jan–27 Feb	10–3	·	·	W	T	F	S	S
2 Mar–3 Apr	10–4	·	·	W	T	F	S	S
4 Apr–30 Oct	10–4	M	T	W	T	F	S	S
2 Nov–31 Dec*	10–3	·	·	W	T	F	S	S
Gift shop								
1 Jan–27 Feb	11–3	·	·	·	·	·	S	S
4 Mar–3 Apr	10:30–4	·	·	·	·	F	S	S
6 Apr–5 Jun	10:30–4	·	·	W	T	F	S	S
6 Jun–2 Oct	10:30–4	M	T	W	T	F	S	S
5 Oct–30 Oct	10:30–4	·	·	W	T	F	S	S
5 Nov–31 Dec*	11–3	·	·	·	·	·	S	S

*Closed 24 and 25 December.

Grange Barn

Grange Hill, Coggeshall, Colchester, Essex CO6 1RE

 1989

One of Europe's oldest timber-framed buildings, Grange Barn stands as a lasting reminder of the once-powerful Coggeshall Abbey. With oak pillars soaring up to a cathedral-like roof, bearing the weight of centuries, it was saved and restored in the 1980s. This 13th-century building has truly stood the test of time.

Parking: on site.

Dog rating: ❧ **Standard** – Welcome on leads.

Access:

Find out more: 01376 562226 or grangebarn1@nationaltrust.org.uk
nationaltrust.org.uk/grange-barn

Grange Barn		M	T	W	T	F	S	S
3 Apr–10 Apr	11–3:30	·	·	·	·	·	·	S
29 May–5 Jun	11–3:30	·	·	·	·	·	·	S
24 Jul–28 Aug	11–3:30	·	·	·	·	·	·	S

Hatfield Forest National Nature Reserve

near Bishop's Stortford, Essex

1924

When Henry I established a royal hunting forest here in 1100, he could little have guessed that almost a millennium later it would be the best survivor of its kind in the

The boardwalk trail at Hatfield Forest National Nature Reserve in Essex

world. The forest is now an important National Nature Reserve and has been recognised as a Site of Special Scientific Interest since the 1950s, due to its breadth of habitats and wildlife. Explore the wide open plains, grazed by Red Poll cattle, or enjoy the shade of the coppice woodland. With more than 405 hectares (1,000 acres), there are many places for imaginative play or quiet relaxation. **Note**: to protect the forest, the best time to visit is May to September.

Satnav: use CM22 6NE. **Parking**: on site (extremely limited in winter).

Dog rating: ❧ ❧ **Good** – On leads near livestock, in the lake area and woodland (always under close control).

Access:

Find out more: 01279 870678 or hatfieldforest@nationaltrust.org.uk
nationaltrust.org.uk/hatfield-forest

Hatfield Forest		M	T	W	T	F	S	S
Café								
1 Jan–1 Apr	9–3	·	·	W	T	F	S	S
2 Apr–2 Oct	9–5	M	T	W	T	F	S	S
5 Oct–31 Dec*	9–3	·	·	W	T	F	S	S

Kiosk car park: 1 January to 1 April and 5 October to 31 December (excluding 25 to 28 December), Wednesday to Sunday, 9 to 2:30; 2 April to 2 October, daily, 9 to 4; January to April and October to December, spaces limited (booking essential); internal car parks open to dusk; grass car parks open weather permitting. *Café: closed 25 to 28 December.

Horsey Windpump

Horsey, Great Yarmouth, Norfolk NR29 4EE

1948

Restored and standing proud over the Broadland landscape, Horsey Windpump is complete with winding cap and patent sails. Explore this historic building and discover its fascinating story and the connection between man and nature. Fantastic views over Horsey Mere and beyond from the top. **Note**: surrounded by Horsey Estate – managed by the Buxton family.

Parking: on site.

Dog rating: ❋ ❋ **Good** – Welcome on leads outside Windpump.

Access:

Find out more: 01263 740241 or horseywindpump@nationaltrust.org.uk
nationaltrust.org.uk/horsey

Horsey Windpump		M	T	W	T	F	S	S
Windpump								
5 Mar–27 Mar	11–3	·	·	·	·	·	S	S
28 Mar–30 Sep*	10–4	M	T	W	T	F	S	S
1 Oct–31 Oct*	11–3	M	T	W	T	F	S	S
5 Nov–27 Nov	11–3	·	·	·	·	·	S	S
Shop and tea-room								
1 Jan–11 Feb	11–3	·	·	·	·	F	S	S
12 Feb–27 Mar	11–3	M	T	W	T	F	S	S
28 Mar–21 Jul	11–4	M	T	W	T	F	S	S
22 Jul–4 Sep	11–5	M	T	W	T	F	S	S
5 Sep–31 Oct	11–4	M	T	W	T	F	S	S
1 Nov–31 Dec**	11–2	M	T	W	T	F	S	S

*Windpump closed Fridays during school terms.
**Closed 25 December.

Houghton Mill and Waterclose Meadows

Houghton, near Huntingdon, Cambridgeshire PE28 2AZ

1939

Historic watermill in an inspiring riverside setting surrounded by meadow walks. All the family can enjoy a tour of the oldest working watermill on the Great Ouse. You can buy flour, ground in the traditional way on our French burr millstones.

Parking: on site.

Dog rating: ❋ **Standard** – Welcome in grounds on leads (assistance dogs only in Mill).

Access:

Find out more: 01480 301494 (Mill). 01480 499996 (campsite) or houghtonmill@nationaltrust.org.uk
nationaltrust.org.uk/houghton-mill-and-waterclose-meadows

Houghton Mill

Mill: March to October, guided tours (bookable), please check before visiting. Car park: open daily all year (excluding 25 December), 9 to 4.

Letting off steam at Houghton Mill and Waterclose Meadows in Cambridgeshire

Ickworth

The Rotunda, Horringer, Bury St Edmunds, Suffolk IP29 5QE

1956 | 🏠 🏡 ✿ 🎍 🍽 💷 📷 🎬 🧍

An Italianate palace in the heart of an ancient deer park. Formal gardens, pleasure grounds, rolling Suffolk landscape and woodlands invite gentle strolls, long walks, runs, bike rides and picnics. The Italianate Garden mirrors the architecture of the house and celebrates the Hervey family's passion for Italy, while also encasing an idiosyncratic Victorian stumpery. The house is home to one of the finest silver collections in Europe, family portraits by Gainsborough and Reynolds, works by Titian and Velázquez, and Neo-classical sculpture. The servants' quarters recreate domestic service through the stories and memories of those who lived here.

Satnav: may not direct you to main entrance. Access to Ickworth is through Horringer village. **Parking**: on site.

Dog rating: ❀ ❀ ❀ **Best** – Welcome on leads (assistance dogs only in the Italianate Garden and Walled Garden).

Access: 🅿 🐕 ♿ ♿ ♿ ♿ ♿ ♿ ♿ ♿ ♿ ♿ ♿ ♿ ♿

Find out more: 01284 735270 or ickworth@nationaltrust.org.uk
nationaltrust.org.uk/ickworth

Ickworth		M	T	W	T	F	S	S
House*								
7 Mar–30 Oct	11–3	M	T	W	T	F	S	S
Italianate Garden, café, plant and gift shop								
Open all year	10–4**	M	T	W	T	F	S	S

*House: some areas may close occasionally for conservation; limited winter opening. **Welcome point and plant shop: open daily from 9; estate and parkland: open daily all year, 9 to 4 (may close in adverse weather). Everything closed 24 and 25 December.

Ickworth, Suffolk (clockwise from this picture): the Rotunda, looking across fields towards the Walled Garden and enjoying a stroll in the park

Kyson Hill

Broomheath, Woodbridge, Suffolk 1934

Kyson Hill is a small peaceful area of meadowland and specimen trees with views across the River Deben. **Note**: sorry no toilet. For satnav use IP12 4DL. Broomheath public car park, 546 yards (not National Trust).

Find out more: 01394 389700 (Sutton Hoo) or kysonhill@nationaltrust.org.uk **nationaltrust.org.uk/kyson-hill**

Lavenham Guildhall

Market Place, Lavenham, Sudbury, Suffolk CO10 9QZ

1951

The Guildhall of Corpus Christi is a remarkable testament to the last 500 years of village life. This complex of timber-framed buildings provides an atmospheric backdrop to the stories of the people who shaped and influenced its fortunes and, ultimately, the village of Lavenham we see today. Sometimes sad, sometimes uplifting, their tales are poignant and life-affirming. From religious guild to workhouse, family home to nightclub, there is more than

Detail of a medieval carving at Lavenham Guildhall, Suffolk, above, and the tea-room, below left

meets the eye. Take the opportunity to explore Lavenham village, known for its beautiful timber-framed buildings and impressive church.

Parking: in village (free) – not National Trust. Nearest car parks at Prentice Street (200 yards, 24 spaces), use CO10 9RD, and main car park at Church Street (800 yards, 86 spaces), use CO10 9SA.

Dog rating: 🐾 **Standard** – Welcome on leads in garden and tea-room (assistance dogs only in museum).

Access:

Find out more: 01787 247646 or lavenhamguildhall@nationaltrust.org.uk **nationaltrust.org.uk/lavenham-guildhall**

Lavenham Guildhall		M	T	W	T	F	S	S
7 Jan–27 Feb*	10:30–3:30					F	S	S
3 Mar–3 Apr*	10:30–3:30				T	F	S	S
6 Apr–30 Oct	10:30–3:30			W	T	F	S	S
4 Nov–18 Dec*	10:30–3:30					F	S	S

*Minimum openings; tea-room may open daily.
Early December: parts of museum may close.

Melford Hall

Long Melford, Sudbury, Suffolk CO10 9AA

1960 ♠ ❖ ♨ ☕ 🏠 🚶

Melford Hall is a family home that has suffered its fair share of trials and tribulations, from being ransacked during the Civil War to being devastated by fire in 1942. It is thanks to the many generations who have called it home and left their mark, that it continues to survive. It is their stories, and those of the Hyde Parker family who currently live there – ranging from naval exploits to visits from their cousin Beatrix Potter – that make this family home such an intriguing place to explore.

Parking: on site.

Dog rating: ❖ **Standard** – Welcome on leads on park walk (assistance dogs in house and garden).

Access: 🅿️ 🚗 🚻 🖼️ 💺 🔌 📷 ♿ 🔦 👫 ♿

Find out more: 01787 376395 (Infoline). 01787 379228 or melford@nationaltrust.org.uk
nationaltrust.org.uk/melford-hall

Melford Hall		M	T	W	T	F	S	S
6 Apr–2 Oct	12–4:30			W	T	F	S	S
8 Oct–23 Oct	12–4:30						S	S
26 Oct–30 Oct	12–4:30			W	T	F	S	S

House: entry may be by tour or timed ticket; last entry one hour before closing. Open Bank Holiday Mondays, April to October.

Having suffered a turbulent past, Melford Hall in Suffolk, above and below, is an intriguing place to explore

Morston Quay

Quay Lane, Holt, Norfolk NR25 7BH

1973

Set within the shelter of Blakeney Point, which forms a wonderful backdrop, Morston Quay is the perfect spot from which to explore this beautiful coastline. Hop onto a boat (not National Trust) and go to see the seals on Blakeney Point, or simply sit and watch the world go by.

Parking: on site (subject to tidal flooding).

Dog rating: 🐾 🐾 **Good** – Welcome under close control.

Access:

Morston Quay in Norfolk is the perfect starting point for a Blakeney adventure

Find out more: 01263 740241 or morstonquay@nationaltrust.org.uk
nationaltrust.org.uk/morston-quay

Morston Quay		M	T	W	T	F	S	S
Quay								
Open all year		M	T	W	T	F	S	S
Visitor Welcome								
Open all year*	11–2	M	T	W	T	F	S	S

*Opening dependent on tides and boat trips. Closed 25 December. Kiosk: open daily, February to October (subject to tides).

Morven Park

near Potters Bar, Hertfordshire 1928

Originally the 14th-century Toll Bar, Morven Park offers 8 hectares (20 acres) of peaceful parkland. **Note**: sorry no toilet. For satnav use EN6 1HS.

Find out more: 01582 873663 or morvenpark@nationaltrust.org.uk
nationaltrust.org.uk/morven-park

Northey Island

near Maldon, Essex 1978

A peaceful retreat on the Blackwater Estuary, important for coastal wildlife, Northey is also the oldest recorded battlefield in Britain. **Note**: sorry no toilet. For satnav use CM9 5JQ for parking. Working farm – keep to marked trails, routes may vary (dogs on leads/under close control). Access by tidal causeway (no vehicles), March to October, 9 to 6 – email for permit (see permit for links to Maldon tide timetables). Closed November to February to protect overwintering birds.

Find out more:
northeyisland@nationaltrust.org.uk
nationaltrust.org.uk/northey-island

Orford Ness National Nature Reserve

Orford Quay, Orford, Woodbridge,
Suffolk IP12 2NU

Orford Ness National Nature Reserve, Suffolk

Suffolk's secret coast – wild, remote, exposed. Known as the 'Island', only reached by National Trust ferry, the Ness contains the ruined remnants of a disturbing past. Ranked among the most important shingle features in the world, rare and fragile wildlife thrives where weapons, including atomic bombs, were tested and perfected. **Note**: charge for ferry fare (including members).

Parking: at Riverside car park, Quay Street, not National Trust (charge including members). 150 yards to National Trust Orford Quay office to check in for ferry.

Access:

Find out more: 01394 450900 or
orfordness@nationaltrust.org.uk
nationaltrust.org.uk/orford

Orford Ness		M	T	W	T	F	S	S
16 Apr–3 Jul	10–5						S	S
5 Jul–30 Aug	10–5		T		T		S	S
3 Sep–30 Oct	10–5						S	S

Access only by National Trust ferry from Orford Quay, no access from Aldeburgh. Boats depart 10 to 1, returning regularly (last return 5). Main visitor route (Red Route) always available, other routes open seasonally.
Open Good Friday, Easter Monday, Bank Holiday Mondays (May and August), plus Jubilee Bank Holiday days.

Oxburgh Hall

Oxborough, near Swaffham,
Norfolk PE33 9PS

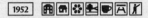

No one ever forgets their first sight of Oxburgh Hall, a romantic moated manor house set beneath sweeping Norfolk skies. Step inside and explore a house filled with portraits and treasured objects, which tell the story of the Bedingfeld family's 500 years of turbulent history. Outside you can catch reflections in the moat, relax in the wildlife-rich seasonal garden, and explore nearly 81 hectares (200 acres) of woodland, streams and parkland.

Parking: on site.

Admiring a tapestry in the Queen's Room at Oxburgh Hall in Norfolk

Dog rating: 🐾 🐾 **Good** – Welcome on leads in garden, park and cafés (assistance dogs only in house).

Access: 👁️🚻♿🅿️🔊🚶🧑🐕♿➡️

Find out more: 01366 328258 or oxburghhall@nationaltrust.org.uk
nationaltrust.org.uk/oxburgh

Oxburgh Hall		M	T	W	T	F	S	S
House								
1 Jan–11 Feb	11–3				T	F	S	S
12 Feb–30 Oct	11–3:45	M	T	W	T	F	S	S
3 Nov–31 Dec*	11–3				T	F	S	S
Garden, park and café								
1 Jan–11 Feb	9:30–4	M	T	W	T	F	S	S
12 Feb–30 Oct	9:30–5	M	T	W	T	F	S	S
2 Nov–31 Dec*	9:30–4			W	T	F	S	S

*Everything closed 24 to 26 December. **Café: opens 30 minutes after garden and park and closes 30 minutes before.

Romantic moated Oxburgh Hall, bottom, boasts acres of wildlife-rich woodland, below

Paycocke's House and Garden

25 West Street, Coggeshall, Colchester, Essex CO6 1NS

| 1924 | 🏠 🐾 🌲 |

Set in an ancient village full of listed buildings, this exquisitely carved half-timbered Tudor cloth merchant's house offers five centuries of craftsmanship and conservation. Explore the many architectural changes and see how the house was saved from demolition and restored to its former glory, then discover the tranquil cottage garden, above.

Parking: on-street parking or public car park in centre of Coggeshall (charge including members).

Dog rating: 🐾 **Standard** – Welcome on leads in garden (assistance dogs only in house).

Access: 👁️🚻🔊🖥️🚶♿🐕🧑

Find out more: 01376 561305 or paycockes@nationaltrust.org.uk
nationaltrust.org.uk/paycockes-house-and-garden

Paycocke's House		M	T	W	T	F	S	S
25 Mar–28 Mar	11–3:30	M				F	S	S
1 Apr–18 Apr	11–3:30	M	T	W	T	F	S	S
22 Apr–18 Jul	11–3:30	M				F	S	S
22 Jul–5 Sep	10:30–4	M	T	W	T	F	S	S
9 Sep–30 Oct	11–3:30	M				F	S	S

Peckover House and Garden

near Wisbech, Cambridgeshire

1943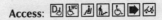

While its riverside setting at Wisbech was popular among merchants, imposing Peckover House stood apart as an oasis of calm, reflecting the Quaker way of life. The Peckovers were bankers and added a specially designed wing to the house; an exhibition tells its story. The family also loved their garden, and you can discover its delights as you explore the unexpected 0.8 hectare (2 acres) of abundance.

Peckover House and Garden, Cambridgeshire, below and right, offers an oasis of calm

Satnav: use PE13 1RG or PE13 2RA for nearest car parks. **Parking**: nearest at Chapel Road or Somers Road, 500 yards (not National Trust). Car parks occasionally used for town events and may not be in use – please check before journey.

Access:

Find out more: 01945 583463 or peckover@nationaltrust.org.uk
North Brink, near Wisbech, Cambridgeshire PE13 1JR
nationaltrust.org.uk/peckover

Peckover House
Opening arrangements not confirmed at time of print, please check before visiting (access by booked tours only).

Pin Mill

near Chelmondiston, Suffolk 1978

A woodland site with pockets of heath crossed by footpaths from the village, with panoramic views over the River Orwell. **Note**: nearest toilets and refreshments in village. For satnav use IP9 1JW.

Find out more:
pinmill@nationaltrust.org.uk
nationaltrust.org.uk/pin-mill

Ramsey Abbey Gatehouse

Hollow Lane, Ramsey, Huntingdon, Cambridgeshire PE26 1DH  1952

This fascinating medieval gatehouse, along with the Lady Chapel, are all that remain of the great Benedictine abbey at Ramsey. **Note**: on school grounds so no public access except on open days. Open April to September on select dates, please email for an appointment.

Find out more: 01480 301494 or ramseyabbey@nationaltrust.org.uk
nationaltrust.org.uk/ramsey-abbey-gatehouse

Rayleigh Mount

Rayleigh, Essex 1923

Medieval motte-and-bailey castle site, with adjacent windmill housing historical exhibition. **Note**: for satnav use SS6 7ED. Open daily, 7 to 6, 27 March to 30 October, and 7 to 4 at all other times; gates close at 2 on Saturdays.

Find out more: 01245 227662 or rayleighmount@nationaltrust.org.uk
nationaltrust.org.uk/rayleigh-mount

Sharpenhoe

near Streatley, Bedfordshire 1939

Managed as a nature reserve; archaeology, geology and nature come together to provide a stunning landscape. **Note**: sorry no toilet. For satnav use LU3 3PR.

Find out more: 01582 873663 or sharpenhoe@nationaltrust.org.uk
nationaltrust.org.uk/sharpenhoe

Shaw's Corner

Ayot St Lawrence, near Welwyn, Hertfordshire AL6 9BX

1944 🏠❄🏠🚶🐕

Step back into the early 20th century when George Bernard Shaw moved to his country retreat. Arts and Crafts-inspired décor, sculptures, paintings, gifts and his Oscar adorn this Edwardian former rectory. Discover the world-class playwright and man with deep connections to global influencers in politics, art and literature. **Note**: access roads are narrow and may flood after heavy rain.

Shaw's Corner, Hertfordshire: the great man's writing shed

Satnav: some routes might take you through a ford and an unsignposted route. **Parking**: very limited (not suitable for large vehicles).

Access:

Find out more: 01438 821968 (Infoline). 01438 820307 or shawscorner@nationaltrust.org.uk
nationaltrust.org.uk/shaws-corner

Shaw's Corner			M	T	W	T	F	S	S
25 Mar–25 Sep	Tour		·	·	·	·	**F**	**S**	**S**

Also open Bank Holiday Mondays, April to September.

Sheringham Park

Upper Sheringham, Norfolk NR26 8TL

1987 🏛🌿♿🔔☕🛍📷🏠🎋🚶

The beach at Sheringham Park in Norfolk, above, and the Temple at dawn, top

Making use of the park's undulating landscape, Humphry Repton created views of the North Norfolk coast that can still be enjoyed today. His 1812 design stated 'Sheringham Park had more natural beauty and advantages than any place he had ever seen'. The Upcher family added an extensive rhododendron collection to Repton's design, bringing an array of colour to the wild garden in the spring. A walk around the varying habitats of the 405-hectare (1,000-acre) estate may be interrupted by the drumming of a woodpecker, the song of skylarks or the sound of a steam train travelling through the park. **Note**: Sheringham Hall is privately occupied. Limited access by written appointment with leaseholder.

Parking: on site. Two electric vehicle charging points in car park.

Dog rating: 🐾 🐾 **Good** – Welcome throughout estate under close control, on leads during bird-breeding season and around livestock.

Access: ♿🚌🚻♿🦽🅿️♿📷♿🏛 ♿➡️♿

Find out more: 01263 820550 or sheringhampark@nationaltrust.org.uk
nationaltrust.org.uk/sheringham

Sheringham Park		M	T	W	T	F	S	S
Park								
Open all year	Dawn–dusk	M	T	W	T	F	S	S
Courtyard Café								
6 Jan–13 Mar*	10–3:30	·	·	·	T	F	S	S
14 Mar–30 Oct	10–4:30	M	T	W	T	F	S	S
3 Nov–31 Dec**	10–3:30	·	·	·	T	F	S	S

*Courtyard Café: open daily during February half term;
**closed 24 to 26 December.

Sundon Hills Country Park

Upper Sundon, Bedfordshire 2000

Wildlife-rich chalk grassland, beech woodland, open meadows and a picnic site with views north towards the Greensand Ridge. **Note**: sorry no toilet. For satnav use LU3 3PE.

Find out more: 01582 873663 or sundonhills@nationaltrust.org.uk

Sutton Hoo

Sutton Hoo, Woodbridge, Suffolk IP12 3DJ

1998 | 🏠🐕☕💼🏠🎪🏃

For 1,300 years Sutton Hoo's secrets were hidden deep within a burial mound until, in 1939, a discovery was made which changed history. From the sandy soil archaeologists unearthed the imprint of a 27-metre-long ship, its timbers long since rotted away. This was revealed to be the ship burial of an Anglo-Saxon king, complete with exquisite gold and silver treasures. Now a full-size ship sculpture, newly designed exhibitions, replicas, the atmospheric Royal Burial Ground and a 17-metre-high viewing tower, offering views over the landscape and River Deben, all bring this fascinating story to life. There is also a variety of walks through the estates acid grass meadows and woodlands.

Sutton Hoo, Suffolk: Anglo-Saxon burial mounds, below, sculpture, above, and exploring, right

Explore how land, buildings and war memorials came to us: ntlandmap.org.uk

Parking: on site.

Dog rating: 🐾 **Standard** – Welcome on leads in reception, shop, café and walks.

Access: ⟦🅿️🅟⟧⟦🅿️🅳⟧♿🚻📶📷🎧♿➡️♿

Find out more: 01394 389700 or suttonhoo@nationaltrust.org.uk
nationaltrust.org.uk/sutton-hoo

Sutton Hoo		M	T	W	T	F	S	S
1 Jan–2 Jan	10–4	.	.	.	.	.	S	S
19 Feb–27 Feb	10–4	M	T	W	T	F	S	S
26 Mar–30 Oct	10–5	M	T	W	T	F	S	S
26 Dec–31 Dec	10–4	M	T	W	T	F	S	.

High Hall exhibition, Tranmer House and second-hand bookshop: at other times open weekends only. Estate walks open daily. For café and gift shop opening hours please check before visiting. Everything closed 24 and 25 December.

Theatre Royal Bury St Edmunds

Westgate Street, Bury St Edmunds, Suffolk IP33 1QR ⟦1974⟧

Last surviving Regency playhouse in Britain, this Grade I-listed theatre offers a vibrant mixed programme. **Note**: managed by Bury St Edmunds Theatre Management Ltd. Tours are free to National Trust members, admission charges apply for shows (including members). Guided tours available (email for details).

Find out more: 01284 769505 or theatreroyal@nationaltrust.org.uk
nationaltrust.org.uk/theatre-royal

Totternhoe Knolls

Castle Hill Road, Totternhoe,
Bedfordshire 2000

The dramatic earthworks of a
Norman castle rise from windswept chalk
grassland habitat. **Note**: sorry no toilet.
For satnav use LU6 1RG.

Find out more: 01582 873663 or
totternhoeknolls@nationaltrust.org.uk

West Runton and Beeston Regis Heath

near West Runton, Norfolk 1925

A lovely place to walk among heath
and woods, with fine views of the coast.
Note: sorry no toilet. For satnav
use NR27 9ND.

Find out more: 01263 820550 or
westrunton@nationaltrust.org.uk
**nationaltrust.org.uk/west-runton-and-
beeston-regis-heath**

Whipsnade Tree Cathedral

Whipsnade, Dunstable,
Bedfordshire 1960

Peaceful place with trees planted in
shape of medieval cathedral. Created
after the First World War to commemorate
fallen comrades. **Note**: for satnav use
LU6 2LQ. Annual service. Open daily.
Car park: open 9 to 7, 27 March to
30 October; 9 to 4, all other dates.

Find out more: 01582 872406 or
whipsnadetc@nationaltrust.org.uk
**nationaltrust.org.uk/whipsnade-tree-
cathedral**

Wicken Fen National Nature Reserve

near Ely, Cambridgeshire

1899

With vast skies above flowering meadows,
sedge and reedbeds, Wicken Fen reveals a
lost fenland landscape. A wealth of wildlife
lives in this important wetland, including
rarities such as hen harriers and bitterns,
numerous dragonflies, moths and wildfowl.
Changing every season, the fen feels wild,
although people have shaped it for

Wicken Fen National Nature Reserve in Cambridgeshire, above and below

centuries; see how they lived and worked in the fenman's yard and cottage. The Wicken Fen Vision, an ambitious landscape-scale conservation project, is opening new areas for wildlife and for exploration. Grazing herds of Highland cattle and Konik ponies

help create a diverse range of new habitats. **Note**: some paths are seasonal. Charges apply for Wicken Lode boat trips (including members).

Satnav: use CB7 5XP. **Parking**: 120 yards.

Dog rating: 🐾 🐾 **Good** – Welcome on leads on wider reserve and in visitor centre (assistance dogs only on Sedge Fen).

Access: ♿ ♿ ♿ ♿ ♿ ♿ ♿ ♿ ♿ ♿

Find out more: 01353 720274 or wickenfen@nationaltrust.org.uk
nationaltrust.org.uk/wicken

Wicken Fen		M	T	W	T	F	S	S
Reserve – Sedge Fen								
Open all year*	10–5	M	T	W	T	F	S	S
Visitor centre, shop and café								
1 Jan–27 Feb	10–4:30**	M	T	W	T	F	S	S
28 Feb–30 Oct	10–5	M	T	W	T	F	S	S
31 Oct–31 Dec*	10–4:30**	M	T	W	T	F	S	S

*Everything closed 25 December (excluding car park).
**Café: closes at 4.

Willington Dovecote and Stables

Willington, Church End, near Bedford, Bedfordshire MK44 3PX `1914`

One of the largest and best-preserved examples of a 16th-century stone dovecote, a remnant of Gostwick's extravagant manorial complex. **Note**: Dovecote and Stables can be viewed by appointment dependent on volunteer availability, contact willingtondovecote@nationaltrust.org.uk. Open April to September on select dates, please email for an appointment.

Find out more: 01480 301494 or willingtondovecote@nationaltrust.org.uk
nationaltrust.org.uk/willington-dovecote-and-stables

Wimpole Estate

Arrington, Royston,
Cambridgeshire SG8 0BW

1976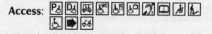

A unique working estate, with an impressive mansion at its heart. Discover Wimpole's acres of parkland, miles of walks, vibrant walled kitchen garden and rare-breed farm. Explore the Hall, where intimate rooms contrast with beautiful Georgian interiors. With its various owners driven by passion and purpose, Wimpole is both a place to escape to and a place to get involved. We continue the 3rd Earl of Hardwicke's passion for trail-blazing food production and design, celebrating the estate's past magnificence and echoing Elsie Bambridge's 20th-century revival.

As owners changed, a roll-call of ingenious architects, artists and landscape designers shaped the estate. Wimpole is an 'all-year-round' place to visit, reflecting the changing seasons, with something to captivate and inspire all visitors.

Satnav: follow the brown signs, entrance via A603. **Parking:** on site, 669 yards to stable block. Electric vehicle charging points in car park.

Dog rating: ❀ ❀ **Good** – Welcome on leads in the parkland (livestock grazing). Assistance dogs elsewhere.

Access:

The mansion which lies at the heart of Wimpole Estate in Cambridgeshire, below. Opposite, resident lamb and visitors

Find out more: 01223 206000 or wimpole@nationaltrust.org.uk
nationaltrust.org.uk/wimpole

Wimpole Estate		M	T	W	T	F	S	S
Hall								
1 Jan–13 Feb	12–3	·	·	·	·	·	S	S
14 Feb–20 Feb	12–3	M	T	W	T	F	S	S
26 Feb–3 Apr*	11:30–3	·	·	·	·	·	S	S
4 Apr–22 Jul	12–3	M	T	W	T	F	S	S
23 Jul–3 Sep	12–3:30	M	T	W	T	F	S	S
4 Sep–30 Oct	12–3	M	T	W	T	F	S	S
5 Nov–31 Dec*	11:30–3	·	·	·	·	·	S	S
Rare-breed farm								
1 Jan–13 Feb	10:30–3	·	·	·	·	·	S	S
14 Feb–30 Oct	10:30–4:30	M	T	W	T	F	S	S
5 Nov–18 Dec	10:30–3	·	·	·	·	·	S	S
20 Dec–31 Dec	10:30–3	M	T	W	T	F	S	S
Food and refreshments								
Open all year	10–4	M	T	W	T	F	S	S
Stable shop								
1 Jan–13 Feb	10:30–4	·	·	W	T	F	S	S
14 Feb–31 Dec	10:30–4	M	T	W	T	F	S	S

*Hall: guided tours available weekdays from 12. Walled garden, pleasure grounds and formal gardens: open daily all year, 9:30 to 4:30. Parkland: open daily all year, 9 to 6. Everything (excluding car park) closed 24 to 26 December.

Exploring the medieval tower at
Tattershall Castle, Lincolnshire

East Midlands

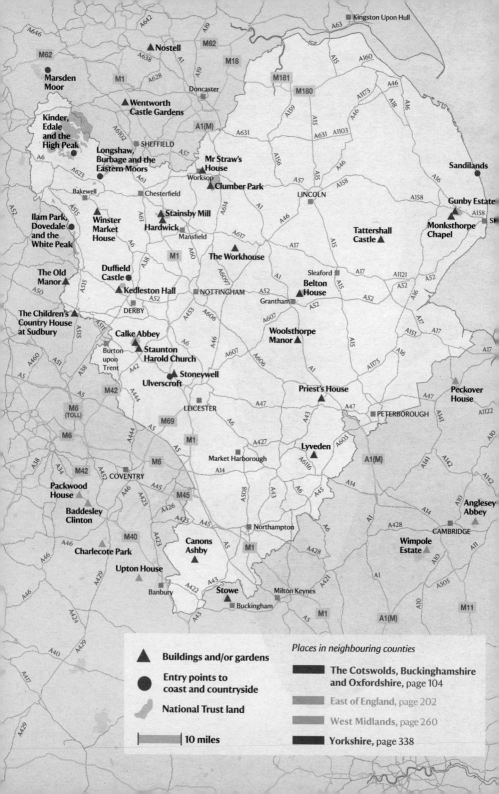

Kingston Upon Hull

Nostell

Marsden Moor

Kinder, Edale and the High Peak

Wentworth Castle Gardens

SHEFFIELD

Longshaw, Burbage and the Eastern Moors

Mr Straw's House

Worksop

Clumber Park

Bakewell

Chesterfield

LINCOLN

Sandilands

Ilam Park, Dovedale and the White Peak

Winster Market House

Stainsby Mill

Hardwick

Mansfield

Gunby Estate

Monksthorpe Chapel

The Old Manor

Duffield Castle

The Workhouse

Tattershall Castle

The Children's Country House at Sudbury

Kedleston Hall

DERBY

NOTTINGHAM

Sleaford

Belton House

Grantham

Calke Abbey

Burton upon Trent

Staunton Harold Church

Woolsthorpe Manor

Stoneywell

Ulverscroft

LEICESTER

Priest's House

PETERBOROUGH

Peckover House

Packwood House

Baddesley Clinton

COVENTRY

Market Harborough

Lyveden

Anglesey Abbey

Wimpole Estate

CAMBRIDGE

Charlecote Park

Upton House

Canons Ashby

Northampton

Banbury

Stowe

Buckingham

Milton Keynes

▲ Buildings and/or gardens

● Entry points to coast and countryside

National Trust land

10 miles

Places in neighbouring counties

The Cotswolds, Buckinghamshire and Oxfordshire, page 104

East of England, page 202

West Midlands, page 260

Yorkshire, page 338

Belton House

Belton House, Belton, near Grantham,
Lincolnshire NG32 2LS

1984

Generations of the Brownlow family made
their mark on Belton, commissioning the
finest designers and craftsmen of their
age to shape the estate we see today.

The house and gardens showcase
cutting-edge design and innovation,
from 17th-century sash windows to a
cast-iron-framed orangery in the Italian
Garden, made possible thanks to the
Industrial Revolution. The interiors are
equally impressive, with a dazzling
collection of silver and porcelain, as well
as a world-renowned library. Today, Belton
welcomes new generations to explore the
ancient deer park, picnic in the pleasure
grounds, or burn off energy in the National
Trust's largest open-air adventure playground.

Belton House, Lincolnshire: the perfect example of a country-house estate

Tackling the maze at Belton House, above, and a family enjoys a leisurely walk in the grounds, left

Access: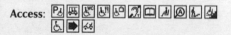

Find out more: 01476 566116 or belton@nationaltrust.org.uk
Belton, near Grantham, Lincolnshire NG32 2LS
nationaltrust.org.uk/belton-house

Satnav: use NG32 2LW. **Parking**: on site.

Dog rating: 🐾 🐾 🐾 **Best** – Welcome on leads in cafés, shops, gardens, parkland and courtyards (assistance dogs only in adventure playground).

Belton House		M	T	W	T	F	S	S
House								
7 Mar–6 Nov	12:30–5*	M	T	W	T	F	S	S
Gardens, parkland and outdoor adventure playground								
Open all year	9:30–5:30**	M	T	W	T	F	S	S
Shops and Stables Café								
Open all year	10–5	M	T	W	T	F	S	S

*House: last entry one hour before closing. **June to August, open to 6; November to February, close 4. Bellmount Woods: open daily (access from separate car park). Everything closed 25 December.

Calke Abbey

Ticknall, Derby, Derbyshire DE73 7JF

| 1985 |  |

Poised between gentle neglect and downright dereliction, Calke Abbey, the un-stately home, is unlike other great country estates. Entering along the Lime Tree Avenue offers views of the historic parkland, home to ancient oaks, secluded ponds and areas of National Nature Reserve. Nestled among peaceful woodland, Calke Explore provides the perfect base to reconnect with nature and explore the wider estate, including once-industrial limeyards. Peeling paintwork and abandoned rooms tell the story of a country house in decline, while a vast collection reveals the varied interests of a caring family who never threw anything away. The walled garden bursts with seasonal colour and produce, while a domed orangery, faded glasshouses and gardener's bothy echo the history of Calke's working garden. **Note**: there may be waiting times for the house on busy days; ask at ticket office.

Parking: on site.

Dog rating: 🐾 🐾 🐾 Best – Welcome on leads in the wider estate and garden.

Access:

The faded grandeur and dilapidation of Calke Abbey in Derbyshire, tells a tale of dramatic decline

Find out more: 01332 863822 or
calkeabbey@nationaltrust.org.uk
nationaltrust.org.uk/calke

Calke Abbey		M	T	W	T	F	S	S
Calke Park National Nature Reserve*								
Open all year	8–6	M	T	W	T	F	S	S
Garden, stableyards, restaurant and shop**								
Open all year	9:30–5	M	T	W	T	F	S	S
House								
1 Mar–30 Oct	11–4:30	M	T	W	T	F	S	S

*Park: open 9:30 to 4:30, January, February, November and
December. **Garden, stableyards, restaurant and shop: close
at 5 when house is open, March to October; at 4 all other
times. Everything closed 24 and 25 December.

One of the many cycling trails at Calke Abbey, below, and examining a dusty corner, above

Canons Ashby

near Daventry,
Northamptonshire NN11 3SD

1981 🏠🏘️❀🎣☕🖼️🏕️🌿

Ancient and peaceful, Canons Ashby is far removed from today's bustling lifestyle. Medieval canons built their priory near the small village of Ashby but, following the Dissolution, the village was lost leaving a curiously truncated church. Nearby, the Elizabethan Dryden family built their home, and over the succeeding 450 years additions and alterations took place, resulting in the current blend of architectural and decorative styles: although little has changed since the 19th century. Outside is a pretty terraced garden, typifying the formal 18th-century style then fashionable, and an ancient parkland and paddock offering space for fun as well as contemplation.

Canons Ashby, Northamptonshire: the south front, above, and playing croquet on the lawn, left

Parking: 200 yards.

Dog rating: 🐾 🐾 **Good** – Welcome on leads in all outdoor spaces.

Access: 🅿️🚌♿🚻♿♿🎨📷📺♿ 🅿️♿♿🚹

Find out more: 01327 861900 or canonsashby@nationaltrust.org.uk
nationaltrust.org.uk/canons-ashby

Canons Ashby		M	T	W	T	F	S	S
House								
12 Feb–25 Mar	11–3	M	T	W	T	F	S	S
26 Mar–30 Oct	11:30–4	M	T	W	T	F	S	S
3 Nov–4 Dec	11–3	·	·	·	T	F	S	S
5 Dec–24 Dec	11–3	M	T	W	T	F	S	S
Tea-room, shop, gardens, priory church and parkland*								
12 Feb–25 Mar	10–3:30**	M	T	W	T	F	S	S
26 Mar–30 Oct	10–5**	M	T	W	T	F	S	S
3 Nov–4 Dec	10–3:30**	·	·	·	T	F	S	S
5 Dec–24 Dec	10–3**	M	T	W	T	F	S	S

*Tea-room, shop, gardens, priory church and parkland: also open 1 and 2 January and 31 December, 10 to 3. **Tea-room and shop: open 30 minutes after and close 30 minutes before rest of property. Some areas of house and garden may close in winter for conservation work.

The Children's Country House at Sudbury

Sudbury, Ashbourne, Derbyshire DE6 5HT

1967 🏛️🏠🍀💼📷🏠🎭

New this year, The Children's Country House at Sudbury is a playful heritage day out. We've worked with children to create a place where kids are invited to use their natural curiosity to explore collections, stories and history. In the Hall, you will find activities inspired by the way each room was used in the past: the Saloon is once again a glittering party space, the

The Children's Country House at Sudbury, Derbyshire

Long Gallery comes alive with energetic games and you're invited to get your hands messy in the kitchen. In the museum, discover how children lived, worked and played over the years and, in the garden, find the secret hidden corners and picnic with the geese by the lake. **Note**: booking is essential at all times.

Parking: 500 yards.

Dog rating: 🐾 **Standard** – Welcome on leads in grounds (assistance dogs only indoors).

The Children's Country House at Sudbury,
above, and one of the young visitors, right

Access: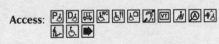

Find out more: 01283 585337 or
cchsudbury@nationaltrust.org.uk
nationaltrust.org.uk/cchsudbury

Children's Country House		M	T	W	T	F	S	S
12 Feb–31 Dec	10–5						**S**	**S**

Open daily during school holidays. Early years specific
offer on Thursdays.

Clumber Park

Worksop, Nottinghamshire S80 3BE

1946

Historically the home of the Dukes of Newcastle, the beauty of Clumber Park is reflected throughout the grand designed landscape. The beauty of the Gothic Revival Chapel, serpentine lake, extensive glasshouse and double herbaceous borders in the Walled Kitchen Garden delight throughout the year, while a network of cycle, walking and running routes allow visitors to explore all 1,537 hectares (3,800 acres) of the estate, which remains undiminished by the absence of the great house. Clumber Park, with its rich animal habitats, is perfect for a spot of bird watching and offers an ideal escape for a picnic or family stroll; a haven for wildlife and for people.

Spring arrives at Clumber Park in Nottinghamshire, below, and exploring the extensive glasshouse, this picture

See how you've helped, and what more you can do: nationaltrust.org.uk/donate

The Chapel of St Mary the Virgin at Clumber Park

Parking: 250 yards.

Dog rating: 🐾 🐾 🐾 Best – Welcome under control.

Access: ♿ 🚻 ♿ ♿ 🔍 ♿ ♿ ♿ ➡ ♿

Find out more: 01909 476592 or clumberpark@nationaltrust.org.uk **nationaltrust.org.uk/clumber-park**

Clumber Park	
Open every day all year*	8–6**

*Excluding 25 December. **29 March to 25 October: visitor facilities open 9 to 5 at weekends and Bank Holidays; 10 to 5 at other times. Food and beverage: open 9.

Duffield Castle

Duffield, Derbyshire ☐1899

Small site nestled in Duffield village where a large medieval castle once stood. **Note**: sorry no toilet or car park. For satnav use DE56 4DW. Steep steps and uneven ground.

Find out more: 01332 842191 or duffieldcastle@nationaltrust.org.uk **nationaltrust.org.uk/duffield**

Gunby Estate, Hall and Gardens

Gunby, Spilsby, Lincolnshire PE23 5SS

1944

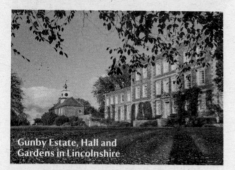

Gunby Estate, Hall and Gardens in Lincolnshire

Set at the foot of the Lincolnshire Wolds, it's no wonder the Massingberd family chose this location for their home in 1700. It feels as if the family have just popped out as you visit their gardens full of colour, whatever the season. The estate is perfect for walks.

Satnav: entrance is off roundabout (not beyond or before). **Parking**: on site.

Dog rating: 🐾 🐾 **Good** – Welcome on leads in the gardens, courtyard and grounds. Dog bowl and dog bin available in the courtyard.

Access:

Find out more: 01754 890102 or gunbyhall@nationaltrust.org.uk
nationaltrust.org.uk/gunby-hall

Gunby Estate		M	T	W	T	F	S	S
House*								
12 Feb–30 Oct	11–2	M	T	W	·	·	S	S
Gardens and tea-room								
12 Feb–30 Oct	10–4**	M	T	W	T	F	S	S

*House: entry may be by timed tickets allocated on site on day.
**Everything closes at 3 in February and March.

Gunby Hall Estate: Monksthorpe Chapel

Monksthorpe, near Spilsby, Lincolnshire PE23 5PP 2000

Monksthorpe Chapel, dated 1701, was made to look like a barn to avoid detection and features a rare open-air baptistry. **Note**: grounds open every day all year. You can collect and drop off the key for the chapel from Gunby's tea-room during opening times.

Find out more: 01754 890102 or monksthorpe@nationaltrust.org.uk
nationaltrust.org.uk/monksthorpe-chapel

Hardwick

near Chesterfield, Derbyshire

1959

One of the finest Elizabethan buildings in the country, Hardwick Hall is a remarkable house, built by a remarkable woman. Architectural prowess abounds, from the audaciously impressive glass windows, to the turrets, bearing the initials 'E. S.' – Elizabeth of Shrewsbury, known as Bess of Hardwick. Let the three floors take you on a journey, from the finest collections of Elizabethan tapestries and embroideries in Europe to cosy Forties' furnishings. Outside, the gardens offer bright seasonal colour and so much to explore, including the orchard and herb garden, full of scents. Follow walks through the picturesque parkland and oak-scattered Grade I-listed woodland pasture. Hardwick sits on high ground overlooking rolling hills, with impressive views that will take your breath away. **Note**: Old Hall owned by the National Trust and administered by English Heritage.

Even in autumn, the gardens at Hardwick, Derbyshire, offer bright seasonal colour, while the house is still as striking as when it was built

Statue at the top of the Yew Alley at Hardwick

Satnav: use S44 5RW.
Parking: 600-space car park.

Dog rating: 🐾 🐾 **Good** – Welcome on leads in stableyard, park and car park.

Access: 🅿️ 🏛️ 🚻 ♿ 📷 🖥️ 📺 ♨️ 🅰️ ♿ ♿ ➡️

Find out more: 01246 850430 or
hardwickhall@nationaltrust.org.uk
Doe Lea, near Chesterfield,
Derbyshire S44 5QJ
nationaltrust.org.uk/hardwick

Hardwick Estate: Stainsby Mill

Doe Lea, Chesterfield, Derbyshire S44 5RW

| 1976 | 🏠 🚶 |

An atmospheric gem on the Hardwick Estate. Watch the Victorian watermill turn and see the cogs and machinery work to grind the flour as our millers still do. Join one of our booked experiences and explore this delightful building, then pick up a bag of Stainsby milled flour. **Note**: nearest toilets and refreshments at Hardwick Hall.

Parking: limited on-road parking (not National Trust).

Dog rating: 🐾 **Standard** – Welcome on leads at nearby Hardwick parkland (assistance dogs only in Mill).

Access: 🖼️ ♨️ ♿

Find out more: 01246 850430 or
stainsbymill@nationaltrust.org.uk
nationaltrust.org.uk/stainsby-mill

Stainsby Mill

Opening arrangements not confirmed at time of print, please check before visiting.

Hardwick Estate: Stainsby Mill, Derbyshire

Hardwick		M	T	W	T	F	S	S
Hall*								
1 Jan–1 Apr	11–3:30	M	T	W	T	F	S	S
2 Apr–31 Oct	11–4	M	T	W	T	F	S	S
1 Nov–31 Dec**	11–3:30	M	T	W	T	F	S	S
Garden, restaurant and shop								
1 Jan–1 Apr	9:30–5†	M	T	W	T	F	S	S
2 Apr–31 Oct	9–6†	M	T	W	T	F	S	S
1 Nov–31 Dec**	9:30–5†	M	T	W	T	F	S	S
Park								
Open all year		M	T	W	T	F	S	S

*Hall: experience varies; closes occasionally due to the collection's fragility and for conservation.
**Closed 24 and 25 December. †Shop: opens at 10.

Ilam Park, Dovedale and the White Peak

Ilam, Ashbourne, Derbyshire

1934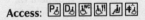

The stepping stones at Dovedale lead to a riverside walk through the National Nature Reserve full of caves and pinnacles, rich in wildlife and fossils. A 1½-mile walk across fields links Dovedale and Ilam Park, a tranquil parkland nestled beneath steep-sided hills on the River Manifold. The park is dotted with majestic mature trees and offers views of the church, the rugged backdrop of Thorpe Cloud and Bunster Hill. A 1-mile circular parkland route makes this a popular choice for families and dog walkers. The Church of the Holy Cross contains stories of St Bertram, buried within. **Note**: Ilam Hall let to YHA. Dovedale toilets not National Trust (charge including members).

Satnav: use DE6 2AZ. **Parking**: at Ilam Park (119:132507) and Dovedale.

Dog rating: 🐾 **Standard** – Welcome on leads – seasonal access.

Access: 🅿️ 🅰️ 🚻 ♿ ♿ ♿

Find out more: 01335 350503 or peakdistrict@nationaltrust.org.uk **nationaltrust.org.uk/dovedale**

Ilam Park		M	T	W	T	F	S	S
Tea-room								
1 Jan–28 Mar	10–4	M	T	W	T	F	S	S
29 Mar–31 Oct	10–5	M	T	W	T	F	S	S
1 Nov–31 Dec*	10–4*	M	T	W	T	F	S	S

*Tea-room and Stableyard Grab and Go closed 25 December. Ilam bunkhouse: open all year (0344 335 1296). Darfar and Redhurst holiday cottages: available to let all year (0344 800 2070). Ilam Hall: available for overnight accommodation via the Youth Hostel Association (01335 350212).

Walkers at Ilam Park, Dovedale and the White Peak in Derbyshire, left and below

Kedleston Hall

near Derby, Derbyshire

1987 | 🏛️🏚️❀♿☕🛍️🎭🚶

Be inspired by a true 'temple of the arts' – as envisioned by celebrated architect Robert Adam. Experience the grandeur of this lavishly decorated 1760s show palace in Derbyshire, lived in over the centuries by the Curzon family. See objects collected by Lord Curzon during his time as Viceroy of India, representing the rich diversity of cultures and communities across South Asia. The Hall is set in 332 hectares (820 acres) of landscape parkland and Pleasure Grounds, which can be explored on foot all year. The parkland is popular for dog walks, picnics and orienteering. **Note**: the medieval All Saint's Church is managed by the Churches Conservation Trust.

Satnav: for main entrance on Kedleston Road use DE22 5JD.
Parking: 200 yards from hall.

Kedleston Hall in Derbyshire: fiery autumn colours, above, and the newly restored state bedroom, left

Dog rating: 🐾 🐾 **Good** – Welcome on leads in the parkland, gardens and outdoor seating areas.

Access: 🅿️♿🚻♿♿♿♿♿➡️

Find out more: 01332 842191 or kedlestonhall@nationaltrust.org.uk Quarndon, near Derby, Derbyshire DE22 5JH
nationaltrust.org.uk/kedleston-hall

Kedleston Hall		M	T	W	T	F	S	S
Hall								
19 Feb–27 Mar	11–3	M	T		T	F	S	S
28 Mar–30 Oct	11–4	M	T	·	T	F	S	S
2 Dec–23 Dec	11–3	M	·	·	·	F	S	S
Park and Pleasure Grounds								
1 Jan–18 Feb	9–4	M	T	W	T	F	S	S
19 Feb–30 Oct	9–5	M	T	W	T	F	S	S
31 Oct–31 Dec*	9–4	M	T	W	T	F	S	S
Restaurant								
1 Jan–18 Feb	10–3:30	M	T	W	T	F	S	S
19 Feb–27 Feb	10–4	M	T	W	T	F	S	S
28 Feb–30 Oct	10–4:30	M	T	W	T	F	S	S
31 Oct–31 Dec*	10–3:30	M	T	W	T	F	S	S
Shop								
1 Jan–18 Feb	10–3:30	M	·	·	T	F	S	S
19 Feb–30 Oct	10–4	M	·	·	T	F	S	S
31 Oct–31 Dec*	10–3:30	M	·	·	T	F	S	S

*Everything closed 25 December and occasionally for events.

Kinder, Edale and the High Peak

near Hope Valley, Derbyshire

1936 | 🏠🎣🛝⛺

The High Peak, including Kinder, the Vale of Edale and along the Snake moors to the Derwent edges, offers exhilarating walks across heather moors, high gritstone edges and monumental windswept tors. Stories and wild nature abound amid the ancient peat bogs and quiet wooded cloughs. You can follow the route of the 1932 Mass Trespass onto Kinder Scout National Nature Reserve, retracing the steps of those early champions of access to wild places. Alternatively, a short walk up the steps of Mam Tor rewards you with panoramic views from this ancient hilltop fortress.

Note: nearest toilets in villages and visitor centres (not Trust) at Ladybower Reservoir, Edale and Castleton.

Parking: at Mam Nick National Trust car park (110:SK124832). Also non-National Trust parking at Edale, Castleton, Sett Valley and Upper Derwent Valley (charge including members).

Dog rating: 🐾 **Standard** – Welcome on leads – seasonal access.

Find out more: 01433 670368 or peakdistrict@nationaltrust.org.uk **nationaltrust.org.uk/kinder**

Kinder, Edale and the High Peak

Welcome shelters open all year: Lee Barn (110:SK096855), Dalehead (SK101843) and Edale End (SK161864) in the Edale Valley; South Head (SK060854) above Hayfield; Grindle Barns above Ladybower Reservoir (SK189895). Mam Nick car park (SK123832) and Dalehead Bunkhouse (0344 335 1296) open all year.

Kinder, Edale and the Dark Peak in Derbyshire

Longshaw, Burbage and the Eastern Moors

near Sheffield, Derbyshire

Longshaw, Burbage and the Eastern Moors in Derbyshire, left and above

A countryside haven on Sheffield's doorstep, Longshaw, Burbage and the Eastern Moors has a network of footpaths and bridleways you can explore within a typical Peak District landscape of skies and silhouettes. Here you'll find long views, with scooping shapes of rocks and hills and gorges where water tumbles through ancient woods and over mossy boulders. A diverse range of wildlife lives peacefully here among abandoned millstones and packhorse routes of the past. The designed landscape around Longshaw Lodge, a former grouse-shooting estate, offers a warm and friendly starting point for your adventure. **Note**: National Trust/RSPB manage Eastern Moors for Peak District National Park; Burbage for Sheffield County Council.

Satnav: use S11 7TZ (follow brown signs).
Parking: at Woodcroft car park (110: 266800), Wooden Pole and Haywood for Longshaw and at Curbar Gap, Birchen Edge and Shillito Wood for the Eastern Moors. Additional car parks at Surprise View and Burbage, not National Trust (charge including members).

Dog rating: ❧ **Standard** – Welcome on leads – seasonal access.

Access:

Find out more: 01433 631757 (Longshaw). 0114 289 1543 (Eastern Moors) or peakdistrict@nationaltrust.org.uk **nationaltrust.org.uk/longshaw**

Longshaw		M	T	W	T	F	S	S
Tea-room								
1 Jan–28 Mar	10–4	M	T	W	T	F	S	S
29 Mar–31 Oct	10–5	M	T	W	T	F	S	S
1 Nov–31 Dec*	10–4	M	T	W	T	F	S	S

*Closed 25 December. White Edge Lodge: available as holiday cottage all year (0344 800 2070). Longshaw Lodge not open to public.

Lyveden

Harley Way, near Oundle,
Northamptonshire PE8 5AT

1922 🏠🏚🍀🦆☕🏕

Deep in Northamptonshire lies a mysterious garden. Begun by Sir Thomas Tresham in 1595 but never completed, the house stands as testament to his Catholicism. Persecuted for his religious beliefs, Sir Thomas sought solace in the creation of his garden. New visitor facilities at the manor house provide the opportunity for lunch or cake in our new café. During your visit you can discover the wonder of this Elizabethan garden in the order originally intended, as grass paths, viewing mounts and moats lead you upwards from the manor house to the symbolic garden lodge.

Parking: 100 yards.

Dog rating: 🐾 **Standard** – Welcome on leads (assistance dogs only in the manor house and café).

Access: 🅿️♿🚻👶🦷♿↕️➡️🐕‍🦺

Find out more: 01832 205259 or
lyveden@nationaltrust.org.uk
nationaltrust.org.uk/lyveden

Lyveden		M	T	W	T	F	S	S
3 Jan–28 Feb	11–4	**M**	·	·	·	**F**	**S**	**S**
4 Mar–28 Mar	10–5	**M**	·	·	·	**F**	**S**	**S**
1 Apr–30 Oct	10–5	**M**	**T**	**W**	**T**	**F**	**S**	**S**
31 Oct–31 Dec	11–5	**M**	·	·	·	**F**	**S**	**S**

Everything closed 25 and 26 December. Tea-room: last orders 30 minutes before closing.

Bread ovens, top, and the intriguing Elizabethan lodge, below, at Lyveden in Northamptonshire

Mr Straw's House

5–7 Blyth Grove, Worksop,
Nottinghamshire S81 0JG

1990

Within the Sanderson-papered walls of this middle-class home, the family lived thriftily, installing few modern conveniences since 1923. A large and intriguing collection of everyday objects and personal papers has survived alongside traces of the occasional indulgence. The lovingly tended garden and orchard include a cacti collection and fruit trees.

Parking: on site, in orchard opposite property.

Access:

Find out more: 01909 476592 (Clumber Park) or mrstrawshouse@nationaltrust.org.uk
nationaltrust.org.uk/mr-straws-house

Mr Straw's House		M	T	W	T	F	S	S
3 Mar–28 Oct	10–5	·	·	·	**T**	**F**	·	·

House: last admission one hour before closing; admission by booked timed ticket only (bookable online).

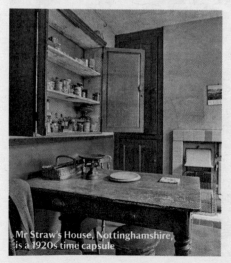

Mr Straw's House, Nottinghamshire, is a 1920s time capsule

The Old Manor

Norbury, Ashbourne,
Derbyshire DE6 2ED 1987

An idyllic medieval hall featuring a rare king post and well-preserved Tudor door, set within beautiful gardens. **Note**: open Thursday, May to September, 11 to 3.

Find out more: 01283 585337 or oldmanor@nationaltrust.org.uk
nationaltrust.org.uk/old-manor

Priest's House, Easton on the Hill

38 West Street, Easton on the Hill, near Stamford, Northamptonshire PE9 3LS 1966

Delightful small late 15th-century building, with interesting local architecture and museum. **Note**: open daily, 10 to 5. Unmanned. Access from neighbouring keyholders listed on property noticeboard.

Find out more: 01832 205259 or priestshouse2@nationaltrust.org.uk
nationaltrust.org.uk/priests-house-easton-on-the-hill

Sandilands

near Sutton-on-Sea, Lincolnshire

2020

This former golf course on Lincolnshire's wild coast will be a new place for nature to thrive. Work to make this happen begins this year, and migratory birds from far-flung places are already stopping off

The former golf course at Sandilands, Lincolnshire, will become a place where nature can thrive

here. Come for a windy walk and see how many species you can spot.

Satnav: may misdirect (look out for former clubhouse). **Parking**: car park (not National Trust) beside former clubhouse.

Dog rating: 🐾 🐾 **Good** – Welcome on leads.

Access:

Find out more: 01754 890102 or sandilands@nationaltrust.org.uk
nationaltrust.org.uk/sandilands

Staunton Harold Church

Staunton Harold Estate, Ashby-de-la-Zouch, Leicestershire LE65 1RW 1954

A rare and imposing church built in 1653, with a landscape lake and rolling wooded hills as its backdrop. **Note**: nearest toilet 500 yards (not National Trust).

Visit by timed, guided tour only (booking essential), 2 April to 30 October. Church services are normally held Easter to Christmas, first and third Sundays.

Find out more: 01332 863822 or stauntonharold@nationaltrust.org.uk
nationaltrust.org.uk/staunton-harold-church

Stoneywell

Whitcroft's Lane, Ulverscroft, Leicestershire LE67 9QE

2012 🏠 ✿ ⛩ 🐕

Stoneywell, Leicestershire: an Arts and Crafts vision

Zigzagging from its rocky outcrop, Stoneywell is the realisation of one man's Arts and Crafts vision within a family home. Original furniture and family treasures fill the cottage's quirky rooms and, outside, every turn conjures childhood memories of holiday excitement – one way to the fort, another to the woods beyond.

Parking: for booked visitors only.

Access: 🅿️ ♿ 🚻 🔲 📺 ♨ 👁 📷 ⓘ 🧗

Find out more: 01530 248040 (Infoline) or stoneywell@nationaltrust.org.uk
nationaltrust.org.uk/stoneywell

Stoneywell		M	T	W	T	F	S	S
4 Mar–31 Oct	10–4:30	M	·	·	·	F	S	S

Tattershall Castle

Sleaford Road, Tattershall,
Lincolnshire LN4 4LR

1925 🏰🏠🎪🏹

Rising proudly from the flat Lincolnshire fens, Tattershall Castle was designed to display wealth, position and power. Built by Lord Ralph Cromwell, Treasurer of England, the Great Tower is one of the earliest and finest surviving examples of English medieval brickwork. Dramatically saved from being dismantled and exported, the castle and its huge Gothic fireplaces were restored from ruin by Lord Curzon of Kedleston between 1912 and 1914. Imagine the splendour of this once-palatial private residence as you wander through the vast echoing chambers. Ascend the spiral staircase from basement to battlements and take in spectacular views of the countryside. **Note**: access to the tower via a spiral staircase only (149 steps). Loose gravel paths throughout.

Parking: 150 yards from entrance. Height restrictions apply, maximum 2.4 metres.

Dog rating: 🐾 **Standard** – Welcome on leads in the grounds.

Access: 🅿️♿🚻🧑‍🦽🎧👁️♿

Fun and games at Tattershall Castle in Lincolnshire, this picture and left

Find out more: 01526 342543 or
tattershallcastle@nationaltrust.org.uk
nationaltrust.org.uk/tattershall

Tattershall Castle		M	T	W	T	F	S	S
16 Feb–31 Mar*	11–3		·	·	**W**	**T**	**F**	**S**	**S**
1 Apr–30 Sep*	10:30–4:30		·	·	**W**	**T**	**F**	**S**	**S**
1 Oct–30 Oct*	11–3		·	·	**W**	**T**	**F**	**S**	**S**

*Open Bank Holiday Mondays. Last entry one hour before closing (may close earlier due to light levels). Great Tower: some rooms close occasionally for weddings.

Ulverscroft Nature Reserve

near Copt Oak, Loughborough,
Leicestershire 1945

Nestled in the ancient Charnwood Forest, the heathland and woodland habitats of Ulverscroft support a rich variety of wildlife. **Note**: sorry no toilet. For satnav use LE67 9QE.

Find out more: 01332 863822 or
ulverscroftreserve@nationaltrust.org.uk
nationaltrust.org.uk/ulverscroft

Winster Market House

Main Street, Winster, Matlock,
Derbyshire DE4 2DJ 1906

A small listed 16th-century market house with displays upstairs – the first Derbyshire place acquired by the National Trust, costing £50. **Note**: unstaffed. Currently closed (please check the website for details).

Find out more: 01335 350503 or
winstermarkethouse@nationaltrust.org.uk
nationaltrust.org.uk/winster-market-house

Woolsthorpe Manor in Lincolnshire was the birthplace and home of Isaac Newton

Woolsthorpe Manor

Water Lane, Woolsthorpe by Colsterworth,
near Grantham, Lincolnshire NG33 5PD

| 1943 |

Find out more: 01476 860338 or
woolsthorpemanor@nationaltrust.org.uk
nationaltrust.org.uk/woolsthorpe

Woolsthorpe Manor		M	T	W	T	F	S	S
12 Feb–31 Oct	11–5*	**M**	·	·	**T**	**F**	**S**	**S**

*Coffee shop open 11 to 4:30. Open for guided tours only (last booking 4). May close early due to low light levels.

The world changed here. Isaac Newton, scientist, mathematician, thinker, craftsman, was born and grew up at Woolsthorpe Manor, doing much of his most important scientific work before he was 26. Sent home from Cambridge by the plague during 1665–7, he experimented obsessively, laying foundations for a groundbreaking scientific revolution. Here he split sunlight into colours with a prism and an apple fell from a tree to inspire his theory of gravity. Newton's genius still resonates through our world today. Visit Woolsthorpe, as Einstein did, and be inspired by Newton's story. **Note**: booking not necessary to visit the Discovery Centre.

Parking: 50 yards.

Access:

The Workhouse, Southwell

Southwell, Nottinghamshire

[2002] 🏠✿🍴🏞️🎋

Walking up the paupers' path towards The Workhouse, it is easy to imagine how the poor might have felt as they sought refuge here. This austere building, the most complete workhouse in existence, was built in 1824 as a place of last resort for the destitute. Its architecture was influenced by prison design, and its harsh regime became a blueprint for workhouses throughout the country. The stories of people who lived and worked here over the years help tell the history of the building's evolution and prompt reflection on how society has tackled social welfare through time.

Three views of The Workhouse, Southwell, in Nottinghamshire

Satnav: use NG25 0QB.
Parking: 200 yards.

Dog rating: ✿ **Standard** – Welcome on leads in front field.

Access: 🅿️♿🚻🔊📖📺🎵:.🔍♿ 🚶♿➡️

Find out more: 01636 817260 or theworkhouse@nationaltrust.org.uk
Upton Road, Southwell,
Nottinghamshire NG25 0PT
nationaltrust.org.uk/southwell-workhouse

The Workhouse		M	T	W	T	F	S	S
16 Feb–31 Jul*	10:30–4**			W	T	F	S	S
1 Aug–31 Aug	10:30–4**	M	T	W	T	F	S	S
1 Sep–30 Oct	10:30–4**			W	T	F	S	S

*Open Bank Holiday Mondays. **Last entry one hour before closing (may close earlier due to light levels).

Enjoying the view at Clent Hills, Worcestershire

West Midlands

Little Moreton Hall

Biddulph Grange Garden

Ilam Park, Dovedale and the White Peak

Hardwick

Mansfield

Congleton

Crewe

STOKE-ON-TRENT

Wrexham

Erddig

Chesterfield

Bakewell

Kedleston Hall

DERBY

Chirk Castle

Oswestry

Downs Banks

Stone

Stafford

The Children's Country House at Sudbury

Calke Abbey

Shugborough Estate

Shrewsbury

Attingham Park

Sunnycroft

Letocetum Roman Baths

Welshpool

Town Walls Tower

Cronkhill

Benthall Hall

Moseley Old Hall

Tamworth

Powis Castle

Wilderhope Manor

Morville Hall

Wightwick Manor

WOLVERHAMPTON

Carding Mill Valley

Wenlock Edge

Dudmaston

Bridgnorth

BIRMINGHAM

Kinver Edge

Roundhouse

Moseley Road Baths
Birmingham Back to Backs

COVENTRY

Knowles Mill

Clent Hills

Kidderminster

Croft Castle

Berrington Hall

Rosedene

Packwood House

Baddesley Clinton

Leominster

Hawford Dovecote

The Firs

Hanbury Hall

Warwick

Wichenford Dovecote

WORCESTER

Coughton Court

Charlecote Park

Farnborough Hall

Cwmmau Farmhouse

Brockhampton

Greyfriars House

Kinwarton Dovecote

Stratford upon Avon

Canons Ashby

The Weir Garden

HEREFORD

Croome

Middle Littleton Tithe Barn

Evesham

Hidcote

Upton House

Banbury

The Fleece Inn

Snowshill Manor

Chipping Norton

Stow-on-the-Wold

Attingham Park

Atcham, Shrewsbury, Shropshire SY4 4TP

1947 🏛 ✿ ❋ ☕ 🏠 🎭 ⚹

Attingham inspires a sense of beauty, space and awe. From the moment you enter the gates, views open up across the 200-year-old parkland towards the Shropshire Hills and the impressive mansion emerges against silhouettes of cedar trees. The house, which sits at the heart of Lord Berwick's estate, is an example of classical design and Italian influence. Outside, cattle graze and fallow deer roam, woodland glades of historic trees offer peace and shade, while the red-brick walled garden is a place of order, productivity and horticulture. The accessible paths around the parkland are perfect for walks, running or exploring the 1,619-hectare (4,000-acre) estate. Full of life and locally loved, there's something for everyone all year round.

The impressive classical façade of Attingham Park, Shropshire, shows its Italian influence

Parking: 25 to 200 yards.

Dog rating: 🐾 🐾 🐾 **Best** – Welcome (dog-walkers' guide available).

Access: [access icons]

Find out more: 01743 708123 (Infoline). 01743 708162 or attingham@nationaltrust.org.uk
nationaltrust.org.uk/attingham-park

Attingham Park		M	T	W	T	F	S	S
Park, Field of Play, Carriage House Café and Stables shop*								
1 Jan–18 Feb	8–5	M	T	W	T	F	S	S
19 Feb–8 Apr	8–6	M	T	W	T	F	S	S
9 Apr–5 Sep	8–6:30	M	T	W	T	F	S	S
6 Sep–30 Oct	8–6	M	T	W	T	F	S	S
31 Oct–31 Dec	8–5	M	T	W	T	F	S	S
Walled Garden								
Open all year	9–5**	M	T	W	T	F	S	S

*Carriage House Café opens 9 and Stables shop opens 10; both close one hour before park (except for 9 April to 5 September, both close 5). **Closes dusk if earlier. Mansion: opening times and experiences vary throughout year. Everything closed 25 December.

The red-brick paved Walled Garden at Attingham Park, below, and a graceful interior, above

Attingham Park Estate: Cronkhill

near Atcham, Shrewsbury,
Shropshire SY5 6JP 1947

Delightful picturesque Italianate hillside villa designed by Regency architect John Nash, with beautiful views across the Attingham Estate. **Note**: house ground floor, garden and stables open as part of visit. Property contents belong to tenant. Open 6 and 8 May, 1 and 3 July, 9 and 11 September, 11 to 4 (admission by booked timed tickets).

Find out more: 01743 708162 or cronkhill@nationaltrust.org.uk
nationaltrust.org.uk/attingham-park-cronkhill

Attingham Park Estate: Town Walls Tower

Shrewsbury, Shropshire SY1 1TN 1930

This last remaining 14th-century watchtower sits on what were once the medieval fortified, defensive walls of Shrewsbury. **Note**: sorry no toilet and 40 extremely steep, narrow steps to top floor. Opening arrangements not confirmed at time of print, please check before visiting.

Find out more: 01743 708162 or townwallstower@nationaltrust.org.uk
nationaltrust.org.uk/town-walls-tower

Wisteria swathes Baddesley Clinton in Warwickshire, above right

Baddesley Clinton

Rising Lane, Baddesley Clinton,
Warwickshire B93 0DQ

1980

The magic of Baddesley Clinton comes from its secluded, timeless setting deep within its own parkland. From refuge to haven, this atmospheric moated manor house has been a sanctuary since the 15th century. Discover Baddesley's late medieval, Tudor and 20th-century histories and uncover its stories, from hiding persecuted Catholics in its priest's holes, to the history of the Ferrers family who lived at Baddesley for more than 500 years. The peaceful gardens include fish pools, walled garden and a lakeside walk, perfect for a tranquil stroll.

You'll find our access guide here: nationaltrust.org.uk/access

Children explore moated Baddesley Clinton, opposite and top. Visitors in the courtyard, above

Parking: 100 yards.

Dog rating: ✤ **Standard** – Welcome on leads in car park and estate public footpaths.

Access: 🅿♿🚻🏠📷📺♿👶🏠♿➡

Find out more: 01564 783294 or baddesleyclinton@nationaltrust.org.uk
nationaltrust.org.uk/baddesley-clinton

Baddesley Clinton		M	T	W	T	F	S	S
1 Jan–18 Feb	9–4	M	T	W	T	F	S	S
19 Feb–30 Oct	9–5	M	T	W	T	F	S	S
31 Oct–31 Dec	9–4	M	T	W	T	F	S	S

House: opening times vary throughout the year, admission by timed ticket (not bookable), last entrance one hour before closing. Closed 24 and 25 December.

Benthall Hall

Broseley, Shropshire TF12 5RX

 1958 🏠🐕❀🎣⛩🚶

Within this fine stone house, below, discover the history of the Benthall family from the Saxon period to the present day. Outside, the garden includes a Restoration church, a plantsman's garden with pretty crocus displays in spring and autumn, and an old kitchen garden. Woodland and parkland walks open all year.

Parking: 100 yards.

Dog rating: ✤ **Standard** – Dogs welcome on parkland and woodland walks.

Access: 🅿♿🚻🚶🏠

Find out more: 01952 882159 or benthall@nationaltrust.org.uk
nationaltrust.org.uk/benthall

Benthall Hall		M	T	W	T	F	S	S
19 Feb–30 Oct	12:30–5:30*	M	T	W	.	.	S	S

*House: open 1 to 5. Estate: open every day all year (excluding 25 December), dawn to dusk.

Berrington Hall

near Leominster, Herefordshire HR6 0DW

1957

Standing proud and strong, this fine Georgian mansion sits within 'Capability' Brown's final garden and landscape. In the house are jewel-like interiors, designed by Henry Holland and home to the Harley, Rodney and Cawley families. Upstairs you can explore the life of Ann Harley, first lady of Berrington, and see a dress fit for a king. Learn more about the Berrington garden project as we continue to revive 'Capability' Brown's final masterpiece, and nurture your mind and body with a walk round the lake. **Note**: major restoration to mansion stonework, lake, woodland and garden paths, and walls.

Parking: 30 yards.

Dog rating: 🐾 🐾 **Good** – Welcome on leads in the garden, courtyard, stables café, second-hand bookshop and parkland.

Berrington Hall in Herefordshire, above and below

Access: ⓟ Ⓓ 🏠 🚻 ♿ 🎫 🪑 ⠿ ♿ 🐾 ⬆
♿ ➡ ♿

Find out more: 01568 615721 or berrington@nationaltrust.org.uk
nationaltrust.org.uk/berrington-hall

Berrington Hall		M	T	W	T	F	S	S
1 Jan–13 Feb	10–4*						S	S
19 Feb–30 Oct	10–5*	M	T	W	T	F	S	S
19 Nov–18 Dec	10–4*						S	S
19 Dec–23 Dec	10–4*	M	T	W	T	F		
27 Dec–31 Dec	10–4*		T	W	T	F	S	

*Mansion: opens 11 (last entry one hour before closing).

Biddulph Grange Garden

Grange Road, Biddulph,
Staffordshire ST8 7SD

1988 ♣ ▣ 🗆 🕺 🐾

Three views of Biddulph Grange Garden, Staffordshire: quirky paradise full of surprises

Biddulph Grange Garden is a remarkable survival, a formal Victorian horticultural masterpiece and a quirky, playful paradise full of intrigue and surprise. Created by its visionary owner, James Bateman, the garden and Geological Gallery express his attempts to reconcile his religious convictions and passion for botany and geology. His international plant and fossil collection includes towering wellingtonia and monkey puzzle trees, rhododendrons, late-flowering dahlias and the oldest golden larch in Britain. A visit is a journey from a stepped Italian terrace to an Egyptian pyramid, via a narrow Himalayan glen and Chinese garden, hidden by tunnels, hedges and rockwork. **Note**: there are 400 uneven steps, narrow paths, dark tunnels and gradients in the garden.

Parking: 50 yards.

Access:

Find out more: 01782 517999 or biddulphgrange@nationaltrust.org.uk
nationaltrust.org.uk/biddulph-grange-garden

Biddulph Grange Garden		M	T	W	T	F	S	S
1 Jan–31 Jan	10–3:30	M	T	W	.	.	S	S
1 Feb–18 Feb	10–3:30	M	T	W	T	F	S	S
19 Feb–18 Mar	10–4:30	M	T	W	T	F	S	S
19 Mar–21 Oct	10–5:30	M	T	W	T	F	S	S
22 Oct–30 Oct	10–4:30	M	T	W	T	F	S	S
31 Oct–30 Nov	10–3:30	M	T	W	.	.	S	S
1 Dec–31 Dec*	10–3:30	M	T	W	T	F	S	S

Closes dusk if earlier. *Closed 25 and 26 December.

Birmingham

Birmingham Back to Backs

55-63 Hurst Street/50-54 Inge Street, Birmingham, West Midlands B5 4TE

2004

Birmingham Back to Backs in the West Midlands offer an insight into a long-gone way of life

Immerse yourself in the life of residents at Birmingham's last surviving court of back to backs and get an insight into how people lived from the 1840s to the 1970s. With privies, coal fires, candlelight and cramped spaces, you'll get a real taste of back-to-back life. **Note**: steep, narrow and winding staircases on some tours.

Parking: nearest at Arcadian Centre, Bromsgrove Street (not National Trust).

Access:

Find out more: 0121 622 2442
(enquiries only, not bookings) or
backtobacks@nationaltrust.org.uk
nationaltrust.org.uk/birmingham-back-to-backs

Birmingham Back to Backs	M	T	W	T	F	S	S
6 Jan–18 Dec	Tour	·	·	**T**	**F**	**S**	**S**

Clent Hills

See page 275.

Moseley Road Baths

497 Moseley Road, Balsall Heath,
Birmingham B12 9BX

Find out more: 0121 439 0320 or
moseleyroadbaths.org.uk

Roundhouse

1 Sheepcote Street, Birmingham B16 8AE

2017

Explore Birmingham and its heritage
from this unique horseshoe-shaped
building at the heart of the city's canal
network. Book now for city walks, kayak
tours and more. **Note**: Roundhouse
Birmingham is an independent charity,
in partnership with Canal & River Trust.

Parking: public car parks nearby,
none National Trust (charge
including members).

Bird's-eye view of Birmingham's Roundhouse

Access:

Find out more:
hello@roundhousebirmingham.org.uk
nationaltrust.org.uk/roundhouse-birmingham

Roundhouse		M	T	W	T	F	S	S
Visitor centre								
12 Jan–31 Mar	10–4	·	·	**W**	**T**	**F**	**S**	**S**
1 Apr–30 Sep	9:30–4:30	·	**T**	**W**	**T**	**F**	**S**	**S**
1 Oct–18 Dec	10–4	·	·	**W**	**T**	**F**	**S**	**S**

Birmingham partners

From intriguing museums to stately
homes, there are several places in the
Birmingham area that offer a special
welcome to our members. You could be
entitled to up to 50% off your entry price
or guided tour when you show your
National Trust membership card.

The list is ever-growing, so the best
way to find a place near you is to
head to our website and search for
'Birmingham partners'.

Brockhampton

Bringsty, near Bromyard,
Herefordshire WR6 5TB

1946 🏠🏘️✤🛆☕🎦🕴️

More than 600 years ago the Dumbleton
family built this moated manor house
tucked away in a Herefordshire valley. Find
out about the lives of the people who lived
here and discover how a once-grand
medieval hall was slowly transformed into
a modest home for farmers. There are miles
of walks through a farming landscape with
parkland, hidden dingles, gushing streams
and wild woodlands waiting to be
discovered. Explore newly replanted
orchards and 'orchard rooms' on accessible
paths, and step on board a replica Trow,
a type of ship which would have once
transported apples and other produce from
Brockhampton. **Note**: some walks include
challenging terrain with steep slopes and
muddy areas.

**Medieval timber-framed Brockhampton
in Herefordshire, above and below**

Parking: 100 yards and 1 mile.

Dog rating: 🐾 🐾 **Good** – Welcome on
leads outdoors.

Access: 🅿️🐕♿🧴🖼️♿♿♿➡️

Find out more: 01885 482077 or
brockhampton@nationaltrust.org.uk
nationaltrust.org.uk/brockhampton

Brockhampton		M	T	W	T	F	S	S
1 Jan–13 Feb	10–4*						S	S
19 Feb–30 Oct**	10–5*	M	T	W	T	F	S	S
26 Nov–18 Dec	10–4*						S	S
19 Dec–23 Dec	10–4*	M	T	W	T	F		
27 Dec–31 Dec	10–4*		T	W	T	F	S	

*House: opens 11. **House: open daily 9 April to 30 October.

Carding Mill Valley and the Long Mynd

near Church Stretton, Shropshire

Discover wildlife-rich heather-covered hills at this valley in the heart of the Shropshire countryside. Here families can enjoy playing in the stream before exploring one of the many waymarked walks. Head up to the top of Long Mynd for that perfect photograph and be rewarded with far-reaching views.

Satnav: use SY6 6JG. **Parking**: 50 yards.

Dog rating: ❀ **Standard** – Welcome on leads and under close control – seasonal access. Welcome in the tea-room.

Access:

Find out more: 01694 725000 or cardingmill@nationaltrust.org.uk
nationaltrust.org.uk/carding-mill-valley-and-the-long-mynd

Carding Mill Valley		M	T	W	T	F	S	S
Tea-room								
1 Jan–20 Feb	10–4	M	T	W	T	F	S	S
21 Feb–30 Oct	10–5	M	T	W	T	F	S	S
31 Oct–31 Dec*	10–4	M	T	W	T	F	S	S

*Closed 25 December.

Charlecote Park

Wellesbourne, Warwick,
Warwickshire CV35 9ER

Charlecote Park, below, was already in its middle age when Elizabeth I arrived 450 years ago, entering through the gatehouse and on to the welcoming red-brick mansion, just as you will today. A family home for more than eight centuries, it is a place of surprising treasures, with collections reflecting the tastes, lifestyle and varied fortunes of the Lucy family. Imagine the hum of activity of a working estate in the domestic 'below-stairs' spaces and in the laundry room and brewhouse in the courtyard. In the stables see the family's carriage collection, while in the parkland Jacob sheep and fallow deer roam across the 'Capability' Brown landscape, a haven for wildlife in which you can picnic and play, walk and wander. **Note**: essential building works may significantly disrupt house access.

Charlecote Park, Warwickshire, clockwise from left:
deer roam freely, the grounds and inside the house

Most places offer last entry 30 minutes before closing

Parking: 300 yards.

Dog rating: 🐾 🐾 **Good** – Welcome on leads (designated areas).

Access: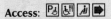

Find out more: 01789 470277 or charlecotepark@nationaltrust.org.uk
nationaltrust.org.uk/charlecote

Charlecote Park		M	T	W	T	F	S	S
Park, garden, café and shop*								
1 Jan–18 Feb	9–4**	M	T	W	T	F	S	S
19 Feb–30 Oct	9–5**	M	T	W	T	F	S	S
31 Oct–31 Dec	9–4**	M	T	W	T	F	S	S
House†								
19 Feb–30 Oct	10:30–3	M	T	W	T	F	S	S
5 Nov–27 Nov	10:30–3	·	·	·	·	·	S	S
28 Nov–31 Dec	10:30–3	M	T	W	T	F	S	S

*Café and shop: open at 9:30. **Park and garden: close dusk if earlier. †House: admission by timed tickets; building projects may impact availability. Everything closed 25 December.

Clent Hills

near Romsley, Worcestershire

Set on the edge of Birmingham and the Black Country, this green oasis with panoramic views, below, is the perfect place for a refreshing walk or a picnic on a sunny day. Families can create their own adventures – building dens, hunting for geocaches or simply getting closer to nature. **Note**: nearest facilities at Nimmings Wood entrance.

Satnav: use B62 0NL for Nimmings Wood entrance. **Parking**: at Nimmings Wood; additional parking at Adam's Hill and Walton Hill. Please note the gates at Nimmings Wood are locked daily with no out-of-hours service – vehicles cannot be retrieved once the gates are locked.

Dog rating: 🐾 **Standard** – Welcome on leads on easy-access path and café (excluding play area). Be aware of livestock grazing.

Access:

Find out more: 01562 887912 or clenthills@nationaltrust.org.uk
nationaltrust.org.uk/clent-hills

Clent Hills

Nimmings Wood car park: open 9 to 5, 1 March to 31 October; 9 to 4 at other times. Café: open 10 to 4. Car park and café: closed 25 December.

Coughton Court

Alcester, Warwickshire B49 5JA

1946

Coughton has been home to the Throckmorton family for more than 600 years. Facing persecution for their Catholic faith, they were willing to risk everything. You can discover their story and find out about a family's struggles, perseverance and intrigues, including their link to the infamous Gunpowder Plot. Coughton is very much a family home with an intimate feel. The Throckmorton family still live here and they created and manage the gardens, including a riverside walk, bog garden and beautiful display of roses in the walled garden. **Note**: building works likely. Picnics welcome in three fenced picnic areas (none in formal gardens please).

Parking: 150 yards.

Access:

Find out more: 01789 400777 or coughtoncourt@nationaltrust.org.uk
nationaltrust.org.uk/coughton-court

Coughton Court		M	T	W	T	F	S	S
3 Mar–31 Mar*	11–4				T	F	S	S
1 Apr–26 Jun	11–5**			W	T	F	S	S
28 Jun–11 Sep	11–5**		T	W	T	F	S	S
14 Sep–30 Sep	11–5**			W	T	F	S	S
1 Oct–29 Oct	11–4**			W	T	F	S	S

House: opening times vary. *Grounds closed. Open Bank Holiday Mondays and Good Friday. **Walled garden: opens 12. Everything closed for private Throckmorton family days 25 June, 13 August, 17 September and 30 October.

Three views of Coughton Court in Warwickshire: a family home for 600 years with an intimate feel

Croft Castle and Parkland

near Leominster, Herefordshire

1957 | (icons)

This intimate house became the Croft family home before the Domesday Book. Its walls conceal a rich and turbulent history, with many compelling 20th-century stories to uncover. The interiors, styled by Thomas Farnolls Pritchard, also tell an 18th- and 19th-century tale. You can take your dog for a stroll to the Iron Age hill fort, exploring the historic parkland with ancient trees along the way, and discover new views and walks in Fishpool Valley. Croft Castle is a place to immerse yourself in 1,000 years of power, politics and pleasure.

Satnav: use HR6 OBL. **Parking**: 100 yards.

Dog rating: 🐾 🐾 **Good** – Welcome on leads in garden, parkland and glazed area of tea-room.

Access: (icons)

Find out more: 01568 780246 or croftcastle@nationaltrust.org.uk
Yarpole, near Leominster, Herefordshire HR6 9PW
nationaltrust.org.uk/croft-castle

Croft Castle		M	T	W	T	F	S	S
1 Jan–13 Feb	10–4*						S	S
19 Feb–30 Oct**	10–5*	M	T	W	T	F	S	S
19 Nov–18 Dec	10–4*						S	S
19 Dec–23 Dec	10–4*	M	T	W	T	F		
27 Dec–31 Dec	10–4*		T	W	T	F	S	

*Castle: opens 11. **Castle: open daily 9 April to 30 October.

Playing outdoor noughts and crosses at Croft Castle and Parkland in Herefordshire

Croome

near High Green, Worcester,
Worcestershire WR8 9DW

1996

Expect the unexpected at Croome and be amazed by the grandest of English landscapes, 'Capability' Brown's masterful first commission, with commanding views over the Malverns. The parkland, nearly lost but now restored, is great for walks and adventures, with a surprise around every corner. At the heart of the park lies Croome Court, once home to the Earls of Coventry. The 6th Earl was an 18th-century trendsetter, and today Croome follows his lead, working with artists, craftspeople and communities to tell the story of its eclectic past in inventive ways. Visitors arrive at the RAF visitor centre, once a secret wartime airbase, now a museum celebrating what was once a hub of activity for thousands of people. **Note**: walled gardens are privately owned.

Satnav: follow signs from main road, not satnav. **Parking**: on site.

Dog rating: 🐾 🐾 **Good** – Welcome on leads in garden and wider estate.

Access: ♿🚐♿🚻🍴📷✏🚶🔍♿🛗
♿➡🚷

There is so much to do at Croome, Worcestershire, this page and left, with acres of park to explore and something fascinating at every turn in the house

Find out more: 01905 371006 or croome@nationaltrust.org.uk
nationaltrust.org.uk/croome

Croome		M	T	W	T	F	S	S
House								
1 Jan–6 Mar	11–4	M	T	W	T	F	S	S
7 Mar–29 Oct	11–4:30	M	T	W	T	F	S	S
30 Oct–31 Dec*	11–4	M	T	W	T	F	S	S
Park, restaurant and shop								
1 Jan–6 Mar	10–4**	M	T	W	T	F	S	S
7 Mar–29 Oct	10–5**	M	T	W	T	F	S	S
30 Oct–31 Dec*	10–4**	M	T	W	T	F	S	S

*Everything closed 24 and 25 December.
**Restaurant and shop close 30 minutes before park.

Cwmmau Farmhouse

Brilley, Whitney-on-Wye, Herefordshire HR3 6JP 1965

A charming 17th-century timbered farmhouse with many original features and stunning views across Herefordshire. **Note**: closed this year. Available for holiday bookings.

Find out more: 01568 780246 or cwmmaufarmhouse@nationaltrust.org.uk
nationaltrust.org.uk/cwmmau-farmhouse

Downs Banks

Washdale Lane, Oulton Heath, near Stone, Staffordshire 1950

A little wilderness of woodlands and heath, with easy access walks, in the heart of the Midlands. **Note**: sorry no toilet. Some steep paths.

Find out more: 01889 880160 or downsbanks@nationaltrust.org.uk
nationaltrust.org.uk/downs-banks

Dudmaston

Quatt, near Bridgnorth,
Shropshire WV15 6QN

1978

Fun in the garden at Dudmaston, Shropshire

Stretching across 1,214 hectares
(3,000 acres) of ancient woodland and
park, Dudmaston is a working estate with a
family home at its heart. Steeped in history
but shaped by modern tastes and radical
thinking, it is a delightful collision of
unexpected contrasts. With remarkable
pieces by Moore and Matisse in the
galleries and modern sculpture in the
garden, art has always found a home here.
Discover the picturesque dingle, or find
a tranquil spot and enjoy the views over
the pool. Explore the wider estate from
Hampton Loade, Sawmill and Comer
Woods – offering multi-use trails, walks
and refreshments. **Note**: the family home
of Mr and Mrs Mark Hamilton-Russell.

Satnav: for Comer Woods use WV15 6QJ;
Hampton Loade WV15 6HD; Sawmill
WV15 6QN. **Parking**: Dudmaston Hall
car park (seasonal) and pay and display
car parks in Comer Woods, Hampton Loade
and the Sawmill.

Dog rating: 🐾 🐾 **Good** – Welcome on
leads across the estate (assistance dogs
only in gardens).

Access:

Find out more: 01746 780866 or
dudmaston@nationaltrust.org.uk
nationaltrust.org.uk/dudmaston

Dudmaston		M	T	W	T	F	S	S
Park, tea-room and second-hand bookshop								
12 Feb–20 Feb*	11–4	·	·	·	·	·	S	S
13 Mar–31 Mar	11–4:30	M	T	W	T	·	·	S
3 Apr–29 Sep**	10:30–4:30	M	T	W	T	·	·	S
2 Oct–31 Oct	11–4:30	M	T	W	T	·	·	S
5 Nov–27 Nov	11–4	·	·	·	·	·	S	S
Galleries†								
13 Mar–31 Mar	12:30–4	M	T	W	T	·	·	S
2 Oct–31 Oct	12:30–4	M	T	W	T	·	·	S
5 Nov–27 Nov	12:30–4	·	·	·	·	·	S	S
Hall and galleries								
3 Apr–29 Sep**	12:30–4	M	T	W	T	·	·	S
Garden								
13 Mar–31 Mar	11:30–4:30	M	T	W	T	·	·	S
3 Apr–29 Sep**	11–4:30	M	T	W	T	·	·	S
2 Oct–31 Oct	11:30–4:30	M	T	W	T	·	·	S

*Dingle walks only. **Open Friday for Platinum Jubilee.
†Tours from 11.

Farnborough Hall

Farnborough, near Banbury,
Warwickshire OX17 1DU 1960

Carolean house with exquisite plasterwork
and grand stairway. Set in landscaped
gardens with a mile-long terrace walk and
parkland views. **Note**: occupied and
administered by the Holbech family. Open
2 April to 28 September, Wednesday and
Saturday, 2 to 5:30 (also open 1 and 2 May).

Find out more: 01295 670266 (option six)
or farnboroughhall@nationaltrust.org.uk
nationaltrust.org.uk/farnborough

The Firs – Birthplace of Edward Elgar

Crown East Lane, Lower Broadheath, Worcester, Worcestershire WR2 6RH

2017

Family treasures tell the story of Sir Edward Elgar's humble beginnings in this intimate cottage. Learn more about Elgar's inspiration in the modern visitor centre and then enjoy the peaceful cottage garden.

Parking: on site.

Dog rating: ❀ **Standard** – Welcome on leads (assistance dogs only in cottage).

Access:

Find out more: 01905 333330 or thefirs@nationaltrust.org.uk
nationaltrust.org.uk/the-firs

The Firs		M	T	W	T	F	S	S
4 Mar–30 Oct	11–5*	M	·	·	·	F	S	S
2 Dec–19 Dec	11–4*	M	·	·	·	F	S	S

*House: last entry one hour before closing; café: shuts 30 minutes before closing time.

The Fleece Inn

Bretforton, near Evesham, Worcestershire WR11 7JE 1978

Medieval half-timbered longhouse, now a traditional village inn, with barn and orchard. Known for folk music, Morris dancing and asparagus. **Note**: open every day all year, 10 to 11 (reduced opening on 25 December).

Find out more: 01386 831173 or fleeceinn@nationaltrust.org.uk
nationaltrust.org.uk/fleece-inn

Greyfriars House and Garden

Friar Street, Worcester, Worcestershire WR1 2LZ

1966

Greyfriars House and Garden in Worcestershire

Set in the heart of historic Worcester, this late 15th-century timber-framed house reflected the fortunes of the city for more than 500 years. Saved from demolition in the 20th century, Greyfriars was brought back to life by unconventional siblings Elsie and Matley Moore.

Parking: none on site, nearest at St Martin's Gate, Cornmarket, Kings Street and Cathedral Plaza, pay and display, not National Trust (charge including members).

Dog rating: ❀ **Standard** – Welcome in the garden.

Access:

Find out more: 01905 23571 or greyfriars@nationaltrust.org.uk
nationaltrust.org.uk/greyfriars

Greyfriars	M	T	W	T	F	S	S
House, garden, café and second-hand bookshop							
15 Feb–17 Dec 10:30–4:30	·	T	W	T	F	S	·

House: access guided tour only (timed tickets allocated on arrival).

Hanbury Hall

School Road, Hanbury, Droitwich Spa,
Worcestershire WR9 7EA

1953 [icons]

A country retreat in the heart of
Worcestershire. The house and garden,
originally a stage-set for summer parties,
offer a glimpse into life at the turn of the
18th century. Don't miss the original
wall-paintings by Sir James Thornhill; full
of drama and politics. The original formal
gardens, designed by George London, have
been faithfully recreated and complement
the relaxed later gardens, with orangery,
orchards and walled garden. If you venture
further afield, our walks into the parkland
will lead you into the remains of ancient
forests and historic avenues.

Parking: 150 yards.

Dog rating: 🐾 🐾 **Good** – Welcome
on leads in the parkland, Stables Café,
stableyard and courtyard behind house.

Access: [icons]

Find out more: 01527 821214 or
hanburyhall@nationaltrust.org.uk
nationaltrust.org.uk/hanbury-hall

Hanbury Hall		M	T	W	T	F	S	S
House								
1 Jan–20 Feb	10–4						S	S
21 Feb–30 Oct	10–4	M	T	W	T	F	S	S
5 Nov–27 Nov	10–4						S	S
28 Nov–31 Dec*	10–4	M	T	W	T	F	S	S
Gardens and parkland								
1 Jan–18 Feb	9:30–4:30	M	T	W	T	F	S	S
19 Feb–30 Oct	9:30–5	M	T	W	T	F	S	S
31 Oct–31 Dec*	9:30–4:30	M	T	W	T	F	S	S
Café								
1 Jan–18 Feb	10–4	M	T	W	T	F	S	S
19 Feb–30 Oct	10–4:30	M	T	W	T	F	S	S
31 Oct–31 Dec*	10–4	M	T	W	T	F	S	S

*Everything closed 24 and 25 December.

Two views of Hanbury Hall in
Worcestershire, below and top right

Hawford Dovecote

Hawford, Worcestershire WR3 7SG 1973

Picturesque dovecote, which has
survived virtually unaltered since the late
16th century, retaining many nesting boxes.
Note: sorry no toilet or tea-room. Please
park carefully to one side of Chatley Lane
without obstructing any private access.

Find out more: 01527 821214 or
hawforddovecote@nationaltrust.org.uk
nationaltrust.org.uk/hawford-dovecote

Kinver Edge and the Rock Houses

near Stourbridge, Staffordshire

1917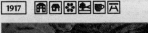

At the Holy Austin Rock Houses discover surprisingly cosy homes carved into the rock of an imposing sandstone ridge. Walks in the surrounding countryside of Kinver Edge cross open heathland, buzzing with wildlife, and woodland trails leading to further rock houses nestled among the trees. Dramatic views across three counties.

Satnav: use DY7 6DL for Rock Houses.
Parking: for the Rock Houses park in lay-by on Compton Road or in the overflow car park on Kingsford Lane. For the wider countryside either park in lay-by on Comber Road or in the car park with toilets on Kingsford Lane.

Dog rating: 🐾 🐾 **Good** – Welcome on leads in gardens of Rock Houses and countryside.

Access: 🅿️ 🎧 ♿

Find out more: 01384 872553 or
kinveredge@nationaltrust.org.uk
Holy Austin Rock Houses, Compton Road,
Kinver, Staffordshire DY7 6DL
nationaltrust.org.uk/kinver-edge

Kinver Edge		M	T	W	T	F	S	S
Rock Houses and café								
1 Jan–13 Feb	11–3						S	S
19 Feb–30 Oct	11–4	M			T	F	S	S
5 Nov–18 Dec	11–3						S	S

Open every day during local school half term, Easter and summer holidays.

Kinwarton Dovecote

Kinwarton, near Alcester,
Warwickshire B49 6HB 1958

Rare 14th-century circular dovecote with metre-thick walls, hundreds of nesting holes and original rotating ladder. **Note**: livestock may be grazing. Sorry no toilet. Open daily, 3 March to 29 October, 9 to 5.

Find out more: 01789 400777 or
kinwartondovecote@nationaltrust.org.uk
nationaltrust.org.uk/kinwarton-dovecote

Knowles Mill

Dowles Brook, Bewdley,
Worcestershire DY12 2LX 1938

Dating from the 18th century, the mill retains much of its machinery, including the frames of an overshot waterwheel. **Note**: Mill Cottage not open to visitors (please respect the resident's privacy). Sorry no toilet.

Find out more: 01527 821214 or
knowlesmill@nationaltrust.org.uk
nationaltrust.org.uk/knowles-mill

Letocetum Roman Baths and Museum

Watling Street, Wall, near Lichfield,
Staffordshire WS14 0AW 1934

Open-air remains of a once-important Roman staging post and settlement, including *mansio* (Roman inn) and bathhouse. **Note**: in the guardianship of English Heritage. Baths: open every day all year, dawn to dusk. Museum: opened by volunteers, please check opening arrangements before visiting.

Find out more: 0370 333 1181 (English Heritage) or letocetum@nationaltrust.org.uk **nationaltrust.org.uk/letocetum-roman-baths**

Middle Littleton Tithe Barn

Middle Littleton, Evesham, Worcestershire WR11 8LN 1975

The largest and finest restored 13th-century tithe barn in the country. **Note**: sorry no toilet. Open daily, 1 April to 31 October, 10 to 5.

Find out more: 01905 371006 or middlelittleton@nationaltrust.org.uk **nationaltrust.org.uk/middle-littleton-tithe-barn**

Morville Hall

Morville, near Bridgnorth, Shropshire WV16 5NB 1965

Elizabethan gem with a Georgian makeover. Enchanting gardens spill down to the Mor Brook against the backdrop of Shropshire Hills. **Note**: property contents are a mix of items on loan and tenant's own. Opening arrangements not confirmed at time of print, please check before visiting.

Find out more: 01746 780866 (Dudmaston Hall) or morvillehall@nationaltrust.org.uk **nationaltrust.org.uk/morville-hall**

Moseley Old Hall

Moseley Old Hall Lane, Fordhouses, Wolverhampton, Staffordshire WV10 7HY

1962 🏠🏠🧩🎑🍵🏞🥾

Atmospheric Moseley Old Hall in Staffordshire

This atmospheric farmhouse, built circa 1600, holds many secrets. Charles II hid here after escaping the 1651 Battle of Worcester. Inside, a log fire crackles as 17th-century domestic life surrounds you. Outside, explore the walled garden, containing herbs and vegetables, the orchard and knot-garden. Beyond is King's Walk Wood.

Parking: on site.

Dog rating: ✿ **Standard** – Welcome on leads in garden and grounds.

Access: 🅿♿🚾🍴🎠📷🎵🔍♿🐾➡

Find out more: 01902 782808 or moseleyoldhall@nationaltrust.org.uk **nationaltrust.org.uk/moseley-old-hall**

Moseley Old Hall		M	T	W	T	F	S	S
14 Feb–27 Mar*	10–4	M				F	S	S
28 Mar–30 Oct*	10–5	M				F	S	S
5 Nov–27 Nov	10–4						S	S
28 Nov–24 Dec	10–4	M				F	S	S
28 Dec–31 Dec	10–4			W	T	F	S	

House: opens 11 (entry at very busy times by timed ticket); access to top floor may be limited for safety. *Open daily 21 to 27 Feb; 11 to 24 April; 30 May to 5 June; 25 July to 4 September and 24 to 30 October.

Packwood House

Packwood Lane, Lapworth,
Warwickshire B94 6AT

1941 🏛️ ✤ 🦮 🍽️ 🏠 🎋 🏃

Surrounded by beautiful gardens and
countryside, Packwood was described by
a guest in the 1930s as 'a house to dream
of, a garden to dream in'. Lovingly restored
at the beginning of the 20th century by
Graham Baron Ash, you can discover the
detail behind the man, his passion for
collecting and his collection. The gardens
include brightly coloured 'mingled style'
herbaceous borders, famous sculpted
yews and an 18th-century gentleman's
kitchen garden.

Parking: 150 yards.

Dog rating: 🐾 🐾 **Good** – Welcome in the
barnyard, park footpaths and café terrace.

**The garden at Packwood House in Warwickshire,
below, and discovering the house, right**

Access: 🅿️ 🚗 🚾 ♿ 🖥️ ⠿ ♿ ♿

Find out more: 01564 782024 or
packwood@nationaltrust.org.uk
nationaltrust.org.uk/packwood

Packwood House		M	T	W	T	F	S	S
1 Jan–18 Feb	9–4*	M	T	W	T	F	S	S
19 Feb–30 Oct**	9–5*	M	T	W	T	F	S	S
31 Oct–31 Dec	9–4*	M	T	W	T	F	S	S

*Formal gardens: open 10; some areas may close at short
notice. **Yew garden: open 12. House: opening times
vary throughout the year, admission by timed ticket
(not bookable), last entrance one hour before closing.
Everything closed 24 and 25 December.

Rosedene

Victoria Road, Dodford, near Bromsgrove,
Worcestershire B61 9BU 1997

Restored 1840s cottage with an organic
garden and orchard, illustrating the
mid-19th-century Chartist movement.
Note: available to hire as a 'back to basics'
holiday cottage. Closed this year.

Find out more: 01527 821214 or
rosedene@nationaltrust.org.uk
nationaltrust.org.uk/rosedene

Shugborough Estate in Staffordshire:
the River Sow meanders through the
parkland, passing the Georgian mansion

Shugborough Estate

Milford, near Stafford,
Staffordshire ST17 0UP

1966

Shaped by its illustrious and maritime
history, Shugborough embodies utility,
style, grandeur and comfort, a rich blend
of landscape gardens and architecture.
Join us on an exciting journey as the estate
rejuvenates itself over the years and the
stories and histories that led to it being
described as a 'perfect paradise' are
uncovered. You can explore the sweeping
parkland, wander through a landscape
peppered with monuments and discover
Park Farm, created at the cutting-edge
of agricultural reforms. In the Georgian
mansion, unearth prized treasures and
experience life 'below stairs', then enter
a world of glamour and royalty in the
apartment of Patrick Lichfield, 5th Earl
and fashion photographer.

Parking: 25 yards from reception.

Dog rating: ❅ ❅ **Good** – Welcome on
leads in formal gardens and parkland.

Access: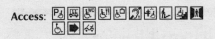

Find out more: 01889 880160 or
shugborough@nationaltrust.org.uk
nationaltrust.org.uk/shugborough

Shugborough Estate		M	T	W	T	F	S	S
Park and gardens*								
1 Jan–18 Feb	9–4	M	T	W	T	F	S	S
19 Feb–8 Apr	9–5	M	T	W	T	F	S	S
9 Apr–4 Sep	9–6	M	T	W	T	F	S	S
5 Sep–30 Oct	9–5	M	T	W	T	F	S	S
31 Oct–31 Dec	9–4	M	T	W	T	F	S	S
Mansion								
28 Mar–30 Oct	11–4:30	M	T	W	T	F	S	S
26 Nov–23 Dec	11–3:30	M	T	W	T	F	S	S
Shop, café and tea-room**								
1 Jan–18 Feb	10–3	M	T	W	T	F	S	S
19 Feb–8 Apr	10–4	M	T	W	T	F	S	S
9 Apr–4 Sep	10–5	M	T	W	T	F	S	S
5 Sep–30 Oct	10–4	M	T	W	T	F	S	S
31 Oct–31 Dec	10–3	M	T	W	T	F	S	S

*Walled Garden and Visitor Reception: open as park
and gardens. **Park Farm Café: opens 9:30 daily.
Everything closed 25 December.

**Shugborough Estate: the Walled Garden,
below, and learning about the house, above**

Sunnycroft

Wellington, near Telford, Shropshire

 1999 🏠 🏡 ✿ ⛺ 🎿

Sunnycroft, Shropshire: an estate in miniature

Hidden behind an avenue of towering redwoods this rare survival of a Victorian 'estate in miniature', with red-brick villa, glasshouses and garden, was a much-loved family home. The wide lawn is perfect for games, and the pretty borders and orchard offer a haven to relax in. **Note**: open on limited dates; workshops and activities run all year.

Satnav: use TF1 2DP (exit seven from M54).
Parking: 150 yards.

Dog rating: ✿ **Standard** – Welcome on leads in grounds only.

Access: 🅿️ 🅳 ♿ 💻 📺 📷 🔧 🚻 ➡️

Find out more: 01952 242884 or
sunnycroft@nationaltrust.org.uk
200 Holyhead Road, Wellington,
near Telford, Shropshire TF1 2DR
nationaltrust.org.uk/sunnycroft

Sunnycroft
Opening arrangements not confirmed at time of print, please check before visiting.

Upton House and Gardens

near Banbury, Warwickshire OX15 6HT

1948 🏠 🏡 ✿ 🍴 📷 🎿 ✕

Lord and Lady Bearsted made Upton House and Gardens their country home in 1927 and extensively remodelled it to create the perfect family retreat. Inside, dedicated spaces were crafted to showcase Lord Bearsted's world-class art and porcelain collection, including works by Bosch, Stubbs and El Greco. Outside, making the most of the natural landscape, the gardens are situated atop an ice-age valley and drop away from the edge of the sweeping south lawn to the Mirror Pool below. Over the next five years we will be offering new perspectives on Upton's collections of paintings, porcelain and garden plants.

Upton House and Gardens, Warwickshire: the gracious façade, below, and Library, above

Note: steep paths and open water.

Satnav: on arrival follow brown signs to car park. **Parking**: 300 yards.

Access:

Find out more: 01295 670266 or uptonhouse@nationaltrust.org.uk
nationaltrust.org.uk/upton

Upton House		M	T	W	T	F	S	S
House								
8 Jan–6 Feb	12–4*	.	.	.	.	.	S	S
7 Feb–30 Oct	11–4*	M	T	W	T	F	S	S
31 Oct–2 Dec	12–4*	M	.	.	.	F	S	S
3 Dec–24 Dec	12–4*	M	T	W	T	F	S	S
Gardens, café and shop								
1 Jan–6 Feb	12–4	.	.	.	.	.	S	S
7 Feb–30 Oct	10–5**	M	T	W	T	F	S	S
31 Oct–2 Dec	12–4	M	.	.	.	F	S	S
3 Dec–24 Dec	12–4	M	T	W	T	F	S	S
27 Dec–31 Dec	12–4	.	T	W	T	F	S	.

*House: last entry one hour before closing.
**Café and shop: open 10:30. Gardens: November to March, open by winter walk only.

The Weir Garden

Swainshill, Hereford;
Herefordshire HR4 7QF

1959

Whatever the season, the natural beauty of this riverside garden is completely captivating. During spring, the ground beneath the ancient trees is carpeted with bulbs; then, in summer, a picnic by the river while watching the wildlife is irresistible. Autumn brings an abundance of seasonal produce in the walled garden. **Note**: sturdy footwear recommended.

Parking: on site.

Access: [WC] [♿]

Find out more: 01981 590509 or
theweir@nationaltrust.org.uk
nationaltrust.org.uk/weir

The Weir Garden		M	T	W	T	F	S	S
29 Jan–30 Sep*	10:30–4:30	M	·	·	T	F	S	S
1 Oct–22 Oct	10–4	·	·	·	·	·	S	S
23 Oct–30 Oct	10–4	M	T	W	T	F	S	S

*29 January to 18 February: closes 4; open daily during
school holidays.

Wenlock Edge

near Much Wenlock, Shropshire 1981

A ribbon of ancient woodland along
a narrow limestone escarpment, with
flower-rich grasslands, old quarries,
lime kilns and far-reaching views.
Note: nearest toilets in Much Wenlock.
For satnav use TF13 6AS for Much Wenlock
car park and TF13 6DQ for Presthope.
Some steep paths and steps.

Find out more: 01694 725000 or
wenlockedge@nationaltrust.org.uk
nationaltrust.org.uk/wenlock-edge

Wichenford Dovecote

Wichenford, Worcestershire WR6 6XY 1965

Small but striking 17th-century
half-timbered dovecote at Wichenford
Court. **Note**: no access to Wichenford
Court (privately owned). Sorry no toilet.

Find out more: 01527 821214 or
wichenforddovecote@nationaltrust.org.uk
nationaltrust.org.uk/wichenford-dovecote

Wightwick Manor and Gardens

Bridgnorth Road, Wolverhampton,
West Midlands WV6 8BN

1937 [icons]

A place where liberal dreams for the future
mix with a love for unfashionable art. The
Mander family's political ideals inspired
them to share their home and fill it with art
for the nation to enjoy. Their belief in social
activism, the right to roam, fairness for

their employees and confronting fascism combines with a home bursting with works by the greatest artists of the pre-Raphaelite and Arts and Crafts movements. A house of colour and comfort; a garden of yew and roses; and a gallery of De Morgan treasures – the legacy of one remarkable family and their friends.

Parking: entrance off A454.

Dog rating: ✿ **Standard** – Welcome on leads in garden.

Access: [icons]

Find out more: 01902 761400 or wightwickmanor@nationaltrust.org.uk
Wightwick Bank, Wolverhampton, West Midlands WV6 8EE
nationaltrust.org.uk/wightwick-manor

Wightwick Manor		M	T	W	T	F	S	S
1 Jan–27 Mar*	10–4	M	T	W	T	F	S	S
28 Mar–30 Oct**	10–5	M	T	W	T	F	S	S
31 Oct–31 Dec*	10–4	M	T	W	T	F	S	S

*House: closed 12/13, 19/20, 26/27 January and 9/10, 16/17 and 23/24 November for conservation. **House and Gallery: summer freeflow entry, 11 to 4. Winter freeflow entry, 11 to 3. Everything closed 25 and 26 December.

Wightwick Manor and Gardens in the West Midlands, above and below

Wilderhope Manor

Longville, Much Wenlock, Shropshire TF13 6EG 1936

Charming Elizabethan manor house with commanding views across a secluded valley with many original features inside and lovely walks outside. **Note**: Youth Hostel, access may be restricted. Open 2 to 4 on Sunday, 2 January to 27 March and 2 October to 18 December; also Wednesday and Sunday, 30 March to 25 September.

Find out more: 01694 771363 (Warden YHA) or wilderhope@nationaltrust.org.uk
nationaltrust.org.uk/wilderhope-manor

The grounds at
Quarry Bank, Cheshire

North West

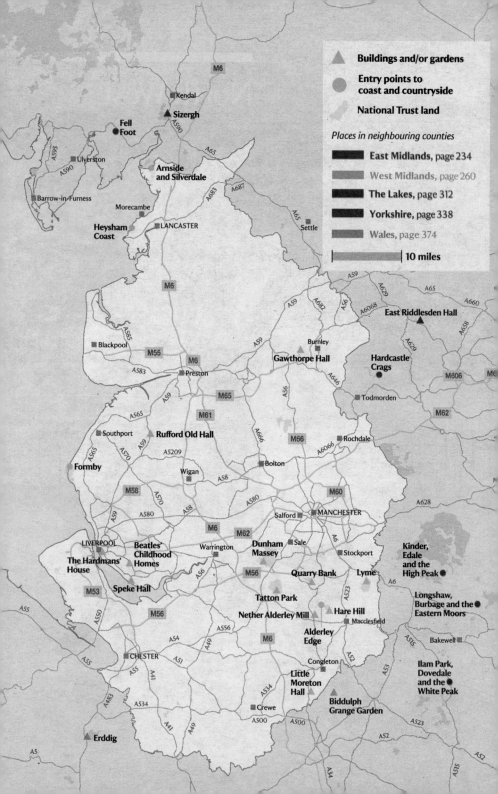

M6

Kendal

▲ Sizergh

Fell
Foot ●

Ulverston

Arnside
and Silverdale

Barrow-in-Furness

Morecambe

Heysham
Coast

LANCASTER

Settle

M6

Blackpool

M55

M6

Preston

A59

M65

Burnley

Gawthorpe Hall ▲

East Riddlesden Hall ▲

Hardcastle
Crags

Todmorden

M62

Southport

M61

Rufford Old Hall ▲

Formby ●

Wigan

Bolton

M66

Rochdale

M58

M60

MANCHESTER

Salford

A628

LIVERPOOL

Beatles'
Childhood
Homes

Warrington

Dunham
Massey

Sale

Stockport

Kinder,
Edale
and the
High Peak ●

The Hardmans'
House

M62

M6

M56

Quarry Bank

Lyme

Longshaw,
Burbage and the
Eastern Moors ●

M53

Speke Hall ▲

Tatton Park ▲

Hare Hill

Macclesfield

Bakewell

Ilam Park,
Dovedale
and the
White Peak ●

M56

Nether Alderley Mill

Alderley
Edge

CHESTER

Congleton

Little
Moreton
Hall

Crewe

Biddulph
Grange Garden

Erddig ▲

Alderley Edge and Cheshire Countryside, Cheshire:
Kitty's Flash at Thurstaston Common

Alderley Edge and Cheshire Countryside

Nether Alderley, near Macclesfield, Cheshire

1946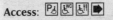

The dramatic red sandstone escarpment of Alderley Edge has far-reaching views over the Cheshire Plain and towards the Peak District. There are plenty of paths to follow through open pasture and woodland. It's a Site of Special Scientific Interest because of its geology and history of copper mining dating back to the Bronze Age, and is also known for its wizard myth, which inspired the novel *The Weirdstone of Brisingamen*. There's more Cheshire countryside to explore: Bickerton, Bulkeley and Helsby Hills on the Sandstone Ridge, Thurstaston Common on the Wirral, and The Cloud and Mow Cop on the Staffordshire border. **Note**: toilets at Alderley Edge car park only.

Satnav: use SK10 4UB for Alderley Edge; ST7 3PA for Mow Cop; SY14 8LN for Bickerton. **Parking**: at Alderley Edge, Mow Cop ST7 3PA and Bickerton SY14 8LN (plus roadside elsewhere).

Dog rating: ❀ **Standard** – Welcome under close control; on leads near livestock and ground-nesting birds.

Access:

Find out more: 01625 584412 or alderleyedge@nationaltrust.org.uk
nationaltrust.org.uk/alderley-edge

Alderley Edge
Alderley Edge car park: open daily, 8 to 5 (28 March to 30 October, closes 8).

A young naturalist gets close to nature at Alderley Edge and Cheshire Countryside

Arnside and Silverdale

near Arnside, Cumbria

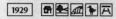 1929

Looking across the River Kent Estuary at Arnside and Silverdale in Cumbria

This wildlife-rich coastal landscape of grassland, woodland, meadows and rugged limestone pavement has miles of footpaths to explore, with views over Morecambe Bay. Arnside Knott and Eaves Wood are home to butterflies and wild flowers, while Jack Scout's cliffs are perfect for watching the sunset or spotting passing migrant birds.

Satnav: use LA5 0BP for Arnside Knott; LA5 0UG for Eaves Wood (Silverdale), both nearby. **Parking**: at Arnside Knott (signposted from Arnside Promenade) and Eaves Wood, Silverdale. Also in Silverdale village (not National Trust).

Dog rating: 🐾 🐾 **Good** – Welcome under close control (on leads near livestock).

Find out more: 01524 701178 or arnsidesilverdale@nationaltrust.org.uk
nationaltrust.org.uk/arnside-and-silverdale

The Beatles' Childhood Homes

Woolton and Allerton, Liverpool

2002

Explore Mendips and 20 Forthlin Road, the childhood homes of John Lennon and Paul McCartney and where The Beatles met, composed and rehearsed many of their earliest songs. You can walk through the back door into the kitchen and imagine John's Aunt Mimi cooking him his tea, or stand in the spot where Lennon and McCartney composed 'I Saw Her Standing There'. This is the opportunity to take a fascinating trip down memory lane in these two atmospheric houses, so typical of Liverpool life in the 1950s. **Note**: handbags, cameras and recording equipment must be left in secure facilities at both houses.

The Beatles' Childhood Homes, Liverpool: Mendips, opposite and right, and 20 Forthlin Road, above

Parking: parking available at Speke Hall for tours departing from there. Check website for information about parking at Liverpool South Parkway railway station.

Access: 🏷️ 🔊 💻 🚹 ⊡ 🅿️ ♿

Find out more: 0151 427 7231 (Speke Hall) or thebeatleshomes@nationaltrust.org.uk
nationaltrust.org.uk/beatles

Beatles' Childhood Homes		M	T	W	T	F	S	S
2 Mar–27 Nov	Tour	·	·	**W**	**T**	**F**	**S**	**S**

Tour times and departure points vary (booking essential).

Dunham Massey

Altrincham, Greater Manchester WA14 4SJ

1976 🏠🐕❄🛍☕🛍🖼🚶

Tucked away south of urban Manchester, Dunham Massey is a green haven – a place to meet, walk and escape. You can take a gentle stroll through the deer park and gardens, home to wildlife and ancient trees. Among the seasonal highlights in the gardens are snowdrops, bluebells, tulips, roses and one of the largest winter gardens in the UK. Explore inside the historic buildings for stories and collections amassed over 300 years. The surrounding canals and footpaths make exploring the 1,200 hectares (3,000 acres) of rolling farmland easy all year round. Treat yourself to a coffee and cake in one of the cafés and take home something to remember your day when you visit the shop.

Dunham Massey, Greater Manchester: flowers in the Winter Garden

The green haven of Dunham Massey, left and above, offers so much for children

Parking: on site.

Dog rating: 🐾 🐾 **Good** – Welcome on short leads in gardens (after midday) and park (assistance dogs only in historic buildings).

Access: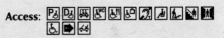

Find out more: 0161 942 3989 (Infoline). 0161 941 1025 or dunhammassey@nationaltrust.org.uk
nationaltrust.org.uk/dunham-massey

Dunham Massey		M	T	W	T	F	S	S
Deer park, gardens, café, restaurant and shop								
1 Jan–11 Feb*	9:30–4**	M	T	W	T	F	S	S
12 Feb–30 Oct	9:30–5**	M	T	W	T	F	S	S
31 Oct–31 Dec*	9:30–4**	M	T	W	T	F	S	S
House and historic buildings†								
14 Mar–30 Oct	12–4	M	T	W	.	.	S	S

*Everything closed 27 January, 9 November and 25 December. Gardens: closed 6 January.
**Gardens: open 10; close at dusk if earlier; last entry 45 minutes before closing; close 3:30 on 'Christmas at Dunham' trail nights (November/December/January). Restaurant: open 10; closes two hours earlier.
†Offer may vary between weekdays and weekends.

Formby

near Formby, Liverpool

1967 ▣ ▣ ▣ ▣ ▣ ▣

Formby is a much-loved coastal nature haven for wildlife and people. Discover some of Europe's best sand-dune habitats, where many rare species thrive, including natterjack toads. Rich in history, you can catch glimpses of the past, with prehistoric footprints and shipwrecks to discover and walks through what were once acres of asparagus fields. Formby's sweeping pinewoods are also home to the iconic red squirrel. Sunny days and holidays can be busy, so you may decide you'll enjoy your visit more on a quieter day. The beach at Lifeboat Road is supervised by lifeguards during summer weekends and holidays. **Note**: toilets open when car parks are staffed.

Satnav: use L37 1LJ for Victoria Road car park; L37 2EB for Lifeboat Road. **Parking**: on site (long traffic queues in summer).

Enjoying the dunes near Formby, Liverpool, below, and exploring an accessible path, above

Dog rating: ✿ **Standard** – Welcome on leads on Squirrel Walk and under close control elsewhere.

Access: ▣ ▣ ▣ ▣ ▣ ▣

Find out more: 01704 878591 or formby@nationaltrust.org.uk
nationaltrust.org.uk/formby

Formby

Car park: open daily, 9 to 5 (October to December, closes 4). Closed 25 December.

Gawthorpe Hall

near Burnley, Lancashire

 1972

Gawthorpe Hall in Lancashire

This Elizabethan house, in the heart of urban Lancashire, has extravagant 19th-century interiors by Sir Charles Barry (known for his role in rebuilding the Houses of Parliament). The Hall displays textiles from the Gawthorpe Textile Collection, including needlework, lace and embroidery. Outside, you can enjoy the garden and woodland walks. **Note**: cared for in partnership with Lancashire County Council.

Satnav: use BB12 8SD then follow brown signs. **Parking**: 150 yards, narrow access road (passing places).

Dog rating: ❧ **Standard** – Welcome under close control in grounds.

Access: [icons]

Find out more: 01282 771004 or gawthorpehall@nationaltrust.org.uk
Burnley Road, Padiham, near Burnley, Lancashire BB12 8UA
nationaltrust.org.uk/gawthorpe

Gawthorpe Hall	
Grounds	
Open every day all year	8–7

Hall: opening arrangements not confirmed at time of print, please check before visiting; last entry 45 minutes before closing.

The Hardmans' House

59 Rodney Street, Liverpool, Merseyside L1 9ER

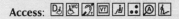 2003

Discover Liverpool's best-kept secret and step inside a true time capsule – the home and studio of a 1950s society photographer. The handsome Georgian house, both glamorous workplace and modest home for Edward Chambré Hardman and his talented wife Margaret, is packed with vintage treasures and fascinating photography. **Note**: entrance on Pilgrim Street at rear of property.

Parking: none on site. Car parks at Anglican Cathedral and Slater Street, not National Trust (charge including members).

Access: [icons]

Find out more: 0151 709 6261 or thehardmanshouse@nationaltrust.org.uk
nationaltrust.org.uk/hardmans

The Hardmans' House

Opening arrangements not confirmed at time of print, please check before visiting.

The Hardmans' House, Merseyside, is a time capsule of the 1950s

Hare Hill

Over Alderley, Macclesfield,
Cheshire SK10 4PY

1978 ⚙🏛🎎🏕🏹

Hare Hill is a place to refresh the senses as well as the soul. Surrounded by farmland, this wooded garden is full of twists, turns and surprises, hidden paths and ponds. At its heart is the walled garden with its white flowering borders, which offers an oasis of tranquillity.

Satnav: postcode takes you 109 yards west of car park. **Parking**: on site.

Access: 🅿🚻♿➡

Find out more: 01625 829973 or harehill@nationaltrust.org.uk
nationaltrust.org.uk/hare-hill

Hare Hill		M	T	W	T	F	S	S
19 Feb–30 Oct*	10:30–5			W	T	F	S	S

*Also open on Bank Holiday Mondays 18 April, 2 May and 29 August.

Heysham Coast

Heysham, near Morecambe,
Lancashire 1996

Sandstone headland with a scenic walk through grassland and woodland, passing a ruined Saxon chapel and unusual rock-cut graves. **Note**: nearest facilities in village (not National Trust); park in the main village car park. For satnav use LA3 2RW.

Find out more: 01524 701178 or heysham@nationaltrust.org.uk
nationaltrust.org.uk/heysham-coast

Little Moreton Hall

Congleton, Cheshire CW12 4SD

1938 🏛🎎🎎♿🍴🏕🏹

As you cross the moat into this Tudor fantasy you leave the chaos of modern life behind. Built to impress by craftsmen more than 500 years ago, the Hall has a unique quirky charm and homely feel. With its crooked walls and uneven floors, it seems so resilient yet still so fragile. Outside there's a knot garden and borders with herbs and vegetables used by the Tudors. You can step back in time and reflect on the

Built to impress more than 500 years ago, Little Moreton Hall in Cheshire is a Tudor fantasy, with unique quirky charm

ups and downs of life at Little Moreton Hall, a remarkable survivor with an inspiring story to tell.

Parking: 100 yards.

Access: 🅿️ ♿ 🚻 🔊 📷 VT ♿ ⠿ Ⓐ 🦽 ♿ ➡️

Find out more: 01260 272018 or littlemoretonhall@nationaltrust.org.uk
nationaltrust.org.uk/little-moreton-hall

Little Moreton Hall		M	T	W	T	F	S	S
16 Feb–30 Oct*	11–5**		·	**W**	**T**	**F**	**S**	**S**

*Open Bank Holiday Mondays and daily during school holidays: 21 to 27 February, 4 to 24 April, 30 May to 5 June, 25 July to 4 September and 24 to 30 October.
**Upper floors may close early if light levels are poor.

Lyme

Disley, Stockport, Cheshire SK12 2NR

1947 🏛️ 👀 ❄️ 🌿 ☕ 🛍️ 🏠 🎭 🚶

If you imagine a classic English country house, you're probably picturing somewhere just like Lyme. The house sits in 570 hectares (1,400 acres) of moorland and deer park, with views across Manchester and Cheshire. Home to the Legh family for over 550 years, the interiors tell the story of centuries of change up to and beyond its Regency heyday, when Thomas Legh created the house and garden you see today. You may recognise Lyme as 'Pemberley' from the BBC's *Pride and Prejudice*, starring Colin Firth. Lyme's ever-changing gardens, with its lake, Orangery and Rose Garden, are an ideal place to unwind. Explore the diverse scenery of the park on its many footpaths, including links to the Gritstone Trail.

Lyme in Cheshire: a Highland cow on the moor by Lantern Wood

Lyme: the imposing mansion seen from across the Reflection Lake

Download the app to get opening details on your phone – scan the QR code on page 3

The Library at Lyme: a classic
English country house

Parking: 200 yards.

Dog rating: 🐾 🐾 **Good** – Welcome under
close control (on leads near livestock,
vehicles and in the garden) with further
seasonal restrictions.

Access: [icons]

Find out more: 01663 762023 or
lyme@nationaltrust.org.uk
nationaltrust.org.uk/lyme

Lyme		M	T	W	T	F	S	S
House								
12 Feb–30 Oct	11–5*	M	T		T	F	S	S
3 Dec–24 Dec**	11–4*	M				F	S	S
Garden, cafés and shops†								
1 Jan–11 Feb	10:30–3:30††	M	T	W	T		S	S
12 Feb–29 Oct	10:30–5††	M	T	W	T	F	S	S
30 Oct–31 Dec	10:30–3:30††	M	T	W	T	F	S	S
Estate								
1 Jan–26 Mar	8:30–5¹	M	T	W	T	F	S	S
27 Mar–29 Oct	8:30–8¹	M	T	W	T	F	S	S
30 Oct–31 Dec	8:30–5¹	M	T	W	T	F	S	S

*House: last entry one hour before closing. **Parts of house
open for Christmas. †At least one café and shop is open
each day (please check on arrival). Timber Yard Café opens
at 10 daily. ††Cafés and shops open 11 to 4. ¹Gates are
locked at closing time. Everything closed 25 December.

Congleton Road, Nether Alderley,
Macclesfield, Cheshire SK10 4TW

1950 [icons]

Hidden under the long sloping roof of
this medieval building is a fully restored,
working corn mill. Learn about the life
of a miller and spot centuries-old
graffiti, then watch the waterwheels
turn, powering the huge millstones that
grind the flour. **Note**: booked tours
only. Uneven floor, steep stairs and
low ceilings. Sorry no toilet.

Parking: limited.

Access: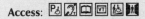

Find out more: 01625 527468 or
netheralderleymill@nationaltrust.org.uk
nationaltrust.org.uk/nether-alderley-mill

Nether Alderley Mill
Occasional opening by booked guided tour only,
please check before visiting.

**Medieval Nether Alderley Mill in Cheshire
is fully restored and operating**

Quarry Bank

Styal, Wilmslow, Cheshire SK9 4LA

1939 | 🏛️ 🦇 ❀ ⚔️ ☕ 🛍️ 🏠 🎋 🕴️

Standing in the gardens, you can almost feel the tranquillity of the river valley giving way to the clatter and bustle of a giant cotton mill as it led the way into the Industrial Revolution. The people here lived during a time of great change, from the mill-owning Greg family in Quarry Bank House, to the workers living in Styal village and the Apprentice House. Discover what life was like for the men, women and children toiling long hours in the heat of the mill, where you can still see working historic machinery in action. The very different lives led by the mill owners becomes apparent when you walk through their estate, picturesque gardens and elegant family home.

Parking: on site. Two electric vehicle charging points.

Quarry Bank in Cheshire, clockwise from above: the 18th-century water-powered cotton mill, Apprentice House and the historic looms

Dog rating: 🐾 🐾 **Good** – Welcome under close control on estate. On leads in garden, mill yard and meadow.

Access: ♿ 🚌 🚻 🔄 ⬆ 👁 ♿ ⬆ 👫
♿ ➡ ♿

Find out more: 01625 527468 or
quarrybank@nationaltrust.org.uk
nationaltrust.org.uk/quarry-bank

Quarry Bank		M	T	W	T	F	S	S
8 Jan–18 Feb	10:30–4*	·	·	W	T	F	S	S
19 Feb–30 Oct	10:30–5*	M	T	W	T	F	S	S
2 Nov–18 Dec	10:30–4*	·	·	W	T	F	S	S
19 Dec–31 Dec**	10:30–4*	M	T	W	T	F	S	S

Also open 1 to 3 January. *Apprentice House, Quarry Bank
House and Worker's Cottage: opening times may vary.
Some buildings open by guided tour only.
**Closed 24 and 25 December.

A moment of quiet reflection at Rufford Old Hall in Lancashire, above, and discovering the garden, below

Rufford Old Hall

200 Liverpool Road, Rufford, near Ormskirk, Lancashire L40 1SG

1936

This black-and-white Tudor building, with its contrasting mellow red-brick Jacobean wing, hunkers in the low-lying mosslands of south-west Lancashire. More than 500 years old, this family home has many stories to tell about the intriguing people who used to live here, as well as a Great Hall that might make your jaw drop! Children can get closer to nature and you can unwind in the Victorian-style garden and grounds, with their colourful seasonal displays – from carpets of bluebells in spring, to golden leaves in autumn.

Parking: on site.

Dog rating: ❖ **Standard** – Welcome on leads in the courtyard and woodland.

Access:

Find out more: 01704 821254 or ruffordoldhall@nationaltrust.org.uk
nationaltrust.org.uk/rufford-old-hall

Rufford Old Hall		M	T	W	T	F	S	S
11 Feb–27 Mar	10:30–3:30					F	S	S
28 Mar–30 Oct	10:30–4:30	M	T			F	S	S
4 Nov–18 Dec	10:30–3:30					F	S	S

House opens 11. Car park shuts 30 minutes after closing.

Speke Hall

Speke, Liverpool L24 1XD

1944

Almost 500 years ago, the Norris family replaced a medieval manor house on the banks of the River Mersey with the very latest in Tudor architecture. The iconic black-and-white Hall has seen centuries of turbulent history but was sympathetically restored in Victorian times as a cosy home. Surrounded by tranquil gardens and semi-ancient woodland, it's a slice of the past in the urban surroundings of Liverpool. Drive through the gates and leave the 21st century behind as you enter a peaceful world where you can be as restful or as active as you choose. The grounds are full of things to discover, from spring carpets of daffodils and bluebells, to natural woodland play trails.

Parking: on site.

Dog rating: 🐾 🐾 **Good** – Welcome on leads in outdoor areas (except Moat Garden, Kitchen Garden, play areas and Childe of Hale trail).

Now a place for family fun, Speke Hall in Liverpool has seen turbulent times over its 500-year-old history

Iconic black-and-white Tudor Speke Hall, above, offers something fascinating at every turn, left

Access: 🅿♿🚌♿🚻♿📷📖♿📷♿ ♿➡♿

Find out more: 0151 427 7231 or spekehall@nationaltrust.org.uk
nationaltrust.org.uk/speke-hall

Speke Hall		M	T	W	T	F	S	S
House*								
9 Mar–30 Oct	12:30–5	·	·	**W**	**T**	**F**	**S**	**S**
25 Nov–11 Dec	12:30–4	·	·	·	·	**F**	**S**	**S**
Gardens, grounds and restaurant								
1 Jan–8 Mar	10:30–4**	**M**	**T**	**W**	**T**	**F**	**S**	**S**
9 Mar–30 Oct	10:30–5**	**M**	**T**	**W**	**T**	**F**	**S**	**S**
31 Oct–31 Dec†	10:30–4**	**M**	**T**	**W**	**T**	**F**	**S**	**S**

*House open Bank Holidays. **Restaurant closes 30 minutes earlier. †Everything closed 24 to 26 December.

Tatton Park

Knutsford, Cheshire

| 1960 |

This grand country estate has sweeping landscapes and 400 hectares (1,000 acres) of parkland, where deer freely wander. The fragrant, formal gardens, developed over 300 years, take you around the world – a highlight being the Japanese Garden's symbolic harmony with nature. Nestled in this historic landscape, the 18th-century mansion displays the well-travelled Egerton family's treasured collections. In a household inspired by innovation, the servants' quarters reveal how this influenced daily duties. Once at the heart of this complete estate, the working farm brings to life a 'field to fork' story, through 'bygone' farm workers, rare-breed animals and seasonal demonstrations. **Note**: managed and financed by Cheshire East Council on behalf of the National Trust.

Satnav: use WA16 6SG. **Parking**: on site. Parkland vehicle entry charges apply (including members).

Dog rating: ❧ **Standard** – Welcome on leads within the farm and under close control in the parkland.

Access: ♿ symbols

Find out more: 01625 374400 or tatton@cheshireeast.gov.uk
Knutsford, Cheshire WA16 6QN
nationaltrust.org.uk/tatton-park

Tatton Park		M	T	W	T	F	S	S
Mansion*								
26 Mar–2 Oct	1–5			W	T	F	S	S
5 Oct–30 Oct	12–4			W	T	F	S	S
Parkland, gardens and restaurants								
1 Jan–27 Mar	10–4**		T	W	T	F	S	S
28 Mar–30 Oct†	10–6**	M	T	W	T	F	S	S
1 Nov–31 Dec	10–4**		T	W	T	F	S	S
Farm††								
1 Jan–27 Mar	11–4						S	S
29 Mar–30 Oct	11–4		T	W	T	F	S	S
5 Nov–24 Dec	11–4						S	S
Shops								
1 Jan–25 Mar	12–4		T	W	T	F	S	S
26 Mar–30 Oct	11–5	M	T	W	T	F	S	S
1 Nov–31 Dec	12–4		T	W	T	F	S	S

*Open Bank Holiday Mondays and for Christmas events.
**Parkland: closes one hour later. †Restaurants: close 5.
††Also open 21 to 25 February, Bank Holiday Mondays and 24 October (closed during RHS Flower Show).
Old Hall: special opening times/charges apply. Mansion, farm, gardens, parkland: last entry one hour before closing (farm entry charges apply, including members). Opening arrangements may be subject to change, please check before visiting. Everything closed 25 December.

The Japanese Garden at Tatton Park in Cheshire, left, and deer in the parkland, below

Discovering Elterwater, in the valley
of Great Langdale. Sticklebarn and
The Langdales, Cumbria

The Lakes

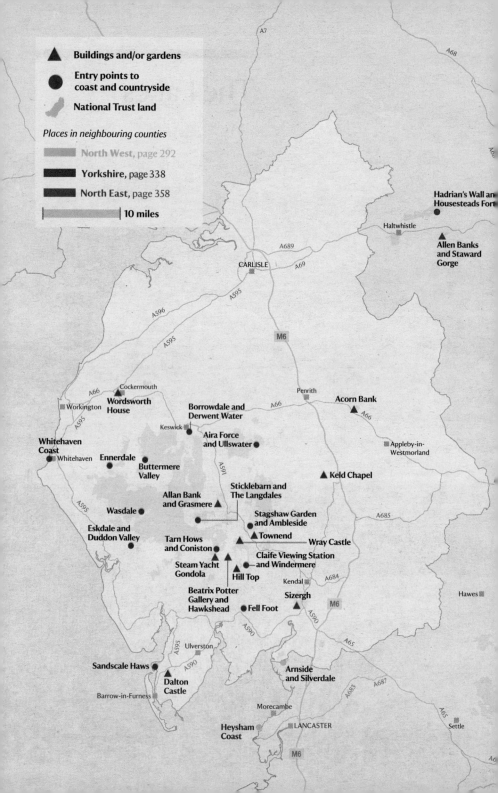

Buildings and/or gardens

Entry points to coast and countryside

National Trust land

Places in neighbouring counties

North West, page 292

Yorkshire, page 338

North East, page 358

10 miles

A7

A68

Hadrian's Wall and
Housesteads Fort

Haltwhistle

Allen Banks
and Staward
Gorge

A689

CARLISLE

A69

A596

A595

M6

A595

Cockermouth

Penrith

A66

Acorn Bank

Workington

Wordsworth
House

Keswick

Borrowdale and
Derwent Water

A66

Appleby-in-
Westmorland

Whitehaven
Coast

Aira Force
and Ullswater

Whitehaven

Ennerdale

Buttermere
Valley

A591

Keld Chapel

Wasdale

Allan Bank
and Grasmere

Sticklebarn and
The Langdales

A685

Eskdale and
Duddon Valley

Tarn Hows
and Coniston

Stagshaw Garden
and Ambleside

Townend

Wray Castle

Steam Yacht
Gondola

Claife Viewing Station
and Windermere

Hill Top

Kendal

A684

Hawes

Beatrix Potter
Gallery and
Hawkshead

Fell Foot

Sizergh

M6

Sandscale Haws

Ulverston

A590

Arnside
and Silverdale

A65

A687

Dalton
Castle

A590

Barrow-in-Furness

Morecambe

A683

A65

Settle

Heysham
Coast

LANCASTER

M6

Acorn Bank

Temple Sowerby, near Penrith,
Cumbria CA10 1SP

1950

Close to Penrith and with views to the Lake
District and Howgill Fells, Acorn Bank is a
tranquil haven in the heart of the Eden
Valley. Established by the Knights Templar
around the 13th century, people have lived
and worked here for more than 800 years.
Today the walled gardens shelter the largest
medicinal herb garden in the National
Trust's care, colourful and varied
herbaceous borders, a lily-filled pond and
traditional orchards carpeted with spring
daffodils. Woodland walks reveal a half-
hidden story of gypsum mining, a working
19th-century watermill and a wildlife-rich
estate. **Note**: house partially open,
including second-hand bookshop. Paths
may close following wet weather.

Parking: on site.

Dog rating: ❀ **Standard** – Welcome in the
woodland and wider estate.

Access:

Find out more: 017683 61893 or
acornbank@nationaltrust.org.uk
nationaltrust.org.uk/acorn-bank

Acorn Bank		M	T	W	T	F	S	S
Garden and parkland*								
14 Mar–4 Sep	10:30–5	M	T	W	T	F	S	S
5 Sep–30 Oct	10:30–5	M	·	·	T	F	S	S
Watermill**								
19 Mar–30 Oct	11–3	·	·	·	·	·	S	S

*Car park open as garden and parkland. House: partially
open. **Watermill: also open Bank Holidays, March to
October. Café: open most days.

The sandstone manor house at Acorn Bank in Cumbria, below, sits within a wildlife-rich estate, above

Aira Force and Ullswater, Cumbria:
looking across Ullswater at dawn

Aira Force and Ullswater

near Watermillock, Penrith, Cumbria

1906

An 18th-century pleasure ground, Aira
Force was the backdrop for William
Wordsworth's poem 'Somnambulist' – a
Gothic tale of love and tragedy. There are
so many woodland trails to discover in this
landscape of contrasts. Quiet glades give
way to dramatic waterfalls, with Aira Beck
thundering down a 65-foot drop past ferns
and rocks. If you walk to the summit of
Gowbarrow, you will be rewarded with
panoramic views over Ullswater. Starting
your day in Glenridding, arriving at Aira
Force by boat, then strolling back along the
lakeshore, allows you to take in the
wonderful Ullswater Valley sights.
Note: boat rides on Ullswater operated by
Ullswater 'Steamers', not National Trust.

Satnav: use CA11 0JS for Aira Force;
CA11 0NQ for Glencoyne Bay. **Parking**: at
Aira Force, Aira Force High Cascades, Aira
Force Park Brow and Glencoyne Bay.

Dog rating: 🐾 🐾 **Good** – Welcome
on leads.

Access:

Find out more: 017684 82067 or
ullswater@nationaltrust.org.uk
nationaltrust.org.uk/aira-force

Aira Force and Ullswater		M	T	W	T	F	S	S
Tea-room								
1 Jan–28 Feb	10:30–3:30	M	T	W	T	F	S	S
1 Mar–31 Oct	10–5	M	T	W	T	F	S	S
1 Nov–31 Dec*	10:30–3:30	M	T	W	T	F	S	S

*Closed 25 December. Opening times may vary
during winter season.

**One of the many woodland trails
at Aira Force and Ullswater**

Allan Bank and Grasmere

near Ambleside, Cumbria

1920 🏠🏡🎴🏛🚪

Views of Grasmere lake and the surrounding fells can be enjoyed from the large bay windows and woodland grounds of this relaxed house. Once home to National Trust co-founder Canon Rawnsley, Allan Bank is now only partially decorated. Red squirrels play in the grounds, there are picnic spots and plenty of places for children to run free. Secret hideaways, such as the Victorian viewing tunnel, create an air of mystery. Lakeshore strolls and adventurous fell-top rambles can be started from nearby Grasmere village. **Note**: follow directions on foot from The Inn at Grasmere.

Satnav: use LA22 9TA for nearest car park.
Parking: nearest in village, not National Trust (charge including members).

Dog rating: 🐾 🐾 **Good** – Welcome on leads.

Access: 🅿️ 🚾 🎱 ♿

Find out more: 015394 35143 or
allanbank@nationaltrust.org.uk
near Ambleside, Cumbria LA22 9QB
nationaltrust.org.uk/allan-bank

Allan Bank and Grasmere		M	T	W	T	F	S	S
Allan Bank								
13 Feb–30 Mar*	11–3:30		T	W				S
3 Apr–30 Oct*	10–4:30		T	W				S
1 Nov–27 Nov	11–3:30		T	W				S
2 Dec–18 Dec	11–3:30					F	S	S
27 Dec–31 Dec	11–3:30		T	W	T	F	S	

Open Bank Holiday Mondays. *Also open Thursdays and Saturdays during school holidays: 12 to 20 February, 2 to 24 April, 31 May to 5 June, 19 July to 4 September and 18 to 30 October.

Allan Bank and Grasmere, Cumbria, above and below: saved from fire, the house is partially furnished

Beatrix Potter Gallery and Hawkshead

Main Street, Hawkshead,
Cumbria LA22 0NS

1947

Take in changing exhibitions of Beatrix Potter's original artwork, illustrations and letters, within the 17th-century building which once served as the office of Beatrix's solicitor husband. Each year you can discover new stories about this inspiring woman and her life. If you've ever been charmed by Beatrix's endearing characters, you can take a closer look at some of her miniature masterpieces and enjoy a unique opportunity to see the delicate watercolours in the surroundings that inspired them. Quaint Hawkshead village makes the perfect base for exploring the countryside much-loved by Beatrix and

Beatrix Potter Gallery and Hawkshead in Cumbria: original artwork and letters to discover

Beatrix Potter Gallery, above, and Hawkshead village, below

many other famous poets, writers and artists. **Note**: nearest toilets 300 yards in main village car park (not National Trust).

Parking: 300 yards, not National Trust (charge including members).

Access:

Find out more: 015394 36355 (Gallery) or beatrixpottergallery@nationaltrust.org.uk **nationaltrust.org.uk/beatrix-potter-gallery**

Beatrix Potter Gallery		M	T	W	T	F	S	S
Gallery								
27 Mar–14 Jul	10:30–4	M	T	W	T	.	.	S
16 Jul–4 Sep	10–4	M	T	W	T	.	S	S
5 Sep–30 Oct	10:30–4	M	T	W	T	.	.	S

Entry by timed ticket, booking advisable (places limited). Open 10 to 4:30 and Saturdays in Easter holidays, May and October half term. Open Friday 3 June (Bank Holiday).

Borrowdale and Derwent Water

near Keswick, Cumbria

From the lakeshore at Crow Park, a few minutes' walk from the centre of the busy Lakeland town of Keswick, there are views across Derwent Water and its islands to the high central fells, framed by Cat Bells and Walla Crag. Castle Crag sits between the lake and upper Borrowdale, where scenic drives, traditional hamlets and waymarked walks await. Nine car parks in the valley make it easy to access some of Lakeland's most photographed views and walks.

During the summer Seatoller and Bowder Stone offer the best chance of a parking spot. October brings rich auburns and golden evening light to Ashness Bridge and Surprise View, and from Kettlewell the autumn colours are reflected in the lake.

Borrowdale and Derwent Water, Cumbria: the view from the lakeshore, below, and rock hopping, above

Borrowdale and Derwent Water in autumn, above, and the tranquil lakeshore, below

Satnav: use CA12 5UP for Great Wood car park. **Parking**: at Great Wood (CA12 5UP), Ashness Bridge (CA12 5UN), Surprise View (CA12 5UU), Watendlath (CA12 5UW), Kettlewell (CA12 5UN), Bowder Stone (CA12 5XA), Rosthwaite (CA12 5XB), Seatoller (CA12 5XN) and Honister Pass (CA12 5XN).

Dog rating: 🐾 **Standard** – Welcome, under close control at lambing time.

Access: 🚾 ➡️

Find out more: 017687 74649 or borrowdale@nationaltrust.org.uk
nationaltrust.org.uk/borrowdale

Buttermere Valley

near Cockermouth, Cumbria

1935

Hiking in the Buttermere Valley, Cumbria

This dramatic valley encompasses the lakes of Buttermere, Crummock Water and Loweswater, all offering easy low-level lakeshore walks and access onto the high fells. Buttermere's 4½-mile round-the-lake path takes in shingle beaches, cascading waterfalls and a hand-cut Victorian tunnel, perfect for family adventures. Top tip: arrive early to get parking. **Note**: toilets at Buttermere village only (not National Trust).

Satnav: use CA13 9UZ for Buttermere; CA13 0RT for Crummock Water; CA13 0RU for Loweswater. **Parking**: at Honister Pass (CA12 5XN), just outside Buttermere village (CA13 9UZ), Lanthwaite Green (CA13 9UY), Crummock Water (CA13 0RT) and Maggie's Bridge (CA13 0RU) at Loweswater.

Dog rating: 🐾 **Standard** – Welcome, under close control at lambing time.

Access: ▶

Find out more: 01768 74649 or buttermere@nationaltrust.org.uk **nationaltrust.org.uk/buttermere**

Claife Viewing Station and Windermere West Shore

near Far Sawrey, Cumbria LA22 0LW

1962

Claife Viewing Station and Windermere West Shore in Cumbria

Perched on the tranquil west shore of Windermere, minutes from the Bowness ferry, Claife Viewing Station was built in the 1790s for the first tourists to the Lake District. Today, you can enjoy the same panoramic views of the lake from the platform, framed by coloured glass. At the café you can sit by a cosy fire or enjoy your food outside in the courtyard. There are

Watery fun at Windermere West Shore, above, and Claife Viewing Station, below

4 miles of lakeside paths leading towards Wray Castle for cycling or walking, or you could explore the landscape around Hill Top and Hawkshead that so inspired Beatrix Potter. **Note**: toilets at nearby Ferry House. Passenger boats operated by Windermere Lake Cruises; car ferry council-run.

Satnav: use LA22 0LP for Ash Landing; LA22 0LR for Harrowslack; LA22 0JH for Red Nab (all nearby). **Parking**: at Ash Landing and Harrowslack for Claife Viewing Station and Windermere west shore. Red Nab is further north along the lakeshore, close to Wray Castle.

Dog rating: 🐾 🐾 **Good** – Welcome under close control.

Access: 🅿️ ♿ ♿

Find out more: 015394 41456 or claife@nationaltrust.org.uk
nationaltrust.org.uk/claife-viewing-station

Claife Viewing Station and Windermere

Claife Viewing Station: open every day all year, dawn to dusk.

Dalton Castle

Market Place, Dalton-in-Furness, Cumbria LA15 8AX 1965

Standing proud in Dalton town centre, this impressive 14th-century tower was once the manorial courthouse of Furness Abbey. **Note**: opened on behalf of the National Trust by the Friends of Dalton Castle. Open Saturdays, 26 March to 24 September, 2 to 5.

Find out more: 015395 60951 or daltoncastle@nationaltrust.org.uk
nationaltrust.org.uk/dalton-castle

Ennerdale

Bowness Knott, Croasdale,
Ennerdale Bridge, Cumbria

 1927

Peaceful, yet dramatic, Ennerdale is
home to one of the UK's largest wildland
partnerships – Wild Ennerdale. A horseshoe
of rugged fells surrounds the wooded valley
where Galloway cattle roam free and the
untamed River Liza flows. The views widen
across Ennerdale Water, which is circled
by lakeshore paths and beaches.
Note: sorry no toilet.

Satnav: CA23 3AU for Bowness Knott;
CA23 3AS for Bleach Green.
Parking: at Bowness Knott and Bleach
Green (not National Trust).

Dog rating: 🐾 **Standard** – Welcome,
under close control near livestock.

Access: ➡

Find out more: 01768774649 or
ennerdale@nationaltrust.org.uk
nationaltrust.org.uk/ennerdale

**Ennerdale, Cumbria: tranquil Ennerdale Water
is surrounded by a horseshoe of rugged fells**

Eskdale and Duddon Valley

Eskdale, near Ravenglass; Duddon Valley,
near Broughton in Furness, Cumbria

 1926

Camping at Eskdale and Duddon Valley, Cumbria

Eskdale is a valley of contrasts.
Upper Eskdale leads to the high
mountains, including Scafell and Bowfell;
the valley floor has meandering riverside
and woodland paths, including the Eskdale
Trail, for walkers and cyclists. Across high
mountain passes lies the Duddon Valley,
with meadows, woodlands, mountains,
hill farms and rivers.

Parking: small car parks in some villages
(not National Trust).

Dog rating: 🐾 **Standard** – Welcome
under close control (please follow local
and seasonal guidance). On leads
around livestock.

Find out more: 01946726064 or
eskdaleandduddon@nationaltrust.org.uk
nationaltrust.org.uk/eskdale

Eskdale and Duddon Valley

Eskdale Campsite: for opening times and bookings
please visit nationaltrust.org.uk/lake-district-camping
or call 01539432733.

Fell Foot

Newby Bridge, Windermere, Cumbria

1948

Less than a 20-minute drive from the M6 at the most southern end of Windermere, Fell Foot is one of the few places where you can access England's largest lake. This family-friendly park is perfect for paddling, boat hire and swimming, whether you're a seasoned pro or a beginner, and state-of-the-art changing facilities at the Active Base offer a

Download the app to get opening details on your phone – scan the QR code on page 3

comfortable place to dry off after a day on the water. If you'd rather stay on land, relax on the lawn for a summer picnic with impressive mountain views, or stroll along the paths to the meadows and Pinetum – the park's collection of specimen trees. Three recently restored Gothic Revival boathouses uncover the park's rich history. **Note**: additional charge (including members) for Active Base, launch facilities and boat hire.

Satnav: use LA12 8NN. **Parking**: two large car parks on site.

Dog rating: 🐾 🐾 🐾 Best – Welcome in all areas on leads.

Fell Foot in Cumbria, this page and opposite, offers so many activities, both on and off the water, for all ages

Access:

Find out more: 015395 31273 or fellfoot@nationaltrust.org.uk
nationaltrust.org.uk/fell-foot

Fell Foot		M	T	W	T	F	S	S
Park and Active Base								
1 Jan–25 Mar	10–4*	M	T	W	T	F	S	S
26 Mar–30 Oct	10–5*	M	T	W	T	F	S	S
31 Oct–31 Dec**	10–4*	M	T	W	T	F	S	S
Boathouse Café								
1 Jan–9 Jan	10–3:30						S	S
10 Jan–25 Mar	10–3:30	M	T	W	T	F	S	S
26 Mar–30 Oct	10–5	M	T	W	T	F	S	S
31 Oct–31 Dec**	10–3:30	M	T	W	T	F	S	S

*Out of hours access available to Active Base members (additional charge for membership, please see website). Car park: open as Park and Active Base. **Everything closed 25 December. Site may close occasionally early in the year due to building work (please check before visiting).

Hill Top

Near Sawrey, Hawkshead, Ambleside,
Cumbria LA22 0LF

1944 🏠❄️📷

Beatrix Potter's beloved farmhouse
Hill Top was her sanctuary and a source of
inspiration for her much-loved children's
tales. Near Sawrey village and Beatrix's
garden path are home to landmarks and
scenes from her illustrations. Filled with her
personal possessions, including Lakeland
furniture and trophies for her prize-winning
Herdwick sheep, the house is a true
reminder of Beatrix's legacy. It remains
much as she left it when it came into the
Trust's care in 1944. Pick up something
exclusive from the Hill Top shop and enjoy
a coffee and piece of cake in the orchard
from the pop-up café.

Parking: limited and for visitors to
Hill Top only.

Dog rating: ❄️ **Standard** – Welcome
on leads in garden. Assistance dogs
only in house.

Access: 🅿️📷📖♿🚻♿👨‍🦽

**Hill Top in Cumbria: Beatrix Potter's
beloved farmhouse**

Find out more: 015394 36269 or hilltop@nationaltrust.org.uk
nationaltrust.org.uk/hill-top

Hill Top		M	T	W	T	F	S	S
House, garden and shop								
12 Feb–23 Mar	10–4	M	T	W	·	·	S	S
26 Mar–25 May	10–5*	M	T	W	·	·	S	S
28 May–4 Sep	10–5*	M	T	W	T	·	S	S
5 Sep–30 Oct	10–5*	M	T	W	·	·	S	S
Garden and shop								
5 Nov–18 Dec	10–3	·	·	·	·	·	S	S

House: entry by timed ticket, booking essential (places limited). Open daily during school holidays (excluding Christmas). *Garden and shop: 19 April to 30 October, open 10 to 4 on days when house closed.

Keld Chapel

Keld Lane, Shap, Cumbria CA10 3NW [1918]

Tucked away in east Cumbria, this rustic 16th-century stone chapel was once the chantry for Shap Abbey. **Note**: for satnav use CA10 3NW. Closed for conservation.

Find out more: 017683 61893 or keldchapel@nationaltrust.org.uk
nationaltrust.org.uk/keld-chapel

Sandscale Haws National Nature Reserve

near Barrow-in-Furness, Cumbria [1984]

This beach has wild, grass-covered dunes and Lakeland mountain views; it's the perfect habitat for rare wildlife, including natterjack toads. **Note**: for satnav use LA14 4QJ.

Find out more: 01524 701178 or sandscalehaws@nationaltrust.org.uk
nationaltrust.org.uk/sandscale-haws

Sizergh

Sizergh, near Kendal, Cumbria LA8 8DZ

1950 | 🏠🐾❀🎒🍵🏛🎍

Standing at the gateway to the National Park, this striking medieval manor is the perfect stop off on your Lake District adventure. Home to the Strickland family for more than 750 years, Sizergh is still lived in today and filled with thousands of items collected by 26 generations, including the internationally renowned Inlaid Chamber. The peaceful gardens have something for every season, from springtime daffodils in the Stumpery to vibrant autumnal acers in the Rock Garden. See what's ready to harvest in the Kitchen Garden, which has been producing vegetables since the 1750s. Choose from a variety of walks, all offering extensive views, through 647 hectares (1,600 acres) of countryside, including wetland, woodland and orchards – home to rare wildlife. **Note**: house may close occasionally for private events.

Garden for all seasons at Sizergh in Cumbria

There is so much to discover at medieval Sizergh, above and opposite, which is still a family home

Satnav: use LA8 8DZ – takes you to the Strickland Arms, then follow National Trust signs. **Parking**: 250 yards (cars and bikes only).

Dog rating: 🐾 🐾 **Good** – Welcome in the café, shop and wider estate on leads.

Access: 🅿️🐕♿🔠🧏📷📺🚶♿🚻
♿➡️♿

Find out more: 015395 60951 or sizergh@nationaltrust.org.uk
nationaltrust.org.uk/sizergh

Sizergh		M	T	W	T	F	S	S
House*								
26 Mar–30 Oct	12–3:30			W	T	F	S	S
Garden, café and shop**								
1 Jan–9 Jan	10–3:30						S	S
10 Jan–25 Mar	10–3:30	M	T	W	T	F	S	S
26 Mar–30 Oct	10–5	M	T	W	T	F	S	S
31 Oct–31 Dec	10–3:30	M	T	W	T	F	S	S
Estate†								
Open all year	Dawn–dusk	M	T	W	T	F	S	S

*House: also open 18 April, 2 May and 29 August.
**Garden: areas subject to closure. †Car park: open daily, 9 to 6. Everything closed 25 December.

Stagshaw Garden and Ambleside

near Windermere, Cumbria

Stagshaw Garden and Ambleside in Cumbria

Perched above Ambleside, this quiet, informal woodland garden is hidden from the hustle and bustle of the town below. Rambling paths and unusual combinations of shrubs, trees and plants give an enchanted feel. In spring it becomes a kaleidoscope of colour with daffodils, bluebells, azaleas and rhododendrons in full bloom. **Note**: Ambleside Roman Fort is owned by the National Trust and managed by English Heritage.

Satnav: use LA22 0HE for Stagshaw Garden and Skelghyll Woods; LA22 9AN for Bridge House. **Parking**: small car park at Stagshaw Garden. Several car parks in Ambleside, not National Trust (charge including members).

Dog rating: ❧ **Standard** – Welcome on leads.

Find out more: 015394 46402 or stagshawgarden@nationaltrust.org.uk
nationaltrust.org.uk/ambleside

Stagshaw Garden and Ambleside

Stagshaw Garden: open every day all year, dawn to dusk. Garden is at its best April to July.

Steam Yacht Gondola

Coniston Pier, Lake Road, Coniston, Cumbria LA21 8AN

A steam-powered yacht on Coniston Water, Steam Yacht Gondola was rebuilt by the National Trust based on the original 1859 version. With inspiration taken from a traditional Venetian 'Burchiello' boat, Gondola's elegant saloons and ornate decoration reflect the tastes of the Victorians. The open-sided engine-room allows passengers to see and hear steam power in action. The Coniston Fells provide an impressive backdrop to your cruise, with opportunities to alight at jetties around the lake. As you pass famous landmarks, the crew provide a commentary on Gondola's history on the lake and association with the famous *Swallows and Amazons*.
Note: cruises depart from Coniston Pier (subject to weather). Sorry no toilet on scheduled sailings.

Aboard Steam Yacht Gondola

Parking: at Coniston Pier, 50 yards, not National Trust (charge including members).

Dog rating: 🐾 **Standard** – Welcome in outside areas.

Access: 🅿️🚻♿️🔯♿️

Find out more: 015394 32733 or sygondola@nationaltrust.org.uk
nationaltrust.org.uk/gondola

Steam Yacht Gondola

Sailing 26 March to 31 October, subject to weather conditions. Booking essential (charge including members), check website for timetable. All sailings depart from Coniston Pier.

Sticklebarn and The Langdales

near Ambleside, Cumbria

1925 🏠🚶♿️🏕️

Sticklebarn and The Langdales in Cumbria: the pub offers a welcome respite to weary walkers

A striking U-shaped valley, Langdale was described by the leading English art critic John Ruskin as 'the loveliest rock scenery, chased with silver waterfalls that I have ever set foot or heart upon'. This outdoor playground offers miles of walking, cycling and climbing routes, from a high-level scramble on the Langdale Pikes to a low-level stroll around Blea Tarn. Below the peaks sits Sticklebarn, a National Trust-run pub serving food and drink that celebrate Cumbria's food heritage and local produce. An outdoor terrace and open fires offer the perfect place to share stories of adventures on the fells over a pint of Cumbrian ale.

The Langdales offer routes for serious hikers, above, as well as gentle walkers, below

Satnav: use LA22 9JU for Sticklebarn; LA22 9PG for Blea Tarn; LA22 9HP for Elterwater; LA22 9HJ for High Close Estate.
Parking: at Stickle Ghyll, Old Dungeon Ghyll, Blea Tarn, Elterwater village and High Close Estate.

Dog rating: 🐾 🐾 **Good** – Welcome on leads.

Access: 🅿️ ♿ 🚻 🍴 ♿ ♿

Find out more: 015394 37356 (Sticklebarn) or sticklebarn@nationaltrust.org.uk
nationaltrust.org.uk/sticklebarn

Sticklebarn and The Langdales		M	T	W	T	F	S	S
Sticklebarn								
1 Jan–9 Jan	11–6	M	T	W	T	F	S	S
24 Jan–28 Feb	11–6	M	T	W	T	F	S	S
1 Mar–31 Oct	11–9	M	T	W	T	F	S	S
1 Nov–31 Dec*	11–6	M	T	W	T	F	S	S
Great Langdale Campsite**								
Open all year		M	T	W	T	F	S	S

*Closed 24 and 25 December. **For detailed opening times and bookings please visit nationaltrust.org.uk/lake-district-camping or call 015394 32733.

Tarn Hows and Coniston

near Coniston, Cumbria

The circular walk at Tarn Hows and Coniston, Cumbria

An accessible walk for all the family whatever the weather, Tarn Hows showcases ever-changing scenery and views of the high fells. The circular 1¾-mile path through a 19th-century man-made landscape makes it a favourite with walkers of all abilities. Arrive early or late for a meditative moment with mountain views. **Note**: toilets in main car park. Mobility scooters free to hire (donations welcome). Livestock grazing.

Satnav: does not work, instead follow signs from B5285, Coniston or Hawkshead Hill. **Parking**: on site at Tarn Hows, also at Glen Mary nearby. Parking available in Coniston (not National Trust).

Dog rating: ❀ ❀ **Good** – Welcome on leads.

Access:

Find out more: 015394 41456 or tarnhows@nationaltrust.org.uk **nationaltrust.org.uk/tarn-hows**

Tarn Hows and Coniston

Hoathwaite Campsite: for opening times and bookings please visit nationaltrust.org.uk/lake-district-camping or call 015394 32733.

Townend

Troutbeck, Windermere, Cumbria LA23 1LB

1948

A cosy farmhouse near Windermere brimming with character. Home to the Browne family for 400 years, Townend is full of intricately carved furniture and rare books, including 44 that are the only remaining copies in the world. Warm yourself by the open fire and spend time in the cottage garden.

Parking: 300 yards.

Dog rating: ❀ **Standard** – Welcome in the garden only.

Access:

Find out more: 015394 32628 or townend@nationaltrust.org.uk **nationaltrust.org.uk/townend**

Townend

Opening arrangements not confirmed at time of print, please check before visiting.

The cottage-style garden at Townend in Cumbria

Wasdale

near Gosforth, Cumbria

1920 [icons]

Taking a welcome break to enjoy
the view from Great End in Wasdale

Wasdale sits below some of England's
highest mountains, creating ever-changing
reflections in Wastwater below. Great Gable
stands at the head of the valley with Scafell
Pike nearby. This is a remote mountain
landscape for hill-walking, climbing and
exploring. Towards the southern end of the
lake and Nether Wasdale, winding paths
weave through woodland and along the
water's edge, revealing a gentler aspect to
the valley. In the summer the valley can get
very busy and parking is limited. Planning
ahead will give you the best experience:
remember to check the weather forecast,
prepare well and enjoy your day.

Parking: at Lake Head CA20 1EX;
Overbeck CA20 1EX (limited);
Nether Wasdale CA20 1ET (limited).

Dog rating: ❀ **Standard** – Welcome under
close control and on leads around livestock
(please follow local and seasonal guidance).

Find out more: 019467 26064 or
wasdale@nationaltrust.org.uk
nationaltrust.org.uk/wasdale

Wasdale

Wasdale Campsite: open every day all year. For detailed
opening times and bookings please visit nationaltrust.org.uk/
lake-district-camping or call 015394 32733.

Nearing the summit of Brown Tounge
on Scafell Pike at Wasdale in Cumbria

Whitehaven Coast

Whitehaven, Cumbria 2008

Coast with a proud mining past. Enjoy
bracing clifftop walks to St Bees Head
from the sandstone Georgian harbour.
Note: sorry no toilet. For satnav use
CA28 9BG for clifftop car park and
CA28 7LY for Whitehaven Harbour.

Find out more: 017687 74649 or
whitehavencoast@nationaltrust.org.uk
nationaltrust.org.uk/whitehaven-coast

Wordsworth House and Garden

Main Street, Cockermouth,
Cumbria CA13 9RX

 1938

Wandering among the heritage fruit trees, flowers and vegetables of William Wordsworth's garden as the River Derwent flows by, it's easy to picture the wild child born here more than 250 years ago and imagine how his childhood home inspired a love of nature and a lifetime of creativity. Indoors, hands-on rooms, animations and audio offer a window into the Georgian world. Some days you may even spot costumed servants cooking in the kitchen, while they gossip and tell tales.

Parking: in town-centre car parks, none National Trust (charge including members). Please note long-stay car park signposted as coach park, 300 yards, Wakefield Road.

Access:

Find out more: 01900 820884 (Infoline). 01900 824805 or wordsworthhouse@nationaltrust.org.uk
nationaltrust.org.uk/wordsworth-house

Wordsworth House		M	T	W	T	F	S	S
2 Apr–6 Nov	10–4:30	M	T	W			S	S

House closes 4. Open Good Friday.

Wordsworth House and Garden, Cumbria: roses in June, left, and a chat in the sun, below

Wray Castle

Low Wray, Ambleside, Cumbria LA22 0JA

1929

In the 1840s a surgeon and an heiress from Liverpool began building a castle with panoramic Lake District views that would only ever have to defend itself from the Cumbrian weather. Last inhabited in the 1920s, and with the furniture and artwork long gone, the castle has had mixed use and first opened to visitors in 2011. A work in progress, we are continually learning more about the castle's history. Indoors is open to discover the church-like rooms. Outdoors, with the castle's turrets and towers providing the atmosphere, explore the grounds and enjoy walks along the shore of Windermere. **Note**: steep walk from jetty if arriving by boat.

Parking: restricted car parking. Please come by boat, bike or boot to avoid disappointment.

Cycling at Wray Castle, Cumbria, below, and looking up into the tower from the Entrance Hall, above

Dog rating: 🐾 **Standard** – Welcome on leads everywhere, excluding castle.

Access: 🅿️ 🅿️ ♿ ♿ 🔁 ♿ ♿

Find out more: 015394 33250 or wraycastle@nationaltrust.org.uk
nationaltrust.org.uk/wray-castle

Wray Castle		M	T	W	T	F	S	S
Castle*								
26 Mar–17 Jul	10:30–4	·	·	W	T	F	S	S
18 Jul–4 Sep	10:30–4	M	T	W	T	F	S	S
7 Sep–30 Oct	10:30–4	·	·	W	T	F	S	S
Grounds								
Open all year	9–6	M	T	W	T	F	S	S
Low Wray Campsite**								
28 Mar–30 Oct		M	T	W	T	F	S	S

*Castle: open daily in Easter holidays and May and October half term. Open Monday 2 May (Bank Holiday).
**For detailed opening times and bookings please visit nationaltrust.org.uk/lake-district-camping or call 015394 32733.

Autumn colours at Wray Castle

Having fun in the woodland play area at Nostell, West Yorkshire

Yorkshire

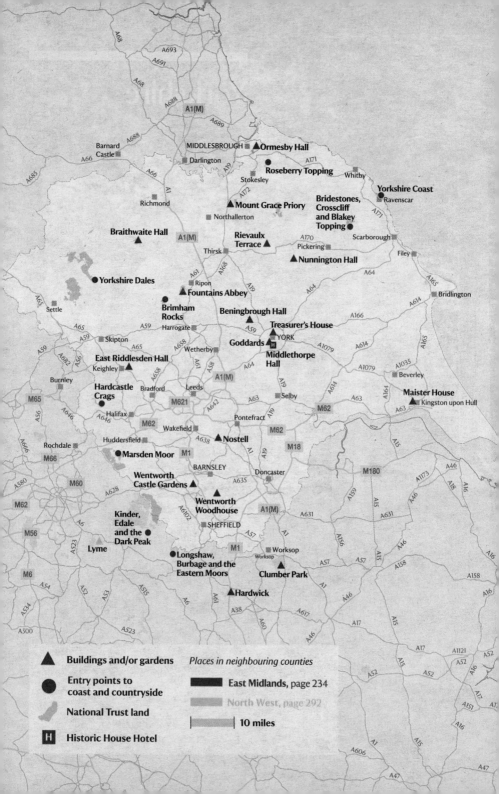

A68
A693
A691
A68
A688
A1(M)
A689
Barnard
Castle
A66
A688
A685
A66
A66
A1
MIDDLESBROUGH ▲**Ormesby Hall**
Darlington
A19
A171
●**Roseberry Topping**
Stokesley
Whitby
A172
Richmond
▲**Mount Grace Priory**
Bridestones,
Crossliff
and Blakey
Topping ●
Yorkshire Coast
Ravenscar
A171
Northallerton
A171
A170
Scarborough
●**Yorkshire Dales**
A61
Rievaulx
Terrace ▲
Pickering
Thirsk
A168
A170
Filey
Braithwaite Hall ▲
A1(M)
▲**Nunnington Hall**
A165
A64
Bridlington
Ripon
A19
A64
A614
▲**Fountains Abbey**
Brimham
Rocks ●
A59
Beningbrough Hall
A166
Settle
Harrogate
A59
A65
A59
Treasurer's House
A614
Skipton
A658
YORK
A65
Wetherby
Goddards H
A1079
A614
A65
A61
A58
Middlethorpe
Hall
A1079
A1035
East Riddlesden Hall ▲
A64
A19
Beverley
Keighley
A658
A1(M)
A59
Burnley
A658
Bradford
Leeds
A614
Maister House
M65
A642
A63
A63
▲**Kingston upon Hull**
Hardcastle
Crags
M621
Selby
M62
A646
Halifax
A56
M66
M62
Wakefield
M62
A63
Rochdale
Huddersfield
Pontefract
M18
A638
▲**Nostell**
M62
●**Marsden Moor**
M1
M580
BARNSLEY
Wentworth
Doncaster
M180
M60
Castle Gardens ▲
A635
M66
A628
▲
Wentworth
A46
M62
A6102
Woodhouse
A1(M)
A631
A159
A15
A173
A46
M56
●
Kinder,
SHEFFIELD
A631
A18 A16
A523
Edale
A57
A156
A46
and the
Dark Peak
M1
A157 A158
●**Lyme**
M1
Worksop
A15 A16
M6
●**Longshaw,**
Worksop
Clumber Park
Burbage and the
A57
A1
A158
Eastern Moors
A534
A52
A158
A500
A6
▲**Hardwick**
A46
A17
A15
A523
A61
A17
A1121 A52
A38
A60
A617
A46
A52
A52
A16
A15
A17
A151
A16
A606
A1
A47

Beningbrough Hall, Gallery and Gardens

Beningbrough, York,
North Yorkshire YO30 1DD

1958	🏛 ❀ 🎣 ☕ 🏠 🎋

From the wealthy teenager who inherited it, to its time as an RAF billet, Beningbrough has been shaped for more than 300 years by the people who lived here. The garden is enjoying a revival, with designs by award-winning landscape architect Andy Sturgeon. Look out for the recently planted ha-ha walk and pergola, which contrast with the traditional herbaceous borders, sweeping lawns and American garden. The walled kitchen garden provides year-round interest, from the first blossom through to harvest season, and further afield the parkland walks give glimpses back to the hall.

Parking: on site.

Dog rating: 🐾 🐾 **Good** – Welcome on short leads in the garden and parkland only.

Beningbrough Hall, Gallery and Gardens in North Yorkshire, above and below

Access:

Find out more: 01904 472027 or
beningbrough@nationaltrust.org.uk
nationaltrust.org.uk/beningbrough

Beningbrough Hall		M	T	W	T	F	S	S
1 Jan–20 Feb	10–3:30*						S	S
21 Feb–27 Feb	10–3:30*	M	T	W	T	F	S	S
2 Mar–31 Mar	10–5**			W	T	F	S	S
1 Apr–30 Sep	10–5**	M	T	W	T	F	S	S
1 Oct–23 Oct	10–5**			W	T	F	S	S
24 Oct–30 Oct	10–5**	M	T	W	T	F	S	S
5 Nov–18 Dec	10–3:30*						S	S
26 Dec–31 Dec	10–3:30*	M	T				S	

Hall and Gallery: opening arrangements not confirmed at time of print, due to major conservation work, please check before visiting. *Shop: opens 10:30. **Shop: opens 12. Also open 1 and 2 January 2023.

Braithwaite Hall

East Witton, Leyburn,
North Yorkshire DL8 4SY 1941

Grand 17th-century tenanted farmhouse
in the heart of Coverdale, close to the
River Cover and surrounded by farmland
and woodland. **Note**: sorry, no toilet.
Parts of the Hall are open in June,
July and August (by arrangement
in advance with the tenant).

Find out more: 01969 640287 or
braithwaitehall@nationaltrust.org.uk
nationaltrust.org.uk/braithwaite-hall

Bridestones, Crosscliff and Blakey Topping

near Pickering, North Yorkshire 1944

On the North York Moors, the
Bridestones are geological wonders –
rock formations with moorland views,
woodland walks and grassy valleys.
Note: nearest toilets at Staindale Lake
car park. For satnav use YO18 7LR.
Access to the Bridestones is via Dalby
Forest Drive toll road, open daily 8 to 8
(closed 25 to 26 December and 1 January).

Find out more: 0191 529 3161 or
bridestones@nationaltrust.org.uk
nationaltrust.org.uk/bridestones

Brimham Rocks

Summerbridge, Harrogate,
North Yorkshire HG3 4DW

 1970

Brimham Rocks, which offer panoramic
views across Nidderdale and the wider
Yorkshire countryside, are an incredible
collection of eye-catching rock formations.
Sculpted by 320 million years of ice, wind
and continental movement, these rocks
have been moulded into magical shapes
and have names such as the Dancing Bear
and Druid's Writing Desk. They're a natural
playground for those seeking adventure,
but also offer tranquillity when exploring
the surrounding moorland, with its rare
wildlife habitat and internationally
important plants. Brimham is a great place
for walkers, climbers, nature-spotters and
artists, as well as families looking for the
freedom to explore. **Note**: nearest toilets
600 yards from car park.

**Brimham Rocks, North Yorkshire:
these formations make an eye-catching
collection of sculptural shapes**

Walkers can enjoy panoramic views from Brimham Rocks

Parking: on site.

Dog rating: 🐾 🐾 **Good** – Welcome on leads.

Access:

Find out more: 01423 780688 or brimhamrocks@nationaltrust.org.uk
nationaltrust.org.uk/brimham

Brimham Rocks

Car park: main gate closes at 9 (or dusk if earlier). Refreshment kiosk: open daily May half term to October half term, 10 to 4. Winter opening times vary, please check before visiting. Closed 24 and 25 December.

East Riddlesden Hall

Bradford Road, Riddlesden, Keighley, West Yorkshire BD20 5EL

1934

East Riddlesden Hall in West Yorkshire: a hidden gem saved from demolition

This hidden gem was saved from demolition in 1934 and today offers a friendly welcome to all who pass through its doors. Discover a historic manor house and 17th-century barn, once the heart of a vast agricultural estate. The intimate gardens offer a relaxing space all year, with fresh buds in spring, roses in summer and trees laden with fruit in autumn. The natural play area, with mud-pie kitchen and den-building, will spark the imagination of the whole family. The tea-room serves up a range of tasty treats and locally sourced gifts can be found in the shop.

Parking: 250 yards (overflow parking on field during peak times).

East Riddlesden Hall, above, and the intimate gardens, below

Dog rating: 🐾 **Standard** – Welcome on lower field (assistance dogs only in house, garden, shop and tea-room).

Access: 🅿️ 🅳 🚾 ⬚ ⬚ 📖 ⬚ ⬚ 🅰️ ♿ ♿

Find out more: 01535 607075 or eastriddlesden@nationaltrust.org.uk
nationaltrust.org.uk/east-riddlesden-hall

East Riddlesden Hall		M	T	W	T	F	S	S
8 Jan–20 Feb**	10–4*						S	S
21 Feb–30 Oct	10–4*	M	T	W			S	S
5 Nov–18 Dec**	10–4*						S	S

*House and shop: open 11. **House: please check winter opening before visiting.

Fountains Abbey and Studley Royal Water Garden

near Ripon, North Yorkshire HG4 3DY

| 1983 | 🏛️ 🏠 ✿ 🦌 ☕ 🏠 📷 🚶

Deep within the Skell Valley lies Fountains Abbey and Studley Royal, a World Heritage Site waiting to be explored. Humans have tamed and teased the valley's wild waters over hundreds of years, creating an expansive landscape with sweeping Georgian water garden and imposing abbey ruins. Cistercian monks chose this place to establish Fountains Abbey in 1132, and the walls echo with centuries-old stories. A riverside path leads to Studley Royal, a playful water garden designed by visionaries John and William Aislabie in the 18th century. Venture beyond the lake to Studley Royal deer park, with ancient tree avenues and red, fallow and sika deer. There are holiday cottages available and a children's play area at the Visitor Centre.

Fountains Abbey and Studley Royal Water Garden in North Yorkshire, below and opposite

Parking: on site at visitor centre (six electric vehicle charging points), West Gate car park and Studley Lakeside.

Dog rating: **Best** – Welcome on leads (dog-friendly eating areas at visitor centre restaurant).

Access:

Find out more: 01765 608888 or fountainsabbey@nationaltrust.org.uk
nationaltrust.org.uk/fountains-abbey

Fountains Abbey		M	T	W	T	F	S	S
Abbey, Water Garden, Visitor Centre refreshments and shop								
1 Jan–31 Jan	10–4*	M	T	W	T		S	S
1 Feb–27 Mar	10–4*	M	T	W	T	F	S	S
28 Mar–30 Oct	10–5*	M	T	W	T	F	S	S
31 Oct–31 Dec**	10–4*	M	T	W	T		S	S
Deer-park								
Open all year	6–6	M	T	W	T	F	S	S

*Visitor Centre shop: opens 11; car parks: close two hours after last entry. **Closed 24 and 25 December; open 30 December. Fountains Hall, Mill, Studley tea-room and St Mary's Church: opening times vary, please check before visiting.

A wintry walk at Fountains Abbey and Studley Royal Water Garden

Goddards

27 Tadcaster Road, Dringhouses, York, North Yorkshire YO24 1GG

1984

Meander through the two hectares (five acres) of Arts and Crafts garden 'rooms' of the former home of the Terry family (think Chocolate Orange). Discover herbaceous borders, a fragrant garden, rock garden and glasshouse. The Terry factory clock tower can be seen from the paddock orchard overlooking the racecourse.

Satnav: enter 27 Tadcaster Road, Dringhouses, York, not postcode.
Parking: designated parking or drop-off only. Park on Knavesmire Road (off A1036) by York racecourse, 1 mile, or at city car parks, none National Trust (charge including members), 1 to 2 miles.

Dog rating: **Standard** – Welcome on leads in the garden.

Access:

Find out more:
01904 624247 (Treasurer's House) or goddards@nationaltrust.org.uk
nationaltrust.org.uk/goddards

Goddards		M	T	W	T	F	S	S
Garden								
3 Mar–30 Oct	11–4				T	F	S	S

Hardcastle Crags

near Hebden Bridge, West Yorkshire

1950 🏠🎣🍴🏛🪑

This picturesque valley has more than 25 miles of footpaths and 160 hectares (400 acres) of woodland to explore. You'll see towering trees, tumbling streams, waterfalls and natural flood management interventions. It's home to a range of wildlife, including the northern hairy wood ant and internationally rare waxcaps. Seasonal highlights include sweet-smelling bluebells in late spring, carpets of golden leaves in autumn and rare, delicate frost flowers in winter. You can walk along the riverside to Gibson Mill, a former cotton mill, where you'll find the café and information showing how the valley has changed over the past 200 years. **Note**: steep paths, rough terrain. Toilets and café at Gibson Mill, 1 mile from car parks.

Satnav: for Midgehole car park use HX7 7AA; Clough Hole car park HX7 7AZ. **Parking**: at Midgehole car park, 1 mile to Gibson Mill, or Clough Hole car park, ¾ mile (steep walk).

There is so much to explore at Hardcastle Crags in West Yorkshire, below and above right

Dog rating: 🐾 🐾 **Good** – Welcome under close control, including in café. On leads near livestock.

Access: 🅿️♿🚾🛗🍴♿🚶♿🚻

Find out more: 01422 844518 (weekdays). 01422 846236 (weekends) or hardcastlecrags@nationaltrust.org.uk **nationaltrust.org.uk/hardcastle-crags**

Hardcastle Crags		M	T	W	T	F	S	S
Gibson Mill and Weaving Shed Café*								
1 Jan–27 Mar	10–3	·	·	·	·	F	S	S
28 Mar–30 Oct**	10–4	M	T	W	T	F	S	S
4 Nov–31 Dec	10–3	·	·	·	·	F	S	S

*Café: open additional days during school holidays. Closed 25 December. **Mill: closes occasionally for private events (please check before visiting).

Maister House

160 High Street, Hull, East Yorkshire HU1 1NL 1966

A merchant family's tale of fortune and tragedy is intertwined with the intriguing history of the 18th-century Maister House. **Note**: staircase and entrance hall only on show. Sorry no toilet. Opening arrangements not confirmed at time of print, please check before visiting.

Find out more: 01904 472027 (Beningbrough Hall) or maisterhouse@nationaltrust.org.uk **nationaltrust.org.uk/maister-house**

Marsden Moor

near Huddersfield, West Yorkshire

1955 [icons]

Exploring Marsden Moor in West Yorkshire

This Site of Special Scientific Interest, with far-reaching views across the South Pennines and Peak District, has more than 2,000 hectares (5,500 acres) of countryside to explore. There's plenty of wildlife to spot, and a variety of walks to discover online to take you through the moorland landscape. **Note**: sorry no toilet.

Satnav: use HD7 6DH for the Information Room and Marsden village. HD3 3FT for Buckstones and HD9 4HW for Wessenden Head. **Parking**: Marsden village (not National Trust), Buckstones and Wessenden Head.

Dog rating: ❖ **Standard** – Welcome on leads (livestock roaming and ground-nesting birds).

Find out more: 01484 847016 or marsdenmoor@nationaltrust.org.uk **nationaltrust.org.uk/marsden-moor**

Middlethorpe Hall and Spa

Bishopthorpe Road, York, North Yorkshire YO23 2GB

2008 [icons]

Middlethorpe Hall is a William III country house just outside York, built in 1699 and set in 8 hectares (20 acres) of gardens. Furnished with antiques and paintings, Middlethorpe retains the look and feel of a well-kept manor house. The bedrooms are complemented by elegant public rooms, including the drawing room and wood-panelled dining room, where imaginative meals are served. The gardens include a rose garden, walled garden, meadow and lake. The spa has a gym, swimming pool and sauna. **Note**: access is for guests staying at the hotel, using the spa or enjoying meals. Children over the age of six welcome.

Find out more: 01904 641241 or info@middlethorpe.com **middlethorpe.com**

Mount Grace Priory, House and Gardens

Staddle Bridge, Northallerton, North Yorkshire DL6 3JG 1953

Explore the well-preserved ruins of a medieval priory, set in woodland with gardens and an Arts and Crafts manor house. **Note**: managed by English Heritage; National Trust members free, except on event days. Visit english-heritage.org.uk for detailed opening times.

Find out more: 01609 883494 or mountgracepriory@nationaltrust.org.uk **nationaltrust.org.uk/mount-grace-priory**

Nostell

Doncaster Road, Nostell, near Wakefield,
West Yorkshire WF4 1QE

| 1954 | 🏛️🏠✤🎣🍵📷📖🎿🏃 |

One of the north of England's great treasure houses, Nostell is a Georgian architectural masterpiece that was built to impress. Generations of the Winn family employed the best architects, craftsmen and artists to create a showcase for fashionable design. Discover a world-class collection of furniture, textiles and wallpaper supplied by Thomas Chippendale, historic paintings, a treasured Georgian doll's house, Robert Adam interiors and a rare John Harrison clock.

Nostell in West Yorkshire, right and below: a wildlife-rich estate surrounds the imposing house

Nostell's purpose-built cycling trails offer opportunities for all ages

Home to wildlife, including swans, kingfishers and bats, the surrounding 121-hectare (300-acre) estate includes parkland, meadows, lakes, a working kitchen garden, orangery and Menagerie Garden. There are seasonal displays of snowdrops, magnolia, bluebells and roses, while active adventurers can explore the woodland play area and purpose-built trails for walking and cycling.

Parking: 650 yards.

Dog rating: 🐾 🐾 **Good** – Welcome under close control, on leads when requested, in park (assistance dogs only in house and gardens).

Access:

Find out more: 01924 863892 or nostell@nationaltrust.org.uk
nationaltrust.org.uk/nostell

Nostell		M	T	W	T	F	S	S
House*								
2 Mar–30 Oct	11–4**			W	T	F	S	S
Gardens, shop and café								
Open all year†	10–4††	M	T	W	T	F	S	S
Parkland								
Open all year	7–5	M	T	W	T	F	S	S

*House: open April, May and August Bank Holidays and additional days over winter. **House: last entry 45 minutes before closing. †Gardens: open 11; some areas may be closed for maintenance in winter. ††Last entry one hour before closing. Everything closed 25 December.

Nunnington Hall

Nunnington, near York,
North Yorkshire YO62 5UY

 1953 🏛 ❀ ☕ 🖼 🍴

At this welcoming house and garden, in
its beautiful setting on the River Rye, you
can discover stories about the Fife family
in the 1920s, as well as the rise and fall
of Lord Preston during the 17th century.
The organic garden is ideal for relaxing
and you can picnic in the wildflower
meadows and fruit orchards. Inside the
house there is the Carlisle Collection
of miniature rooms, renowned for its
high-quality craftsmanship, as well as
a diverse programme of art exhibitions
throughout the year to enjoy.

Parking: on site.

Dog rating: ❀ **Standard** – Welcome on
leads in the garden and tea garden.

The Panelled Bedroom at Nunnington Hall

Access: ♿ 🚾 ♿ ♿ ♿

Find out more: 01439 748283 or
nunningtonhall@nationaltrust.org.uk
nationaltrust.org.uk/nunnington

Nunnington Hall		M	T	W	T	F	S	S
19 Feb–27 Feb	10:30–4	·	T	W	T	F	S	S
1 Mar–29 May	10:30–5	·	T	W	T	F	S	S
30 May–2 Oct	10:30–5	M	T	W	T	F	S	S
4 Oct–30 Oct	10:30–5	·	T	W	T	F	S	S
25 Nov–18 Dec	10:30–4	·	·	·	·	F	S	S

Last entry 45 minutes before closing. Open Mondays during
school holidays and on Bank Holidays.

The south front of Nunnington Hall
in North Yorkshire

Ormesby Hall

Ladgate Lane, Ormesby,
near Middlesbrough,
Redcar & Cleveland TS3 0SR

1962 | 🏠🏡❄️♿🍵👜🚶

Ruth and Jim Pennyman, the last residents
of Ormesby Hall, offered a warm welcome
to everyone who visited their house – the
Pennyman family home for 400 years.
Today you'll find a Georgian mansion,
with a listed stable block, set in acres
of parkland. The formal garden boasts

Georgian Ormesby Hall in Redcar & Cleveland, above and below

colourful seasonal displays and newly established herbaceous borders, with a wildflower meadow, orchard and pond creating a green oasis. In the year that marks 60 years since the estate was gifted to the National Trust, you can discover more about the community spirit and theatrical daring that still resonates within Ormesby today.

Parking: 200 yards. One electric vehicle charging point.

Dog rating: 🐾 🐾 **Good** – Welcome on leads in garden, courtyards and wider estate.

Access:

Find out more: 01642 324188 or ormesbyhall@nationaltrust.org.uk
Ormesby Hall, Church Lane, Middlesbrough, Redcar & Cleveland TS7 9AS
nationaltrust.org.uk/ormesby-hall

Ormesby Hall		M	T	W	T	F	S	S
12 Feb–24 Jul*	10:30–5	M	·	·	T	F	S	S
25 Jul–4 Sep	10:30–5	M	T	W	T	F	S	S
5 Sep–6 Nov*	10:30–5	M	·	·	T	F	S	S
19 Nov–19 Dec	10:30–4	M	·	·	T	F	S	S

Last entry one hour before closing. *Also open Tuesdays and Wednesdays during school holidays.

Rievaulx Terrace, North Yorkshire: Tuscan Temple

Parking: 100 yards.

Dog rating: 🐾 **Standard** – Welcome on leads in garden.

Access: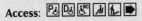

Find out more: 01439 748283 (Nunnington Hall) or rievaulxterrace@nationaltrust.org.uk
nationaltrust.org.uk/rievaulx-terrace

Rievaulx Terrace

Open 10 to 5 on 5/6 March; 2/3 and 15 to 18 April, 30 April and 1 May; 2 to 5 June; 2/3, 22 to 24 and 29 to 31 July; 5 to 7, 12 to 14, 19 to 21 and 26 to 29 August; 2 to 4 September; 1/2 and 28 to 30 October. Last entry one hour before closing.

Rievaulx Terrace

Rievaulx, Helmsley,
North Yorkshire YO62 5LJ

1972 🏠❄️♿️⛩

Designed to impress, Rievaulx Terrace was created by the Duncombe family in the 18th century and is one of Yorkshire's finest examples of a landscape garden from this time. Peaceful woodlands, grand temples and a terrace with views of Rievaulx Abbey make this one of Ryedale's true gems.
Note: no access from Rievaulx Terrace to Rievaulx Abbey (managed by English Heritage).

Roseberry Topping

near Newton-under-Roseberry,
North Yorkshire 1985

Affectionately known as 'Yorkshire's Matterhorn', Roseberry Topping has woodland walks and wildlife on its slopes, and views from its summit. **Note**: nearest toilets in Newton-under-Roseberry car park (not National Trust).
For satnav use TS9 6QR.

Find out more: 0191 529 3161 or roseberrytopping@nationaltrust.org.uk
nationaltrust.org.uk/roseberry-topping

Treasurer's House, York

Minster Yard, York, North Yorkshire YO1 7JL

1930 🏠 ✿ 🍵 🚻 🧗

Tucked behind York Minster, Treasurer's House is not as it first appears. In 1897 it was bought by Frank Green, the grandson of a wealthy industrialist, and by 1900 he had transformed it at great speed into an elaborately decorated town house, ready for the visit of Edward VII. Hear about Frank Green's life and find out how he saved Treasurer's House and changed it into the grand show home we see today. The award-winning garden is an oasis of calm, with unrivalled views of York Minster, making it an ideal place to relax.

Parking: nearest at Lord Mayor's Walk (not National Trust).

Dog rating: ✿ **Standard** – Welcome on leads in the garden.

Treasurer's House: award-winning garden

Access: 🅿 🦽 ▭ 🎧 🔍 ♿ 🧗

Find out more: 01904 624247 or treasurershouse@nationaltrust.org.uk
nationaltrust.org.uk/treasurershouse

Treasurer's House, York		M	T	W	T	F	S	S
2 Apr–28 Jun	Tour	M	T	.	.	.	S	S
2 Jul–9 Nov	Tour	M	T	W	.	.	S	S
19 Nov–18 Dec	11–4	M	T	W	.	.	S	S

Treasurer's House, York, North Yorkshire: the elaborate 18th-century staircase

Most places offer last entry 30 minutes before closing

Wentworth Castle Gardens

Park Drive, Stainborough, Barnsley,
South Yorkshire S75 3EN

| 2019 | ❀ 🖼 ☕ 🛍 🏠 🎪 |

Working together with Barnsley Council
and Northern College, this estate, rooted
in rivalry, provides a space to bring
people together. Royal diplomat Thomas
Wentworth was outraged when a cousin
inherited his family home in 1695 and was
determined to outdo him, creating what
was once known as 'the finest garden in
England'. Today it is South Yorkshire's only
Grade I-listed landscape, with acres of
parkland and gardens to explore. There
are surprises along every avenue, including
a castle that is not what it seems.
Note: house is closed to visitors as it
houses Northern College.

Parking: on site.

Dog rating: 🐾 🐾 🐾 **Best** – Welcome on
leads in the gardens and parkland.

Access: 🅿️♿ 🚻 ♿ ♿ 🖼 ♿ ♿ ♿

Stainborough Castle at
Wentworth Castle Gardens
in South Yorkshire

Wentworth Castle Gardens: Azalea Garden in May

Find out more: 01226 323070 or
wentworthcastlegardens@nationaltrust.org.uk
nationaltrust.org.uk/wentworth-castle-gardens

Wentworth Castle Gardens		M	T	W	T	F	S	S
1 Jan–11 Feb*	10–3:30	·	·	W	T	F	S	S
12 Feb–30 Oct	10–5	M	T	W	T	F	S	S
2 Nov–18 Dec	10–3:30	·	·	W	T	F	S	S
19 Dec–31 Dec**	10–3:30	M	T	W	T	F	S	S

*Also open 3 January. **Closed 25 December.

Wentworth Woodhouse

Wentworth, Rotherham,
South Yorkshire S62 7TQ 2017

Nationally important listed 18th-century
country house with more than 300 rooms
and large gardens – specialist tours and
self-guided experience available.
Note: house operated by Wentworth
Woodhouse Preservation Trust, charge
including members for admission and tours
(but 50 per cent discount). For satnav use
S62 7TQ. Open all year, Wednesday to
Sunday, 10 to 4 (openings may vary,
please check before visiting).

Find out more: 01226 749639 or
info@wentworthwoodhouse.org.uk

Yorkshire Coast

near Ravenscar, North Yorkshire

1976

The coastline from Saltburn to Filey has a
rich heritage. Explore via clifftop walks or
cycling routes, and discover sandy bays
that are perfect for rock-pooling and
fossil-hunting. Ravenscar Visitor Centre and
the Old Coastguard Station, Robin Hood's
Bay, offer refreshments, inspiration for your
visit and displays about coastal life.

Satnav: for Ravenscar use YO13 0NE.
Parking: on roadside at Ravenscar. Pay and
display at Saltburn, Runswick Bay and
Robin Hood's Bay, not National Trust
(charge including members).

Dog rating: 🐾 🐾 🐾 **Best** – Welcome at
most events and in visitor centres. On leads
around livestock and cliff edges.

Access: 🚻 ♿ 🔊 ♿ ⬆

Find out more: 0191 529 3161 or
yorkshirecoast@nationaltrust.org.uk
nationaltrust.org.uk/yorkshire-coast

Yorkshire Coast		M	T	W	T	F	S	S
Old Coastguard Station								
1 Mar–31 Oct	10–5	M	T	W	T	F	S	S
Ravenscar Visitor Centre								
1 Jan–20 Feb	10–4	·	·	·	·	F	S	S
21 Feb–28 Feb	10–4	M	T	W	T	F	S	S
1 Mar–31 Oct	10–5	M	T	W	T	F	S	S
4 Nov–24 Dec	10–4	·	·	·	·	F	S	S
27 Dec–31 Dec	10–4	·	T	W	T	F	S	·

Yorkshire Dales

North Yorkshire

1946 🏠👥🐑⛺🚶

The Yorkshire Dales are a great place to relax and explore the great outdoors. Take in the limestone landscape with its dry-stone walls and barns, fields of sheep and cows, and wildflower meadows and pastures. You can walk along the boardwalk of the National Nature Reserve at Malham Tarn and explore the river and woodland valleys of Upper Wharfedale on foot or by bike. Further north, Hudswell Woods has over 5 miles of footpaths through ancient woodlands, and there are peaceful spots along the River Swale to enjoy a picnic or perhaps skim a stone. **Note**: nearest toilets located at National Park Centre car parks or council car park (Hudswell Woods).

Satnav: use BD23 5JA for Upper Wharfedale; BD24 9PT for Malham Tarn; DL10 4TJ for Hudswell Woods.

Exploring the varied landscapes of the Yorkshire Dales by bike, top, and foot, above

Parking: for Upper Wharfedale use car parks in Kettlewell and Buckden, not National Trust (charge including members). For Malham Tarn parking is either off-road at Waterhouses or at Watersinks car park. For Hudswell Woods use Round Howe car park, not National Trust (charge including members).

Dog rating: 🐾 **Standard** – Welcome (excluding Malham Tarn boardwalk) under close control and on leads near livestock.

Access: ➡️ ♿

Find out more: 01729 830416 or yorkshiredales@nationaltrust.org.uk **nationaltrust.org.uk/yorkshire-dales**

Rugged drama at the Yorkshire Dales, North Yorkshire

Lindisfarne Castle,
Northumberland

North East

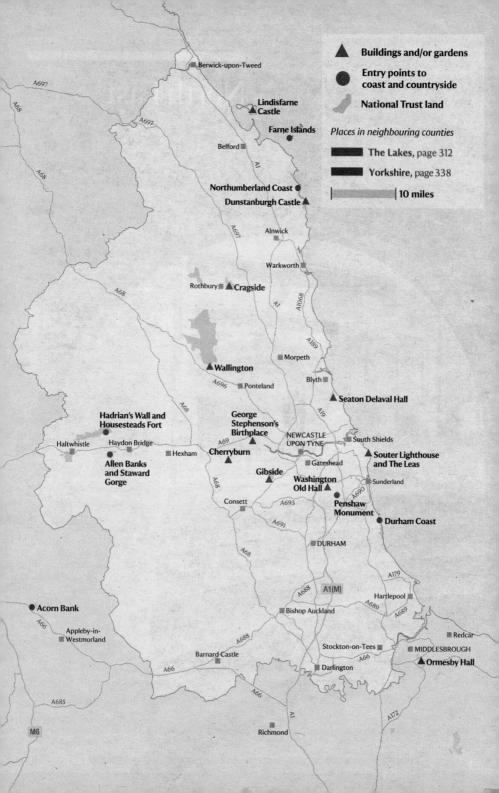

Buildings and/or gardens

Entry points to coast and countryside

National Trust land

Places in neighbouring counties

The Lakes, page 312

Yorkshire, page 338

10 miles

A697

A68

Berwick-upon-Tweed

A697

Lindisfarne Castle

Farne Islands

Belford

A1

Northumberland Coast

Dunstanburgh Castle

Alnwick

Warkworth

A697

A1068

Rothbury

Cragside

A1

A68

A189

Morpeth

Wallington

A696

Ponteland

Blyth

Seaton Delaval Hall

A68

A19

Hadrian's Wall and Housesteads Fort

Haltwhistle

Haydon Bridge

A69

George Stephenson's Birthplace

NEWCASTLE UPON TYNE

South Shields

Hexham

Cherryburn

Souter Lighthouse and The Leas

Allen Banks and Staward Gorge

A68

Gateshead

Gibside

Washington Old Hall

Sunderland

A690

Consett

A693

Penshaw Monument

A691

Durham Coast

DURHAM

A179

A1(M)

A688

Hartlepool

Acorn Bank

A66

Appleby-in-Westmorland

A688

Bishop Auckland

A689

A689

Redcar

Barnard Castle

Stockton-on-Tees

A66

MIDDLESBROUGH

Darlington

Ormesby Hall

A66

A685

M6

A1

A172

Richmond

Allen Banks and Staward Gorge

near Ridley Hall, Bardon Mill, Hexham, Northumberland NE47 7BP

Picnicking at Allen Banks and Staward Gorge in Northumberland

With its deep gorge created by the River Allen, these ancient woods are the ideal backdrop for an outdoor adventure and the perfect place for nature lovers of all ages. The semi-natural woodland is the largest in Northumberland, with miles of waymarked walks, sun-dappled paths and treetop views. **Note**: some level ground but primarily uneven and steep in places with steps on all walks.

Satnav: postcode directs to Ridley Hall – turn left at Ridley Hall gates for Allen Banks car park. **Parking**: at Allen Banks.

Dog rating: ❀ **Standard** – Welcome on leads.

Access: 🅿️ 🚾 ♿

Find out more: 01434 321888 or allenbanks@nationaltrust.org.uk **nationaltrust.org.uk/allen-banks**

Cherryburn

Station Bank, Mickley, Stocksfield, Northumberland NE43 7DD

Set in a tranquil garden with views across the Tyne Valley, this unassuming Northumbrian farmstead was the birthplace of celebrated artist and naturalist Thomas Bewick. Cherryburn is still surrounded by the natural world that inspired his work. Explore the museum with Bewick's pioneering wood engravings.

Satnav: some misdirect, follow brown signs. **Parking**: on site.

Dog rating: ❀ **Standard** – Welcome on short leads in garden and grounds.

Access: 🅿️ 🚾 ♿

Find out more: 01661 843276 or cherryburn@nationaltrust.org.uk **nationaltrust.org.uk/cherryburn**

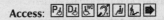

Cherryburn			M	T	W	T	F	S	S
26 May–28 Oct	10–5					T	F		

Opening date may change due to a major project, please check before visiting.

Printing demonstration at Cherryburn in Northumberland

Cragside

Rothbury, Morpeth,
Northumberland NE65 7PX

1977 🏛️🏠♣️⛵🍵🏠🎋

Experience Britain's original smart home.
Illuminated by hydro-electricity and
powered by hydraulics, this pioneering
home is filled with Victorian gadgets for
efficient modern living. Man-made lakes,
waterfalls and swathes of rhododendron
combine to form the surrounding fantasy
mountain landscape, imagined and
engineered by inventor and arms
manufacturer Lord Armstrong and his wife
Lady Margaret. You can wander among the
towering trees in the Pinetum, explore
the weaving paths and tumbling cascades
in the Rock Garden and witness the
changing seasons in the Formal Gardens.

**Two original electric lamps, converted from vases,
in the Library at Cragside, Northumberland**

The vast drawing room at Cragside, left, and exploring the estate, above

See the whole estate by car on the Carriage Drive where waymarked walks and wildlife are waiting to be discovered. Families can adventure through the labyrinth and swoop and slide in the newly extended play area. **Note**: challenging terrain and distances outside, stout footwear essential.

Satnav: may try and bring you through exit. Please follow brown signs to main entrance. **Parking**: nine car parks on estate.

Dog rating: 🐾 🐾 **Good** – Welcome outdoors on leads.

Access:

Cragside: the Iron Bridge that spans Debdon Burn

Find out more: 01669 620333 or
cragside@nationaltrust.org.uk
nationaltrust.org.uk/cragside

Cragside		M	T	W	T	F	S	S
House*								
1 Jan–13 Feb	11–3						S	S
19 Feb–30 Oct	11–5	M	T	W	T	F	S	S
5 Nov–11 Dec**	11–3						S	S
17 Dec–31 Dec**	11–3	M	T	W	T	F	S	S
Gardens and woodland†								
1 Jan–18 Feb	11–3	M	T	W	T	F	S	S
19 Feb–30 Oct	10–5	M	T	W	T	F	S	S
31 Oct–31 Dec	11–3	M	T	W	T	F	S	S

*House: last entry one hour before closing.
**House: frequent closures possible for conservation and
essential maintenance work, please check before visiting.
†Estate: last entry one hour before closing. Everything
closed 24 and 25 December.

Dunstanburgh Castle

Craster, Alnwick,
Northumberland NE66 3TW 1961

This imposing castle ruin occupies a
dramatic position on the Northumberland
coastline, a mile from Craster, towering
over Embleton Bay. **Note**: managed by
English Heritage. Sorry no toilet – closest
at Craster car park. For satnav use NE66 3TT.
Managed by English Heritage, visit
english-heritage.org.uk for further details.

Find out more: 01665 576231 or
dunstanburghcastle@nationaltrust.org.uk
nationaltrust.org.uk/dunstanburgh

Durham Coast

between Seaham and Horden,
County Durham

1987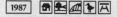

Rocky headlands, sheltered bays, rare
magnesian limestone grasslands and
wildlife-rich wooded valleys characterise
this coastline, part of Durham's Heritage
Coast. The 'black beaches' of the
coal-mining days have been cleaned
up; clifftop paths look over a revitalised
coastal landscape you can now explore.
Note: nearest toilets at Seaham.

Magnificent Durham Coast, County Durham

Satnav: use SR7 7PS for Nose's Point car
park (not National Trust) near Seaham.
Parking: Nose's Point near Seaham,
Easington Colliery and Horden
(none National Trust).

Dog rating: 🐾 🐾 🐾 **Best** – Welcome
(including most events). On leads near
livestock and cliff edges.

Find out more: 0191 529 3161 or
durhamcoast@nationaltrust.org.uk
nationaltrust.org.uk/durham-coast

Farne Islands

Northumberland

| 1925 | 🏠 ⛰ ⚓ 🦆 📷 🪑 🚫 |

Immerse yourself in nature. An exhilarating boat trip takes you into the world of 23 seabird species during nesting season and offers unrivalled close-ups of thousands of seabirds, including puffins (May to July). Each autumn, more than 2,000 grey seal pups are born on the islands. **Note:** Inner Farne Island: basic toilets; easy-access boardwalk. Staple Island: sorry no toilet; challenging terrain.

Satnav: use NE68 7RQ.
Parking: in Seahouses, not National Trust (charge including members).

A ranger welcomes visitors to the Farne Islands, Northumberland

Puffins on the Farne Islands

Find out more: 01289 389244 (Lindisfarne Castle) or farneislands@nationaltrust.org.uk
nationaltrust.org.uk/farne-islands

Farne Islands		M	T	W	T	F	S	S
Shop*								
2 Jan–18 Feb	10–3			W	T	F	S	S
19 Feb–28 Feb	10–4	M	T	W	T	F	S	S
1 Mar–31 Oct	10–5	M	T	W	T	F	S	S
1 Nov–31 Dec**	10–4	M	T	W	T	F	S	S

*Shop: located on Seahouses high street. **Closed 25 and 26 December. Farne Islands: landings on Inner Farne and Staple Island only; opening arrangements not confirmed at time of print, please check before visiting. Landings on both islands subject to rangers' discretion for visitor safety and bird welfare. Longstone bookings arranged through Golden Gate boat company (not National Trust).

George Stephenson's Birthplace

near Wylam, Northumberland
NE41 8DS | 1949 |

Beside the Tyne and Wylam's historic waggonway, this one-room miner's cottage housed a family whose engineering legacy lives on. **Note**: opening arrangements not confirmed at time of print, please check before visiting.

Find out more: 01661 843276 or georgestephensons@nationaltrust.org.uk
nationaltrust.org.uk/george-stephensons-birthplace

Gibside

near Rowlands Gill, Gateshead,
Tyne & Wear NE16 6BG

1974

On the edge of Newcastle, this Georgian landscape garden was built with 'wow' moments in mind. Different walking trails run through acres of garden, taking you past the ruin of Gibside Hall, a columned Palladian chapel, man-made terraces and impressive views. Towering above, the Column to Liberty gives a glimpse into the stormy history of Mary Eleanor Bowes. Nature-rich, Gibside is home to roe deer and red kites, and has amphibian-filled ponds and a fruitful walled garden. On the Explorer Trail, families can play woodland disc golf and zoom along the zip line at Strawberry Castle play area. If you're looking to unwind, you can relax at the café and second-hand bookshop or admire artistic exhibits at The Stables.

Parking: 382 yards from café (uphill walkway). Two electric vehicle charging points.

Dog rating: 🐾 🐾 🐾 **Best** – Welcome on leads (assistance dogs only in chapel, toilets and Market Place Café).

Access: 🅿️ 🚹 🚂 🚻 🍴 ♿ 👶 ➡️ ♿

Find out more: 01207 541820 or gibside@nationaltrust.org.uk
nationaltrust.org.uk/gibside

Gibside		M	T	W	T	F	S	S
Garden, woodlands, café and play area								
1 Jan–13 Mar	10–4	M	T	W	T	F	S	S
14 Mar–16 Oct	10–6*	M	T	W	T	F	S	S
17 Oct–31 Dec**	10–4	M	T	W	T	F	S	S

Chapel: open weekends, times vary, please check before visiting. *Café: closes 5. **Everything closed 24 and 25 December.

Gibside, Tyne & Wear, this page and opposite: today everyone can enjoy this landscape garden, once a pleasure ground preserved solely for use by the Georgian elite

Hadrian's Wall and Housesteads Fort

near Bardon Mill, Hexham,
Northumberland NE47 6NN

1930

A UNESCO World Heritage Site, Housesteads Fort on Hadrian's Wall (above), is the Roman Empire's best-preserved outpost in northern Europe. Sitting high within the dramatic landscape, this epic structure joins geology and human engineering. Follow ancient footsteps, explore challenging walks along the Wall and learn about soldiers' lives at the fort. **Note**: fort is National Trust-owned, English Heritage-managed and is a half-mile uphill walk from visitor centre.

Satnav: can misdirect, please follow brown signs. **Parking**: at Housesteads, Steel Rigg and Cawfields, not National Trust (charge including members).

Dog rating: ❖ **Standard** – Welcome on leads. Livestock in neighbouring fields and on walks along the Wall all year.

Access:

Find out more: 01434 344525 or housesteads@nationaltrust.org.uk
nationaltrust.org.uk/hadrians-wall

Hadrian's Wall and Housesteads Fort

Housesteads Fort: open daily, except some days at Christmas; opening hours vary by season (please check before visiting).

Lindisfarne Castle

Holy Island, Berwick-upon-Tweed,
Northumberland TD15 2SH

1944

Experience the magical feeling of travelling across the causeway to Lindisfarne Castle. Perched high on a crag and commanding far-reaching views over the Northumberland coastline, this iconic castle presides over Holy Island. One of the UK's most recognisable backdrops, it was converted from a fort into a holiday home for the owner of *Country Life* magazine by architect Sir Edwin Lutyens in 1903. Beyond the castle, you can explore the award-winning, summer-flowering Gertrude Jekyll walled garden and Victorian lime kilns and visit the National Trust shop.

Lindisfarne Castle, Northumberland, sits high atop a rocky crag

Note: unfurnished rooms. Limited toilet facilities. Island accessed by tidal causeway – check safe crossing times.

Parking: at main island car park, 1 mile, not National Trust (charge including members). Intermittent locally operated shuttle bus service (not National Trust).

Dog rating: ❧ **Standard** – Welcome on leads in the grounds. Assistance dogs only in castle.

Access: 🅓 ♨ ♿ 👥

Find out more: 01289 389244 or lindisfarne@nationaltrust.org.uk **nationaltrust.org.uk/lindisfarne**

Lindisfarne Castle

Castle: open daily (excluding Friday), 1 March to 30 October. Shop: open daily, 19 February to 30 October (additional days from mid-December). Castle and shop opening times change daily due to tides (always check before visiting). Garden: open every day all year.

Northumberland Coast

Northumberland

1935   🏠 🚻 ♨ 🐑 📷 🍴

From Lindisfarne to Druridge Bay, you'll find wide open skies and miles of sandy beaches, teeming with wildlife. Coastal walks take you past dramatic castle ruins, unspoilt dunes and rock pools. Spot seals, dolphins and wading shorebirds along the coast, and see the nesting shorebirds at Long Nanny shorebird site. **Note**: public car parks only (charge including members).

Satnav: for Low Newton use NE66 3EH; Druridge Bay NE61 5EG; St Aidan's Dunes NE68 7SH.
Parking: limited at Druridge Bay. Also at Holy Island, Seahouses, Beadnell, Newton-by-the-Sea and Craster, none National Trust (charge including members).

Dog rating: ❧ **Standard** – Welcome, some local restrictions may apply. On short leads near and at Long Nanny shorebird site.

Find out more: 01665 576874 or northumberlandcoast@nationaltrust.org.uk **nationaltrust.org.uk/northumberland-coast**

Northumberland Coast: miles of sandy beaches

Penshaw Monument

near Penshaw, Tyne & Wear DH4 7NJ | 1939

This Wearside landmark can be seen from miles around. A sign of home for many, with woodland walks and views. **Note**: sorry no toilet. For satnav use DH4 7NJ. Steps to the top of the hill. Walking routes nearby.

Find out more: 0191 416 6879 or penshaw.monument@nationaltrust.org.uk
nationaltrust.org.uk/penshaw-monument

Seaton Delaval Hall in Northumberland, above and left, has undergone major conservation work

Seaton Delaval Hall

The Avenue, Seaton Sluice, Northumberland NE26 4QR

2009 🏛 🏠 ❄ 🦮 ♨ ☕ ⛱ 🚶

Designed by Sir John Vanbrugh (Castle Howard, Blenheim Palace) and home to the flamboyant Delaval family, the Hall bears the scars of fierce fires which almost condemned it to ruin 200 years ago. In an age known for extremes of behaviour, the 'gay Delavals' were the most notorious of all Georgian partygoers and pranksters, and their dramatic personalities are matched by Vanbrugh's bold architecture. The Hall has

recently undergone major conservation work and parts of the pleasure grounds have been revitalised, creating a new Baroque theatre-inspired woodland play area, an accessible path network and a café in the Brewhouse.

Parking: 300 yards.

Dog rating: 🐾 🐾 **Good** – Welcome on leads outdoors.

Access: ♿ 🚻 ♿ 🔊 📖 🎦 🎵 ⠿ 📷 ♿ ♿ ➡

Find out more: 0191 237 9100 or seatondelavalhall@nationaltrust.org.uk
nationaltrust.org.uk/seaton-delaval-hall

Seaton Delaval Hall		M	T	W	T	F	S	S
1 Jan–20 Feb	10–3*			W	T	F	S	S
23 Feb–30 Oct	10–5*			W	T	F	S	S
2 Nov–31 Dec**	10–3*			W	T	F	S	S

Open Bank Holiday Mondays and daily during school holidays. Last entry one hour before closing. *Indoor spaces open 11. West Wing: due to re-open late spring, please check before visiting. **Everything closed 24 to 26 December.

Souter Lighthouse and The Leas

Coast Road, Whitburn, Sunderland, Tyne & Wear SR6 7NH

1990 [icons]

Breathe in the bracing North Sea air and climb all 76 steps to the top of the first lighthouse in the world designed and built to be lit by electricity. The Engine Room and Keeper's Cottage give a flavour of life in a working lighthouse, while displays and exhibitions tell local stories. To the north of the lighthouse stretches The Leas, with its wildflower meadows dotted with orchids. To the south is Whitburn Coastal Park, cared for by our rangers and great for wildlife – its nature reserve provides nesting sites, water and rest for migrating birds. **Note**: Whitburn Coastal Park owned by South Tyneside Council, leased and managed by the National Trust.

Parking: on site.

Dog rating: 🐾 🐾 🐾 **Best** – Welcome outdoors and on leads in café, lighthouse grounds and near cliff edges.

Access: [icons]

Find out more: 0191 529 3161 or souter@nationaltrust.org.uk
nationaltrust.org.uk/souter

Souter Lighthouse and The Leas		M	T	W	T	F	S	S
Lighthouse								
7 Feb–6 Nov	11–5	M	T	W	T	F	S	S
Café								
1 Jan–28 Feb	10–4	M	T	W	T	F	S	S
1 Mar–31 Oct	10–5	M	T	W	T	F	S	S
1 Nov–31 Dec*	10–4	M	T	W	T	F	S	S

*Closed 25 and 26 December.

Souter Lighthouse and The Leas, Tyne & Wear: the lighthouse shows off its iconic hoops

Wallington

Cambo, near Morpeth,
Northumberland NE61 4AR

1941 🏠🏡🍀🐾☕🛍🏡🎪

Sitting in a rural corner of Northumberland yet only 20 miles from Newcastle-upon-Tyne, Wallington is a large estate where a historic country house sits amid rolling hills, swathes of woodland and an enchanting walled garden. Take time to discover the variety of spaces, both indoors and out, and keep your eyes peeled for the native wildlife – from red squirrels and nuthatches, to white-clawed crayfish and otters. For an active adventure, take to the Dragon Cycle Trail on two wheels, offering far-reaching views across the Northumbrian countryside. Once home to the unconventional and socialist Trevelyan family, the informal house is full of treasured collections, while the four outdoor play areas capture the spirit of the adventurous Trevelyan children. **Note**: cycle hire charges apply (including members).

Parking: on site.

Dog rating: 🐾 🐾 **Good** – Welcome on leads in all outdoor spaces and some indoor spaces.

Cycling trail through the woods at Wallington in Northumberland

Access: 🅿♿🚾♿♿🌳🖼♿♿♿
♿▶♿

Find out more: 01670 773606 or wallington@nationaltrust.org.uk
nationaltrust.org.uk/wallington

Wallington		M	T	W	T	F	S	S
Estate and Walled Garden								
Open all year	10–5*	M	T	W	T	F	S	S
House								
2 Apr–30 Oct	11:30–3:30	M	T	W	T	F	S	S
19 Nov–31 Dec††	11:30–3:30	M	T	W	T	F	S	S
Café and shop**								
1 Jan–18 Feb	10–4†	M	T	W	T	F	S	S
19 Feb–30 Oct	10–5†	M	T	W	T	F	S	S
31 Oct–31 Dec††	10–4†	M	T	W	T	F	S	S

*Walled Garden: 1 January to 27 March and 31 October to 31 December, closes at 4. **Café: last orders 30 minutes before closing. †Shop: opens 11. ††House, café and shop: openings may be extended at Christmas. Everything closed 24 to 26 December.

Autumnal walk at Wallington, above, and the perfect spot for a chat, below

Washington Old Hall

The Avenue, Washington Village, Washington, Tyne & Wear NE38 7LE

1956

Discovering Washington Old Hall, Tyne & Wear

The original Washington and medieval home of George Washington's ancestors. This small manor house has a diverse past, from its links to the first US President to a 17th-century home and even a crowded tenement. Discover tranquil gardens and explore the 'nuttery' – a haven for nature and wildlife.

Parking: unrestricted parking on The Avenue. Designated parking on site (booking essential).

Dog rating: ❁ **Standard** – Welcome on leads in garden only (assistance dogs only in Hall).

Access:

Find out more: 0191 416 6879 or washingtonoldhall@nationaltrust.org.uk **nationaltrust.org.uk/washington-old-hall**

Washington Old Hall		M	T	W	T	F	S	S
1 Apr–31 Oct	12–5	M	·	·	·	F	S	S
House: last entry 3:30. Garden: last entry 4:30.								

Mae adran Cymru hefyd ar gael yn y Gymraeg.
Os hoffech gael copi, gallwch lawrlwytho pdf
yma: **nationaltrust.org.uk/handbook-welsh**

Gallwch hefyd e-bostio **wa.customerenquiries@
nationaltrust.org.uk** neu ysgrifennu at
Swyddfa'r Ymddiriedolaeth Genedlaethol,
Castell Penrhyn, Bangor, Gwynedd, LL57 4HT

This Wales chapter is also available in Welsh.
If you'd like a copy, you can download a pdf
here: **nationaltrust.org.uk/handbook-welsh**

You can also email **wa.customerenquiries@
nationaltrust.org.uk** or write to the
National Trust Office, Penrhyn Castle,
Bangor, Gwynedd, LL57 4HT

The Kitchen Garden at Dyffryn
Gardens, Vale of Glamorgan

Cymru
Wales

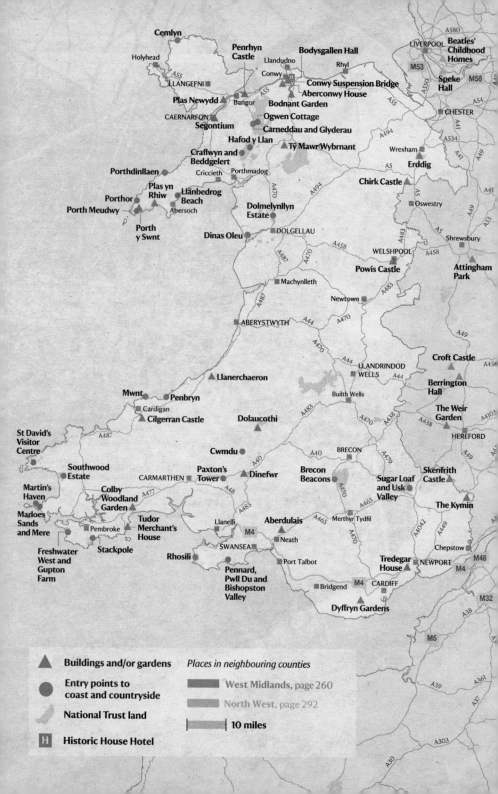

Aberconwy House

Castle Street, Conwy LL32 8AY

1934

This is the only medieval merchant's house in Conwy to have survived the turbulent history of the walled town over seven centuries. Its history includes a coffee shop, a temperance hotel and a bakery, as well as being a home for merchants and sea traders. **Note**: nearest toilets 50 yards. Steps to all parts of property.

Parking: none on site.

Access:

Find out more: 01248 353084 or aberconwyhouse@nationaltrust.org.uk
nationaltrust.org.uk/aberconwy

Aberconwy House

Opening arrangements not confirmed at time of print, please check before visiting.

Medieval Aberconwy House in Conwy has survived turbulent times

Aberdulais

near Neath, Neath Port Talbot

1980

Water from the River Dulais and waterfall were powering industries long before the Industrial Revolution as Aberdulais, above, established its pioneering place as one of the earliest industrial sites in Britain, using cutting-edge technologies to shape the industries that changed the world; from tinplate to copper.

Satnav: postcode misdirects, follow brown signs. **Parking**: 50 yards.

Dog rating: ❧ **Standard** – Welcome on leads throughout site (including inside buildings).

Access:

Find out more: 01639 636674 or aberdulais@nationaltrust.org.uk
Aberdulais, near Neath,
Neath Port Talbot SA10 8EU
nationaltrust.org.uk/aberdulais

Aberdulais

Opening arrangements not confirmed at time of print, please check before visiting.

Bodnant Garden

Tal-y-Cafn, near Colwyn Bay,
Conwy LL28 5RE

 1949

This Grade I-listed garden in Snowdonia's
foothills, with historic plant collections and
breathtaking mountain views, was established
in 1874 by Victorian entrepreneur Henry
Pochin. Five generations of the family have
gone on to transform the 32-hectare
(80-acre) Conwy Valley hillside with rare
trees and shrubs from around the world.
Since 1949 the garden has been nurtured in
collaboration with the National Trust. You
can enjoy Italianate terraces with formal
flowerbeds, pools and parterres, informal
shrub borders, woods, meadows and
riverside dells with waterfalls and towering
conifers. Every season brings new delights –
magnolias and rhododendrons in spring,
roses and water lilies in summer,
followed by rich leaf colour in autumn
and a stunning Winter Garden.
Note: steep paths and open water.

**The golden laburnum arch at
Bodnant Garden in Conwy**

The Pin Mill and Canal Terrace
at Grade I-listed
Victorian Bodnant Garden

Parking: 150 yards. Electric vehicle charging point opposite café.

Dog rating: 🐾 🐾 **Good** – Welcome on short leads (restrictions apply).

Access: ⬜ ⬜ ⬜ ⬜ ⬜ ⬜ ⬜

Find out more: 01492 650460 or bodnantgarden@nationaltrust.org.uk
nationaltrust.org.uk/bodnant-garden

Bodnant Garden		M	T	W	T	F	S	S
1 Jan–28 Feb	10–4	M	T	W	T	F	S	S
1 Mar–31 Oct	10–5	M	T	W	T	F	S	S
1 Nov–31 Dec*	10–4	M	T	W	T	F	S	S

*Garden and tea-room: closed 24 to 26 December.

Bodysgallen Hall and Spa

The Royal Welsh Way, Llandudno, Conwy LL30 1RS

2008 🏛 ✿ 🍽 ☕

This Grade I-listed 17th-century house, set within 89 hectares (220 acres) of parkland, has the most spectacular views towards Conwy Castle and Snowdonia. The romantic gardens, which have won awards for their restoration, include a rare parterre filled with sweet-smelling herbs, as well as several follies, a cascade, walled garden and formal rose gardens. Beyond, the parkland offers miles of stunning walks and views to the coastline. **Note**: access is for paying guests of the hotel, including for luncheon, afternoon tea and dinner, and the spa. Children over the age of six welcome.

Find out more: 01492 584466 or info@bodysgallen.com
bodysgallen.com

On the Beacons Way path between Pont ar Daf and Pen y Fan in the Brecon Beacons, Powys

Brecon Beacons

Powys

 1947

The Brecon Beacons have captivated visitors for hundreds of years with their soaring peaks, including southern Britain's highest mountain, Pen y Fan. From the popular mountaintops to the tranquil valleys, lush farmland to ancient woodland, they are perfect for hill-walking and exploring. Not forgetting South Wales's highest waterfall, Henrhyd Falls, which plunges 90 feet into the wooded Graig Llech Gorge, a haven for rare mosses and ferns. In contrast, you can discover the vast remote moorlands of Abergwesyn Commons in the heart of Wales or ramble over the Begwns with panoramic views of the Brecon Beacons.

Parking: main car park at Pont ar Daf, off A470; alternatives not all National Trust.

Dog rating: ❖ **Standard** – Welcome on leads.

Find out more: 01874 625515 or brecon@nationaltrust.org.uk **nationaltrust.org.uk/brecon-beacons**

Carneddau and Glyderau

Nant Ffrancon, Bethesda, Gwynedd

1951

This 8,498-hectare (21,000-acre) mountainous area includes Cwm Idwal National Nature Reserve, renowned for its geology and Arctic-Alpine plants, such as the rare Snowdon lily. There are eight tenanted upland farms here and nine peaks over 3,000 feet, including the famous Tryfan, where Edmund Hilary trained for his ascent of Everest. The area is home to a variety of wildlife, including otters, feral ponies and rare birds, such as ring ouzel and twite. The 60 miles of footpaths attract more than 500,000 walkers each year, while the bleak, photogenic landscapes have proved popular with artists.
Note: please come well equipped and check the weather. Charges apply in National Park car parks.

Satnav: use LL57 3LZ. **Parking**: at Ogwen Lake (not National Trust).

Dog rating: 🐾 **Standard** – Welcome on leads. Please be mindful of livestock and wildlife, such as ground-nesting birds.

Find out more: 01248 605739 or carneddau@nationaltrust.org.uk
nationaltrust.org.uk/carneddau-and-glyderau

Carneddau and Glyderau, Gwynedd: view of Pen yr Ole Wen from Cwm Idwal, and a mountain pony, top

Cemlyn

Anglesey

1971 🏠♿📈🚶🪑🚶

This Area of Outstanding Natural Beauty along the north-west coast of Anglesey is perfect for walkers with its rugged coastline of rocks, small bays and headland. Cemlyn is a North Wales Wildlife Trust Nature Reserve and a Site of Special Scientific Interest. It becomes a hive of seabird activity in the spring and summer, renowned for its breeding colony of Sandwich, common and Arctic terns that provide a real treat for ornithologists. In autumn and winter, the landscape offers dramatic views and seascapes, with the brackish lagoon separated from the sea by a remarkable shingle ridge.
Note: nearest toilets in Cemaes Bay, 3 miles (not National Trust).

Satnav: use LL67 0DY.
Parking: at Bryn Aber car park, Cemlyn.

Dog rating: 🐾 **Standard** – Welcome on leads. Please be aware of wildlife, such as ground-nesting birds.

Find out more: 01248 714795 or cemlyn@nationaltrust.org.uk
nationaltrust.org.uk/cemlyn

Ruggedly beautiful Cemlyn on the north coast of Anglesey, below, and sea shells, top

Chirk Castle

Chirk, Wrexham LL14 5AF

1981

Completed by Marcher Lord Roger Mortimer in 1310, Chirk is the last Welsh castle from the reign of Edward I still inhabited today. You can explore medieval towers and dungeons, visit the 17th- and 18th-century rooms of the Myddelton family home, including the historic laundry, and discover the story of influential 20th-century tenant and polymath Lord Howard de Walden.

The prized gardens contain clipped yews, herbaceous borders and rock gardens. A terrace gives stunning views over the Cheshire and Shropshire plains, while the large estate, divided by Offa's Dyke, provides habitat for rare invertebrates, wild flowers and veteran trees.

Parking: at Home Farm by ticket office, approximately 220 yards via steep hill to castle. Electric vehicle charging point at Home Farm.

Dog rating: 🐾 🐾 **Good** – Welcome on leads. Assistance dogs only in the gardens, Pleasure Ground Wood and Kitchen Garden.

The richly furnished Saloon at Chirk Castle in Wrexham

Awe-inspiring Chirk Castle

Access:

Find out more: 01691 777701 or
chirkcastle@nationaltrust.org.uk
nationaltrust.org.uk/chirk

Chirk Castle		M	T	W	T	F	S	S
Castle								
28 Feb–6 Nov	12–4	M	T	W	T	F	S	S
3 Dec–31 Dec*	11–4	M	T	W	T	F	S	S
Garden, shop and café								
31 Jan–6 Nov	10–4**	M	T	W	T	F	S	S
12 Nov–27 Nov	10–4	·	·	·	·	·	S	S
3 Dec–31 Dec*	10–4	M	T	W	T	F	S	S

*Closed 24 and 25 December, plus 1 January 2023.
**April to September: closes 5.

Cilgerran Castle

near Cardigan,
Pembrokeshire SA43 2SF `1938`

13th-century castle overlooking the
Teifi Gorge – the perfect location
to repel attackers. Walk the walls
and admire the stunning views.
Note: under the guardianship of
Cadw – Welsh Government's historic
environment service. Please call Cadw on
0300 025 600 for opening arrangements.

Find out more: 01239 621339 or
cilgerrancastle@nationaltrust.org.uk
nationaltrust.org.uk/cilgerran-castle

Colby Woodland Garden

near Amroth, Pembrokeshire SA67 8PP

`1980`

A short walk from the beach, this hidden wooded valley, with its secret garden and industrial past, is a place for play. There are fallen trees to climb, rope swings and playful surprises everywhere. Spring brings bluebells, camellias, rhododendrons and azaleas, while the walled garden gives year-round colour, peace and seclusion. There are woodland walks, meandering streams and ponds with stepping stones and log bridges in the wildflower meadow, and the whole valley teems with wildlife. **Note**: sorry, house not open.

Parking: 50 yards.

Dog rating: 🐾 **Standard** – Welcome on short leads in woodland garden and meadow.

Colby Woodland Garden, Pembrokeshire: the Walled Garden, below, and fun in the wilder areas, left and right

Access: 🅿♿ 🚻 ♿🍴 🚼 ⚲ 🅰 ♿ ➡

Find out more: 01646 623110 or colby@nationaltrust.org.uk
nationaltrust.org.uk/colby-woodland-garden

Colby Woodland Garden		M	T	W	T	F	S	S
Woodland Garden*								
3 Jan–16 Dec	10–5	M	T	W	T	F	S	S
Walled Garden								
9 Apr–6 Nov	10–3	M	T	W	T	F	S	S
Tea-room								
9 Apr–6 Nov	10–4:30	M	T	W	T	F	S	S

*Car parks open as Woodland Garden.

Conwy Suspension Bridge

Conwy LL32 8LD 〔1965〕

Thomas Telford's elegant suspension bridge with its tiny toll-keeper's house, stands alongside Conwy Castle, hidden beside Stephenson's railway bridge. **Note**: sorry no toilet. Conwy Suspension Bridge is currently open for pedestrians and cyclists. The Toll House opening arrangements not confirmed at time of print, please check before visiting.

Find out more: 01248 353084 or conwybridge@nationaltrust.org.uk
nationaltrust.org.uk/conwy-suspension-bridge

Craflwyn and Beddgelert

near Beddgelert, Gwynedd

1994

The 81-hectare (200-acre) Craflwyn Estate is set in the heart of beautiful Snowdonia, within a landscape steeped in history and legend. There's a network of paths and woodland walks to explore and tumbling waterfalls to discover. At Craflwyn you can learn about the princes of Gwynedd before venturing up to nearby Dinas Emrys, legendary birthplace of the red dragon of Wales. Within a couple of miles of Craflwyn, there are great walks for all abilities – from a village stroll at pretty Beddgelert to the rugged Fisherman's Path down the spectacular Aberglaslyn Pass.
Note: Craflwyn Hall and nearby cottages are available as holiday lets.

Craflwyn and Beddgelert in Gwynedd, above and left, in the heart of beautiful Snowdonia

Satnav: use LL55 4NG. **Parking**: in Craflwyn.

Dog rating: ❀ **Standard** – Welcome on leads.

Access: 🧗

Find out more: 01766 510120 or craflwyn@nationaltrust.org.uk
nationaltrust.org.uk/beddgelert

Cwmdu

Llandeilo, Carmarthenshire 1991

Georgian terrace with pub, post office, chapel and vestry. Representing a rural Welsh village of the past. **Note**: for satnav use SA19 7DY. Community-run post office, shop and pub: hours depend on volunteer availability.

Find out more: 01558 685088 or cwmdu@nationaltrust.org.uk

Dinas Oleu

near Barmouth, Gwynedd

Looking down on Barmouth from Dinas Oleu, Gwynedd

Sitting above Barmouth with stunning views across Cardigan Bay and the Llŷn peninsula is the gorse-clad hillside of Dinas Oleu. Thanks to a donation from Mrs Fanny Talbot in 1895 this became the first parcel of land in the care of the National Trust. **Note**: steep rocky terrain and steps to the top.

Parking: nearest in town, not National Trust (charge including members).

Dog rating: 🐾 **Standard** – Welcome on leads.

Find out more: 01341 440238 or dinasoleu@nationaltrust.org.uk

Dinefwr

near Carmarthen, Carmarthenshire

Dinefwr's long history is many-layered and has been instrumental in shaping and reflecting the development of Wales as a nation. Newton House, the Jacobean mansion at the heart of the estate, is a place to relax and reflect, while enjoying a contemporary take on the history of Dinefwr through changing exhibitions. Pause in the garden and savour views out to the deer park, then follow pathways through the historic parkland, protected as a National Nature Reserve, with its flower-rich hay meadows, dense ancient woodland and veteran trees. **Note**: Dinefwr Castle is under the guardianship of Cadw.

Satnav: enter Dinefwr, not postcode.
Parking: 50 yards. Electric vehicle charging point at Home Farm.

Newton House at Dinefwr in Carmarthenshire

Dog rating: 🐾 🐾 🐾 **Best** – Welcome on leads in house ground floor only, outer park and café (assistance dogs only boardwalk/deer park – animals grazing).

Access: [icons]

Find out more: 01558 825910 or dinefwr@nationaltrust.org.uk
Llandeilo, near Carmarthen, Carmarthenshire SA19 6RT
nationaltrust.org.uk/dinefwr

Dinefwr	M	T	W	T	F	S	S
Newton House, second-hand bookshop and café*							
1 Jan–27 Mar	10:30–3:30						S	S
28 Mar–6 Nov	10:30–4:30	M	T	W	T	F	S	S
12 Nov–31 Dec**	10:30–3:30						S	S
Parkland*							
Open all year†		M	T	W	T	F	S	S

*Everything closed 24 and 25 December. **Open daily 23 and 26 to 31 December. †Parkland: open 10 to 4, November to March, and 10 to 5, April to October. Deer park: open 1 March to 6 November.

Newton House at Dinefwr, above and below, sits within a National Nature Reserve

Dolaucothi

Pumsaint, Llanwrda, Carmarthenshire SA19 8US

1941 [icons]

Take a guided tour of the only known Roman gold mine in the UK. Walk among ancient surface workings and go underground to discover more about how the Romans mined for gold. Explore the estate with its wildflower meadows, known as the 'Dolau' in Welsh, which sit alongside the River Cothi, and discover ancient woodlands, upland pasture and expansive views over the surrounding countryside on our walks and multi-user trails.
Note: booked visits only. Steep slopes, sturdy footwear essential. Minimum height 1 metre/no carried children underground.

Parking: on site; woodland car park opposite main entrance.

Dog rating: ✤ **Standard** – Welcome on leads, although not on all guided tours.

Access: 🅿♿🚻♿♿♿

Find out more: 01558 650809 or dolaucothi@nationaltrust.org.uk
nationaltrust.org.uk/dolaucothi

Dolaucothi		M	T	W	T	F	S	S
Mines								
6 Apr–24 Jul*	10–5			W				S
27 Jul–4 Sep	10–5			W	T	F	S	S
7 Sep–30 Oct*	10–5			W				S
Estate and walks								
Open all year		M	T	W	T	F	S	S

*Mines: open Wednesday to Sunday, 11 to 24 April; 30 May to 5 June; 24 to 30 October.

Industrial heritage at Dolaucothi in Carmarthenshire

Dolmelynllyn Estate

Ganllwyd, Near Dolgellau, Gwynedd

1936 🏚♿🚣🚶🏠

The sun rises over ruins on the Dolmelynllyn Estate in Gwynedd

A 696-hectare (1,719-acre) estate, including woodland, two tenanted farms and Grade II-listed Dolmelynllyn Hall, with ornamental lake and parkland. There's a network of paths to explore with highlights which include the impressive Rhaeadr Ddu waterfall, ruins of Cefn Coch gold mines and wildlife-rich oak woodlands.
Note: Dolmelynllyn Hall is a privately run hotel, not a pay-to-enter property.

Satnav: use LL40 2TF. **Parking**: on site.

Dog rating: ✤ **Standard** – Welcome on leads (livestock may be present).

Find out more: 01341 440238 or dolmelynllyn@nationaltrust.org.uk

Dyffryn Gardens

St Nicholas, Vale of Glamorgan CF5 6FZ

2013 🏠✳️🧺🏚️🎴

A garden for all seasons, Dyffryn is slowly being brought back to its Edwardian splendour, while combining its ambition to increase biodiversity and become a space for wellbeing. This journey of restoration means there is always something different to see – from formal gardens to wild meadows, a striking collection of rare cacti and an impressive arboretum. Created in the early 20th century by eminent landscape designer Thomas Mawson, the gardens were the vision of dedicated plant-hunter Reginald Cory, son of wealthy South Wales coal magnate John Cory. The family's imposing Grade II*-listed mansion stands at the heart of the gardens. **Note**: house currently closed as we carry out conservation work and develop plans for its future.

Dyffryn Gardens in the Vale of Glamorgan, this page and opposite, is a garden for all seasons

Parking: on site. Electric vehicle charging point in main car park beside play area.

Dog rating: 🐾 🐾 **Good** – Welcome on short leads throughout garden (assistance dogs only in café and shop).

Access: 🅿️ ♿ 🚻 ♨️ 🎫 📷 🦽 ➡️ ♿

Find out more: 02920 593328 or dyffryn@nationaltrust.org.uk
nationaltrust.org.uk/dyffryn-gardens

Dyffryn Gardens	.	M	T	W	T	F	S	S
1 Jan–18 Feb	10–4*	M	T	W	T	F	S	S
19 Feb–27 Mar	10–5*	M	T	W	T	F	S	S
28 Mar–25 Sep	10–6*	M	T	W	T	F	S	S
26 Sep–23 Oct	10–5*	M	T	W	T	F	S	S
24 Oct–31 Dec**	10–4*	M	T	W	T	F	S	S

Gardens: last entry one hour before closing. *Shop and café: open 10:30 (café: last orders 15 minutes before closing). **Closed 25 and 26 December. House: currently closed.

Erddig

near Wrexham, Wrexham

1973

A haven of natural beauty and a modern sanctuary for wellbeing, Erddig's 485-hectare (1,200-acre) pleasure park, designed by William Emes, welcomes walkers, runners (including their four-legged friends) and those seeking a natural boost in the great outdoors. At its heart, above the River Clywedog, is the house – an unexpected survivor, rescued from dereliction in the 1970s. Discover the story of a family's unique relationship with its servants – a large collection of servants' portraits and carefully preserved rooms capture their lives across the generations, where saw and spade are as treasured as silver and silk. Outdoors, relax in a restored 18th-century walled garden with tranquil water features, trained fruit trees and apple orchards growing more than 180 varieties.

Enjoying the garden and grounds at Erddig, Wrexham, this page, and the opulent Saloon, opposite

Satnav: do not use, follow brown signs.
Parking: on site, 200 yards from ticket office. Electric vehicle charging point in car park.

Dog rating: 🐾 🐾 **Good** – Welcome in country park, Midden Yard and tea garden only.

Access: 🅿️ 🅿️ ♿ ♿ ♿ 🚻 📖 ♿

Find out more: 01978 355314 or erddig@nationaltrust.org.uk
Erddig, near Wrexham, Wrexham LL13 0YT
nationaltrust.org.uk/erddig

Erddig		M	T	W	T	F	S	S
House								
1 Jan–5 Jan	11:30–2:30*	M	T	W			S	S
19 Feb–25 Mar	11:30–2:30*	M	T	W	T	F	S	S
26 Mar–30 Oct	12:30–3:30	M	T	W	T	F	S	S
31 Oct–31 Dec**	11:30–2:30*	M	T	W	T	F	S	S
Garden, restaurant and shop								
1 Jan–25 Mar	11–4	M	T	W	T	F	S	S
26 Mar–30 Oct	10–5	M	T	W	T	F	S	S
31 Oct–31 Dec**	11–4	M	T	W	T	F	S	S

Natural play area: open daily; 19 February to 25 March, 11 to 4, and 26 March to 30 October, 10 to 5.
*Ground-floor servants' quarters only.
**Everything closed 25 and 26 December.

Freshwater West and Gupton Farm

near Castlemartin, Pembrokeshire

| 1976 | 🏠🏖️🎢⛺🍃 |

Freshwater West lies on a wild stretch of coast that's great for water sports and sandy adventures. Beyond the beach, you can discover Gupton Farm, our campsite, Surf Lodge accommodation and visitor hub. The perfect rustic escape for adventurous souls and nature lovers; go wildlife-watching, follow walking trails, make the most of the coast and pitch up on our campsite.

Satnav: for Gupton Farm use SA71 5HW.
Parking: on site.

Dog rating: 🐾 **Standard** – Welcome under close control.

Freshwater West and Gupton Farm in Pembrokeshire: the campsite, below, and wild, sandy coast, above

Access: 🚻♿ 🛗 ⛰️

Find out more: 01646 623110 or freshwater@nationaltrust.org.uk
nationaltrust.org.uk/freshwater-west

Freshwater West and Gupton Farm	M	T	W	T	F	S	S
Campsite							
1 Apr–30 Sep		M	T	W	T	F	S	S

Interpretation room and Surf Lodge (National Trust holiday accommodation) open every day all year.

Green Field

Hafod y Llan

near Beddgelert, Gwynedd

1998

Set in the beautiful Nantgwynant Valley, Hafod y Llan is the largest farm run by the National Trust. Extending from the valley floor to the summit of Snowdon, part of the farm is designated a National Nature Reserve as well as a Site of Special Scientific Interest. Visitors are free to wander the many paths which cross this unique landscape. **Note**: this is a working farm, so access to the farmyard is on foot only.

Satnav: use LL55 4NQ. **Parking**: on farm for campsite guests only. Electric vehicle charging point at campsite for guests. For the Watkin Path, use pay-and-display car park (not National Trust) at Bethannia, opposite farm entrance.

Exploring Hafod y Llan

Dog rating: 🐾 **Standard** – Welcome on leads.

Find out more: 01766 890473 or hafodyllan@nationaltrust.org.uk
nationaltrust.org.uk/hafod-y-llan-farm

Hafod y Llan
Campsite open seasonally.

Looking towards Snowdon with Hafod y Llan, Gwynedd in the distance

The Kymin

Monmouth, Monmouthshire NP25 3SF

 1902 🏠♿🔭

The Kymin in Monmouthshire

Enjoy panoramic views of the Brecon Beacons and Wye Valley; views that once delighted Lord Nelson and Lady Hamilton when they visited the Georgian banqueting house and Naval Temple in 1802. Although the Round House is not open, enjoy lovely walks in the woods and pleasure grounds, perfect for picnics. **Note**: sorry no toilet. Access to car park via steep winding single lane with passing places.

Parking: limited parking on site with designated parking bay adjacent to Round House.

Dog rating: 🐾 **Standard** – Welcome on short leads in the grounds.

Access: 🅿️ 🅳 🎵 ➡️

Find out more: 01874 625515 or kymin@nationaltrust.org.uk
nationaltrust.org.uk/kymin

The Kymin
Grounds: open every day all year. Round House: currently closed, please check the website for details.

Llanbedrog Beach

Llanbedrog, Gwynedd

2000 🏔️🔭

This wonderful stretch of sand, best known for its colourful beach huts, has been enjoyed by generations. Its sheltered waters, fantastic views over Cardigan Bay and adjacent wooded and craggy landscape make this a real gem of Llŷn. **Note**: toilet (not National Trust).

Satnav: use LL53 7TT.
Parking: on site. Electric vehicle charging point beside visitor welcome hut.

Dog rating: 🐾 **Standard** – Welcome, but must be on leads until beyond the beach huts, 1 April to 30 September.

Find out more: 01758 703810 or llanbedrog@nationaltrust.org.uk
nationaltrust.org.uk/llanbedrog-beach

A ranger-led activity at Llanbedrog Beach in Gwynedd

Hands-on fun
in the sands of
Llanbedrog Beach

Cymru Wales

Llanerchaeron

Ciliau Aeron, near Aberaeron,
Ceredigion SA48 8DG

| 1989 | 🏚️🏠♣️🎴🫖📷🎏 |

A remarkably unaltered 18th-century Welsh country estate, comprising the villa, walled gardens, farmyard and pleasure grounds surrounded by parkland and woodlands. The villa (house) is an early example of architect John Nash's work, built in the 1790s, complete with its own service courtyard, including dairy, laundry and salting house – the estate was designed to be self sufficient. The walled kitchen gardens are bursting with colour in summer and the espalier trees abundant with apples in autumn. Explore the pleasure grounds and ornamental lake, before discovering the impressive complex of traditional outbuildings and peaceful woodland or parkland walks.

Parking: 50 yards. Electric vehicle charging point (7kw Type 2) in front of reception.

Llanerchaeron in Ceredigion, clockwise from left: the farmyard, drawing room and courtyard

Dog rating: 🐾 🐾 **Good** – Welcome on leads in the gardens, pleasure grounds and woodland walks.

Access: 🅿️🅿️♿🚽♿🦽📷🎧📷♿♿➡️

Find out more: 01545 570200 or llanerchaeron@nationaltrust.org.uk
nationaltrust.org.uk/llanerchaeron

Llanerchaeron		M	T	W	T	F	S	S
Gardens, farmyard and second-hand bookshop*								
8 Jan–20 Feb	11–3:30**						S	S
23 Feb–6 Nov	10–4:30**			W	T	F	S	S
12 Nov–18 Dec	11–3:30**						S	S
House*								
16 Mar–6 Nov	11–3:30			W	T	F	S	S
Geler Jones Collection								
23 Feb–11 Mar	11:30–2:30			W		F		
16 Mar–4 Nov	11:30–3:30			W		F		

*Open Bank Holiday Mondays. **Second-hand bookshop and reception close 30 minutes before rest of site. Car park, parkland and woodland walks: open daily (excluding 24 to 26 December).

Marloes Sands and Mere

Marloes, Pembrokeshire

A hidden gem on the western edge of Pembrokeshire, Marloes Sands Beach is a long sandy stretch that is perfect for making a splash. Join us for a beach clean, spot marine life and go for a clifftop walk along the coast path. The wetland of Marloes Mere, just inland, is bustling with birdlife. Bring binoculars and get closer to nature at our on-site bird hides.
Note: nearest toilets 164 yards along the track, just past Runwayskiln café.

Satnav: use SA62 3BH. **Parking**: on site. Electric car charging point.

Dog rating: 🐾 **Standard** – Welcome under close control.

Access: ♿🚻 ♿🍴 ⅄ ➡

Find out more: 01646 623110 or marloessands@nationaltrust.org.uk
nationaltrust.org.uk/marloes-sands

Marloes Sands and Mere in Pembrokeshire: the sandy beach, above, and heading towards the sea, below

Fabulously wild Martin's Haven in Pembrokeshire, above and below

Martin's Haven

near Marloes, Pembrokeshire

| 1981 | |

This fabulously wild headland with fine panoramic views of St Bride's Bay is also the gateway to Skomer Island. For a really varied and exciting day, why not combine spotting marine wildlife with discovering traces of ancient settlements?
Note: nearest toilets by the slipway.

Satnav: use SA62 3BJ. **Parking**: on site.

Dog rating: 🐾 **Standard** – Welcome under close control.

Access: 🅿️ ♿

Find out more: 01646 623110 or martinshaven@nationaltrust.org.uk

Mwnt

near Cardigan, Ceredigion | 1963 |

Beautiful secluded bay with a sandy beach – perfect for spotting dolphins, seals and other amazing wildlife.
Note: steep steps to beach with no handrail – not suitable for anyone with limited mobility. For satnav use SA43 1QH.

Find out more: 01545 570200 or mwnt@nationaltrust.org.uk
nationaltrust.org.uk/mwnt

Ogwen Cottage

Nant Ffrancon, Bethesda,
Gwynedd LL57 3LZ 2014

Iconic building long associated with
mountaineering and adventure. There's
a range of rock-climbing, cycling and
mountain-walking routes nearby.
Note: Ogwen Cottage Ranger Base:
usually open during office hours, but
opening times may vary (call for details).

Find out more: 01248 605739 or
ogwen@nationaltrust.org.uk
nationaltrust.org.uk/ogwen-cottage

Paxton's Tower

Llanarthne, near Dryslwyn,
Carmarthenshire 1965

Known as 'Golwg y Byd' (Eye of the World),
Paxton's Tower is said to offer views of
seven counties. **Note**: sorry no toilet. For
satnav use SA32 8HX. Open daily, 8 to 6.

Find out more: 01558 825910 or
paxtonstower@nationaltrust.org.uk

Penbryn

near Sarnau, Cardigan, Ceredigion 1967

One of Ceredigion's best-kept secrets,
this beautifully secluded sandy
cove lies down leafy lanes, edged
with flower-covered banks.
Note: for satnav use SA44 6QL.

Find out more: 01545 570200 or
penbryn@nationaltrust.org.uk
nationaltrust.org.uk/penbryn

Pennard, Pwll Du and Bishopston Valley

near Southgate, Swansea

Pennard, Pwll Du and Bishopston Valley, Swansea

Spectacular cliffs, caves where mammoth
remains have been found, rare birds, an
underground river, bat roosts, silver-lead
mining, ancient woodland, smuggling and
limestone quarrying are just a few of the
wonders of this area. There are also
numerous archaeological features and two
important caves – Bacon Hole and Minchin
Hole. **Note**: due to dangerous rip tides,
swimming in Three Cliffs Bay is not advised.

Satnav: use SA3 2DH.
Parking: at Southgate car park.

Dog rating: ❀ **Standard** – Welcome,
but please be aware livestock graze
freely across Pennard Burrows.

Access: [P♿]

Find out more: 01792 390636 or
pennard@nationaltrust.org.uk
**nationaltrust.org.uk/pennard-pwll-du-
and-bishopston-valley**

Penrhyn Castle and Garden

Bangor, Gwynedd LL57 4HT

1951

Penrhyn Castle is a vast neo-Norman castle and garden with many different tales to tell. Set in 24 hectares (60 acres) of gardens and woodlands, it commands outstanding views across Snowdonia and the North Wales coast, perfect for families, walkers, and nature lovers. Built to impress, the castle's dominating stone façade hides more than just its internal red-brick construction. Inside, experience the luxury of the exquisite carving and furnishings and explore the castle's links to slavery, the slate industry and a bitter industrial dispute that changed Penrhyn's relationship with the local community for ever.

Parking: 500 yards. Electric vehicle charging point in main car park, just below visitor reception.

Dog rating: ✿ **Standard** – Welcome on leads in grounds (assistance dogs only in castle).

Access:

Find out more: 01248 353084 or penrhyncastle@nationaltrust.org.uk
nationaltrust.org.uk/penrhyn-castle

Penrhyn Castle		M	T	W	T	F	S	S
Castle								
5 Mar–30 Oct	10–4*	M	T	W	T	F	S	S
Garden and Victorian Kitchens								
1 Jan–13 Feb**	11–3*						S	S
19 Feb–30 Oct	10–4*	M	T	W	T	F	S	S
5 Nov–18 Dec**	10–4*						S	S
21 Dec–31 Dec†	10–4*			W	T	F	S	S
Shop††								
1 Jan–13 Feb	11–3						S	S
19 Feb–30 Oct	10–4	M	T	W	T	F	S	S
5 Nov–18 Dec	11–3						S	S
Café††								
19 Feb–30 Oct	10:30–4	M	T	W	T	F	S	S
26 Nov–18 Dec	10:30–3:30						S	S

*Last entry one hour before closing.
**Victorian Kitchens: closed 1 January to 13 February and 5 to 25 November.
†Closed 24 to 26 December.
††Opening arrangements may vary.

The dominating Keep of neo-Norman Penrhyn Castle and Garden in Gwynedd

Plas Newydd House and Garden

Llanfairpwll, Anglesey LL61 6DQ

1976 🏠🏚❋🐿🛋🍵📷🏠🎴

With views across the Menai Strait from Anglesey to Snowdonia, this is the perfect place for a house. Transformed into a family home by the 6th Marquess of Anglesey during the 1930s, Plas Newydd's other historic residents include the 1st Marquess, who lost his leg during the Battle of Waterloo, and the flamboyant 5th Marquess. The dining room houses Rex Whistler's 58-foot mural and the Grade I-listed gardens include the Italianate Terrace, Rhododendron Garden and Australasian Arboretum. Perfect for enjoying an outdoor adventure, garden highlights include a hand-built treehouse, nature hides, Frisbee™ golf course, adventure playground and resident red squirrels. **Note**: opening times may vary and some rooms may close occasionally due to essential works.

Parking: 400 yards from main entrance.

Dog rating: ❀ ❀ **Good** – Welcome on short leads in wider garden.

Access: 🅿♿🚜♿♿♿🖼📷🔛◻
🏸♿➡

Find out more: 01248 714795 or plasnewydd@nationaltrust.org.uk
nationaltrust.org.uk/plas-newydd

Plas Newydd		M	T	W	T	F	S	S
Mansion								
4 Mar–6 Nov	11:30–4	M	T	W	T	F	S	S
Gardens, shop and café*								
1 Jan–4 Jan	11–3	M	T	.	.	.	S	S
8 Jan–13 Feb	11–3	.	.	.	.	.	S	S
14 Feb–6 Nov	10:30–5	M	T	W	T	F	S	S
12 Nov–18 Dec	11–3	.	.	.	.	.	S	S
27 Dec–31 Dec	11–3	.	T	W	T	F	S	.

*Gardens: last entry one hour before closing.

Plas Newydd House and Garden, Anglesey: enjoying the view from the battlements, left, and the fine 18th-century house, below

Plas yn Rhiw in Gwynedd, above, sits in glorious gardens, below, with spectacular views over Cardigan Bay

Plas yn Rhiw

Rhiw, Pwllheli, Gwynedd LL53 8AB

1952

Standing on a hillside overlooking Cardigan Bay, Plas yn Rhiw is a beautiful 17th-century manor house with Georgian additions. The house was rescued from neglect and lovingly restored by the three Keating sisters, who bought the property in 1939. The views from the grounds and gardens across the bay are among the most spectacular in Britain. The garden contains many beautiful flowering trees and shrubs, with beds framed by box hedges and grass paths – stunning whatever the season. There are also woodlands, an orchard and meadow to explore.

Parking: 100 yards (narrow lanes). Electric vehicle charging point in top car park beside tea-room.

Dog rating: ❀ **Standard** – Welcome on leads in woodland walk below the visitor reception and toilet facilities (assistance dogs elsewhere).

Access: 🅿 🅳 ♿ 🚻 ♿ ♿

Find out more: 01758 780219 or plasynrhiw@nationaltrust.org.uk
nationaltrust.org.uk/plas-yn-rhiw

Plas yn Rhiw	M	T	W	T	F	S	S
House and garden							
13 Apr–30 Oct 10:30–5		·	**W**	**T**	·	**S**	**S**

House and reception: last entry one hour before closing; booking essential. Open Bank Holiday Mondays.
Tea-room: for opening times, please check before visiting.

Porth Meudwy

near Aberdaron, Gwynedd

1990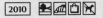

Sheltered cove on the wild, rocky coastline west of Aberdaron. Once the embarkation point for pilgrims to Ynys Enlli (Bardsey Island), today fishermen still bring the daily catch into the cove. Don't miss the unique Aberdaron wooden beach boats, designed to dance nimbly through the waves along the craggy coastline. **Note**: sorry no toilet.

Satnav: use LL53 8DA. **Parking**: ½ mile.

Dog rating: ❀ **Standard** – Welcome on leads (near livestock).

Find out more: 01758 703810 or porthmeudwy@nationaltrust.org.uk

Porth Meudwy in Gwynedd: the cove offers welcome shelter

Porth y Swnt

Henfaes, Aberdaron, Pwllheli, Gwynedd LL53 8BE

2010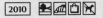

Porth y Swnt, Gwynedd: the interpretation centre

Llŷn's unique culture, heritage and environment are waiting to be discovered at this exciting interpretation centre. You can follow in the footsteps of pilgrims across the Sound in the video pod, form your reflective thoughts in the Sea of Word and see the Ynys Enlli (Bardsey Island) lighthouse's retired optic.

Parking: on site. Electric vehicle charging point behind visitor centre.

Access: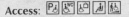

Find out more: 01758 703810 or porthyswnt@nationaltrust.org.uk **nationaltrust.org.uk/porth-y-swnt**

Porth y Swnt		M	T	W	T	F	S	S
14 Apr–30 Oct	10–4				T	F	S	S

Additional openings possible at busy periods, such as school holidays (please check before visiting).

Porthdinllaen

Morfa Nefyn, Gwynedd

1994

This old fishing village really is a jewel. Perched on the end of a thin ribbon of land which stretches out into the Irish Sea, its clear sheltered waters lap against the stout stone houses. You can watch fishermen bring in the daily catch, while relaxing with a drink at the Tŷ Coch Inn. In the summer you can view the ecologically rich seagrasses from a paddleboard – and have fun trying to stand up. **Note**: Porthdinllaen village is approximately 1 mile from nearest car park; no vehicle access.

Satnav: use LL53 6DA.
Parking: on site for beach; 1 mile from village (no vehicular access to village). Electric vehicle charging point in Trust car park, beside visitor welcome hut.

Dog rating: ✿ **Standard** – Under close control, 1 October to 31 March; on east side of beach in summer.

Access:

Find out more: 01758 703810 or porthdinllaen@nationaltrust.org.uk
nationaltrust.org.uk/porthdinllaen

The fine sandy beach and clear waters of Porthdinllaen in Gwynedd, above and below

Porthor

Aberdaron, Gwynedd

| 1981 |

This wonderful beach is famous for its 'whistling sands' and glistening waters. The whistling happens because of the especially fine sand grains on the beach – perfect for building sandcastles. If the joys of sandcastles and sunbathing are not enough for you, then why not have a go at surfing? The sea here is perfect. In addition, the Wales Coast Path runs in both directions from the car park. **Note**: nearest toilet in car park.

Satnav: use LL53 8LG. **Parking**: on site. Electric vehicle charging point.

Dog rating: ❀ **Standard** – Seasonal dog restrictions apply.

Access:

Porthor, Gwynedd, offers 'whistling sands' and fine surf, above, as well as rock pools for everyone to enjoy, below

Find out more: 01758 703810 or porthor@nationaltrust.org.uk
nationaltrust.org.uk/porthor

Powis Castle and Garden

Welshpool, Powys

1952

Once the medieval fortress of Welsh princes, Powis Castle was transformed over centuries into a grand home for the Herbert family, reflecting their wealth and status. Furnished with sumptuous fabrics, world-class artworks, furniture, tapestries and the unique Clive Collection of Indian and East Asian artefacts, the interior reflects the Elizabethan period through to the Edwardian period. With views across the Severn Valley, the garden is one of

Powis Castle and Garden, Powys, this page and opposite: a grand home within one of Britain's finest gardens

Britain's finest. Dating back more than 300 years, it includes 17th-century Italianate terraces lined with vibrant herbaceous borders and gigantic clipped yews, an Edwardian formal garden with century-old apple trees and rose beds, and a woodland area which boasts several champion trees.

Satnav: postcode misdirects; enter Powis Castle. **Parking**: on site. Two electric vehicle charging points in car park.

Dog rating: ✤ **Standard** – Assistance dogs only March to October. Dogs on short leads welcome November to February.

Access:

Find out more: 01938 551920 or
powiscastle@nationaltrust.org.uk
Welshpool, Powys SY21 8RF
nationaltrust.org.uk/powis

Powis Castle		M	T	W	T	F	S	S
Castle								
19 Feb–31 Oct	12–4	M	T	W	T	F	S	S
5 Nov–27 Nov	12–4	.	.	.	.	.	S	S
1 Dec–24 Dec	12–4	M	T	W	T	F	S	S
Garden, café and shop								
1 Jan–31 Mar	10–4*	M	T	W	T	F	S	S
1 Apr–30 Sep	10–5**	M	T	W	T	F	S	S
1 Oct–31 Dec†	10–4*	M	T	W	T	F	S	S

*Shop: opens 11; 1 January to 18 February, open
Friday to Sunday only; closed 24 to 31 December.
**Garden coffee shop and garden shop: opening times vary.
†Closed 25 and 26 December.

Rhosili and South Gower Coast

on the Gower Peninsula, Swansea

| 1933 | 🏠 🚶 🏔 🐑 ☕ 🛍 📷 ⛩ |

Lying at the far end of the beautiful Gower Peninsula, Rhosili is blessed with 3 miles of golden, award-winning sands and spectacular coastal views. It is the perfect base from which to explore the stunning South Gower coastline – most of which is in the care of the National Trust. From the historically and environmentally important medieval strip-farm system known as The Vile, to the instantly recognisable Worm's Head tidal island, Iron Age earthworks, notable wildlife and geology, through to legends, shipwrecks and stories, there is so much to see. Once visited, Rhosili will stay with you for ever. **Note**: steep steps and a slope to the beach.

Satnav: use SA3 1PR. **Parking**: large pay and display car park at end of village. Suitable for motorhomes (no overnight stays). Electric vehicle charging point.

Dog rating: 🐾 **Standard** – Welcome (on leads near livestock please). Beach is dog-friendly all year.

Access: 🅿️ 🚽 ♿ 🚻 📷 🚶 ⬤⬤ 🔍 ➡️

Find out more: 01792 390707 or rhosili@nationaltrust.org.uk **nationaltrust.org.uk/rhosili-and-south-gower-coast**

Rhosili

Outdoor food and beverages: open 1 March to 31 October (weather permitting).

Rhosili and South Gower Coast, Swansea: miles of sands and spectacular views, left and below

St David's Visitor Centre and Shop

Captain's House, High Street, St David's, Pembrokeshire SA62 6SD

 1974 📷🖼🏠🎁

Footpath at St David's Head, Pembrokeshire

This visitor centre and well-stocked shop overlooks the Old Cross in the centre of St David's, Wales's smallest historic city. Why not take a look at our retail collection and then have a chat with one of the team about exploring Pembrokeshire? **Note**: sorry no toilet.

Parking: none on site.

Access: 🦽

Find out more: 01437 720385 or stdavidsshop@nationaltrust.org.uk **nationaltrust.org.uk/st-davids-visitor-centre**

St David's Visitor Centre		M	T	W	T	F	S	S
5 Jan–12 Feb	11–4	·	·	W	T	F	S	·
14 Feb–2 Oct	10–4	M	T	W	T	F	S	S
3 Oct–31 Dec*	11–4	M	T	W	T	F	S	·

*Closed 24 to 27 December.

Segontium

Caernarfon, Gwynedd 1937

Fort built to defend the Roman Empire against rebellious tribes. **Note**: under the guardianship of Cadw – Welsh Government's historic environment service. Museum not National Trust. For satnav use LL55 2LN. Please call Cadw on 0300 025 6000 for opening arrangements.

Skenfrith Castle

Skenfrith, near Abergavenny, Monmouthshire NP7 8UH 1936

Remains of early 13th-century castle, built beside the River Monnow to command one of the main routes from England. **Note**: under the guardianship of Cadw – Welsh Government's historic environment service. Open dawn to dusk.

Find out more: 01874 625515 or skenfrithcastle@nationaltrust.org.uk **nationaltrust.org.uk/skenfrith**

Southwood Estate

Newgale, Roch, Pembrokeshire

2003 🏠📷🖼🏕

The timeless coastline at Southwood Estate in Pembrokeshire

A timeless landscape of wooded valleys, floral fields and craggy cliffs, the Southwood Estate is full of scenic surprises. Follow the waymarked walking trails and explore the best of coast and countryside; spot flora and fauna and see how we're working hard to safeguard this special place. **Note**: access is through a working farm.

Satnav: for Southwood Farm car park use SA62 6AR; Maidenhall car park use SA62 6BD. **Parking**: on site.

Dog rating: ❀ **Standard** – Welcome on a lead. Please be aware of livestock.

Access: 🔧

Find out more: 01646 623110 or southwoodestate@nationaltrust.org.uk **nationaltrust.org.uk/southwood-estate**

Stackpole

near Pembroke, Pembrokeshire

1976 🏠❀🐂🏰🐓🍵🛑♿

A former grand estate stretching down to a beautiful coastline, Stackpole Estate is a National Nature Reserve, recognised for its flora and fauna. It provides easy access to Bosherston Lakes, Stackpole Quay and the award-winning beaches of Broad Haven South, Barafundle Bay and Stackpole Quay. The Lakes, famous for their superb display of lilies and resident otters, and the dramatic cliffs of Stackpole Head are great for wildlife watching. The environmentally friendly Stackpole Centre houses up to 144 guests and includes a theatre, meeting and

South Beach at Broad Haven, Stackpole in Pembrokeshire

classroom space. It is the ideal place for groups, corporate clients, celebrations and family holidays.

Satnav: for Stackpole Quay use SA71 5LS; Broad Haven South SA71 5DR; Bosherston Lakes SA71 5DR; Stackpole Court SA71 5DE. **Parking**: car parks at Stackpole Quay, Broad Haven South, Bosherston Lakes and Stackpole Court. Electric vehicle charging point at Stackpole Centre (SA71 5DQ) and Stackpole Quay (SA71 5LS).

Dog rating: 🐾 **Standard** – Welcome under close control on the estate.

Access: 🅿♿🚻♿🐾➡♿

Find out more: 01646 623110 or stackpole@nationaltrust.org.uk
nationaltrust.org.uk/stackpole

Sugar Loaf and Usk Valley

near Abergavenny, Monmouthshire

 🏠♿🏕

Walking one of the trails at Sugar Loaf and Usk Valley, Monmouthshire

Discover glorious views across Monmouthshire and the borders from the peaks of Sugar Loaf and The Skirrid. Alternatively explore seasonal changes through the ancient woodland that straddles their slopes. By contrast, meander through parkland at Clytha and the Usk Valley, perfect for picnics or short walks. **Note**: sorry no toilet. Some car parks not National Trust (charge including members).

Parking: numerous on-site car parks for Usk Valley.

Dog rating: 🐾 **Standard** – Welcome on leads.

Find out more: 01874 625515 or sugarloaf@nationaltrust.org.uk
nationaltrust.org.uk/sugarloaf-and-usk-valley

Tredegar House

Tredegar House, Pencarn Way,
Newport NP10 8YW

2012 🏛️ 🏠 ❄️ 🏖️ ☕ 🍴 🎡 🌿

Tredegar House and the Morgan family
have been an important part of Newport
and the surrounding area for more than
500 years. Captivating tales of war heroism,
inheritance disputes, Russian princesses
and wide-ranging influence bring alive a
home designed to impress and entertain.
The contrasting formal gardens reflect the
life of the family who once lived here, while
the parkland is a haven for visitors and
wildlife alike. Those who care for the
mansion, gardens and parkland today work
in partnership with the local community,
combining colourful histories and modern
programmes to bring genuine benefit
to all who visit.

Satnav: enter 'Pencarn Way' and
NP10 8YW. **Parking**: on site.
One electrical charging point.

A young visitor explores the Cedar Garden
at Tredegar House in Newport

Dog rating: 🐾 🐾 🐾 **Best** – Well-behaved
dogs welcome in the parkland, formal
gardens and café.

Access: 🅿️🚻♿🍴📷🎨📷♿🕊️ 🚻♿➡️

Find out more:
tredegar@nationaltrust.org.uk
nationaltrust.org.uk/tredegar-house

Tredegar House		M	T	W	T	F	S	S
House and gardens*								
19 Feb–8 Apr	10:30–4	M	T	W	T	F	S	S
9 Apr–30 Sep	10:30–5	M	T	W	T	F	S	S
1 Oct–6 Nov	10:30–4	M	T	W	T	F	S	S
11 Nov–12 Dec	10:30–4	M				F	S	S
16 Dec–22 Dec	10:30–4	M	T	W	T	F	S	S
Café								
1 Jan–8 Apr	10–4	M	T	W	T	F	S	S
9 Apr–30 Sep	10–5	M	T	W	T	F	S	S
1 Oct–31 Dec**	10–4	M	T	W	T	F	S	S
Park								
Open all year	Dawn–dusk	M	T	W	T	F	S	S

*House: opens and closes 30 minutes after and before
these times; last entry one hour before closing.
**Closed 25 December.

Tudor Merchant's House

Quay Hill, Tenby, Pembrokeshire SA70 7BX

1937

Tudor Merchant's House in Pembrokeshire

Over 500 years ago when Tenby was a busy trading port, a merchant built this three-storey house to live in and trade from. The building has been furnished with exquisitely carved replica furniture and brightly coloured wall-hangings which re-create the atmosphere of life in Tudor Tenby. **Note**: sorry no toilet.

Parking: very limited on-street parking. Several pay-and-display car parks, not National Trust (charge including members).

Access:

Find out more: 01646 623110 or tudormerchantshouse@nationaltrust.org.uk
nationaltrust.org.uk/tudor-merchants-house

Tudor Merchant's House		M	T	W	T	F	S	S
3 Mar–7 Apr	11–4	·	·	·	T	·	·	·
14 Apr–2 Jul	11–4	·	·	·	T	·	S	·
5 Jul–30 Aug	11–4	·	·	T	·	T	·	S	·
1 Sep–29 Oct	11–4	·	·	·	T	·	S	·

Booking required.

Tŷ Mawr Wybrnant

Penmachno, Betws-y-Coed, Conwy LL25 0HJ

1951

Modest 16th-century farmhouse with huge cultural significance. Birthplace to Bishop William Morgan, whose 10-year endeavour to translate the Bible into Welsh helped ensure the survival of the language. The house is situated on the old drovers' road and there are several walking trails in the valley. **Note**: access via narrow road from Penmachno.

Satnav: do not use, follow brown signs instead. No access from A470.
Parking: 500 yards.

Dog rating: 🐾 **Standard** – Welcome on leads.

Access:

Find out more: 01766 510120 or tymawrwybrnant@nationaltrust.org.uk
Penmachno, Betws-y-Coed,
Conwy LL25 0HJ
nationaltrust.org.uk/ty-mawr-wybrnant

Tŷ Mawr Wybrnant

Opening arrangements not confirmed at time of print, please check before visiting.

Tŷ Mawr Wybrnant, Conwy: humble yet significant

Flying kites on the beach
at Murlough National Nature
Reserve, County Down

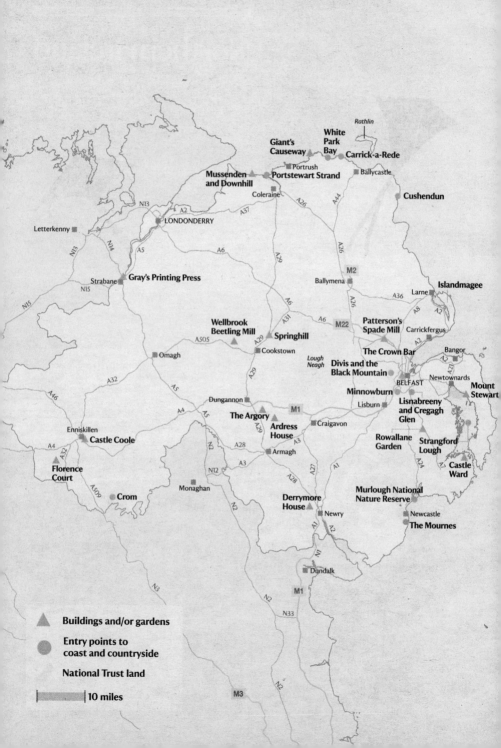

Giant's Causeway

White Park Bay

Carrick-a-Rede

Rathlin

Mussenden and Downhill

Portstewart Strand

Portrush

Ballycastle

Coleraine

Cushendun

N13

A2

A37

A26

A44

LONDONDERRY

Letterkenny

N13

A5

A6

A29

A26

M2

Islandmagee

Gray's Printing Press

Strabane

N14

N15

Ballymena

Larne

A36

A8

A2

N15

A6

A31

A6

M22

A26

Patterson's Spade Mill

Carrickfergus

A2

Bangor

Wellbrook Beetling Mill

Springhill

A505

A29

Cookstown

Lough Neagh

The Crown Bar

A2

A27

Omagh

A32

A5

A29

Divis and the Black Mountain

BELFAST

Newtownards

Mount Stewart

Dungannon

Minnowburn

Lisburn

Lisnabreeny and Cregagh Glen

A46

A4

A5

M1

The Argory

Ardress House

Craigavon

A3

Rowallane Garden

Strangford Lough

Enniskillen

Castle Coole

A32

A28

A29

Armagh

A27

A1

A24

Castle Ward

Florence Court

A509

N2

A3

N12

A28

Murlough National Nature Reserve

Crom

Monaghan

Derrymore House

A1

Newry

Newcastle

The Mournes

N2

A1

A2

N1

Dundalk

N3

M1

N2

N33

▲ **Buildings and/or gardens**

● **Entry points to coast and countryside**

National Trust land

10 miles

M3

Ardress House, County Armagh: the Georgian interior, above, and making a farmyard friend, below

Ardress House

64 Ardress Road, Annaghmore, Portadown, County Armagh BT62 1SQ

1959 🏠🚌❄️♿🏛️🖼️🚶

Set within 40 hectares (100 acres) of rolling countryside, this 17th-century farmhouse surprises with detailed plasterwork and fine Georgian interiors. Outside, the garden and woodland provide the perfect setting for hours of fun and relaxation for everyone.

Parking: 10 yards.

Dog rating: ❀ **Standard** – Welcome on leads in grounds and garden. Assistance dogs only in farmyard.

Access: ♿🚻 👣 ♿

Find out more: 028 8778 4753 or ardress@nationaltrust.org.uk
nationaltrust.org.uk/ardress-house

Ardress House									
House and farmyard									
15 Apr–19 Apr	11–5		M	T			F	S	S
24 Apr–30 Oct	11–5								S
Grounds									
Open all year*	11–5		M	T	W	T	F	S	S

House: last entry one hour before closing.
*Grounds closed 25 and 26 December.

The Argory

144 Derrycaw Road, Moy, Dungannon,
County Armagh BT71 6NA

| 1979 | 🏛️ 🖼️ ❀ ♿ ☕ 📷 🚶 |

This Irish gentry house can trace more than
200 years of history. Built in the 1820s for
the MacGeough Bond family, the house
and surrounding riverside estate came into
existence due to a quirky stipulation in a
will. The interior of this understated and
intimate house still evokes the eclectic
tastes and interests of the family. The
small rose garden with its sundial, pleasure
gardens and wooded walks along the
River Blackwater are ideal for exploring.

The Artificial Sunshine neon
sculpture installation at
The Argory in County Armagh

Check opening dates and times before you set out: nationaltrust.org.uk

Letting off steam at The Argory

Parking: 100 yards.

Dog rating: 🐾 **Standard** – Welcome on leads in grounds and garden.

Access: 🅿️ 🅳 🚻 ♿

Find out more: 028 8778 4753 or argory@nationaltrust.org.uk
nationaltrust.org.uk/argory

Carrick-a-Rede

Ballintoy, County Antrim BT54 6LS

| 1967 | 🏠🍴⛰️☕🏛️🎪🚶 |

Connected to the cliffs by a rope bridge across the Atlantic Ocean, this rocky island is the ultimate clifftop experience. Jutting out from the Causeway Coastal Route, the 30-metre-deep and 20-metre-wide chasm separating Carrick-a-Rede from the mainland is traversed by an amazing rope bridge that was traditionally erected by salmon fishermen. Wildlife-rich and with views across the seas to Rathlin Island, this is also home to Larrybane old quarry, featured in the television series *Game of Thrones*. **Note**: bridge access weather-dependent.

The rope bridge at Carrick-a-Rede, County Antrim, is not for the faint hearted

The Argory									
House and Courtyard coffee shop									
2 Jan–30 Jan	11–4								S
5 Feb–27 Feb*	11–5							S	S
5 Mar–10 Apr	11–5							S	S
11 Apr–24 Apr	11–5	M	T	W	T	F		S	S
30 Apr–29 May	11–5	M						S	S
30 May–27 Jun	11–5	M				F		S	S
1 Jul–31 Aug	11–5	M	T	W	T	F		S	S
3 Sep–25 Sep	11–5							S	S
1 Oct–23 Oct	11–4							S	S
24 Oct–31 Oct	11–4	M	T	W	T	F		S	S
5 Nov–18 Dec	11–4							S	S
Grounds									
Open all year**	11–5	M	T	W	T	F		S	S

House: last entry one hour before closing.
*Also open 17 and 18 February for half term, 11 to 5.
**Grounds: closed 25 and 26 December.

Carrick-a-Rede: the coastline and bridge, above and below

Parking: on site.

Dog rating: 🐾 🐾 **Good** – Welcome on leads (not permitted to cross bridge).

Access:

Find out more: 028 2073 3335 or carrickarede@nationaltrust.org.uk
nationaltrust.org.uk/carrick-a-rede

Carrick-a-Rede

Carrick-a-Rede: opening arrangements not confirmed at time of print, please check before visiting.
Car park: open daily, March to September, 10 to 5.

Castle Coole

Enniskillen, County Fermanagh BT74 6HN

1951 🏠🏚️🎣☕🏠🚶

Surrounded by a stunning landscape park, the majestic 18th-century home of the Earls of Belmore was created to impress. One of the finest examples of Neo-classical architecture in Ireland, the rooms at Castle Coole are brimming with opulence, luxury and colour. There are interesting pieces of history to explore, such as the servants' tunnel and ice house. The parkland, interspersed with mature oaks, woodlands and paths, is perfect for refreshing walks, while the outdoor play area is great for families.

Parking: 150 yards.

Young visitors at Castle Coole, County Fermanagh

Neo-classical Castle Coole was created to impress

Dog rating: 🐾 **Standard** – Welcome under control.

Access: 🅿️🇩♿🚻📖VT♿📷♿♿♿

Find out more: 028 6632 2690 or castlecoole@nationaltrust.org.uk
nationaltrust.org.uk/castle-coole

Castle Coole		M	T	W	T	F	S	S
House and tea-room								
5 Mar–10 Apr	11–4						S	S
15 Apr–23 Apr	11–4	M	T	W	T	F	S	S
24 Apr–30 Apr	11–4						S	S
1 May–30 May	11–4	M		W	T	F	S	S
1 Jun–31 Aug	11–5	M	T	W	T	F	S	S
1 Sep–30 Sep	11–4	M		W	T	F	S	S
Grounds								
1 Jan–28 Feb	10–4	M	T	W	T	F	S	S
1 Mar–31 Oct	10–6	M	T	W	T	F	S	S
1 Nov–31 Dec	10–4	M	T	W	T	F	S	S

House: last entry one hour before closing.
Open Bank Holiday Mondays, Thursday 17 March and all other public holidays in Northern Ireland.

Castle Ward

Strangford, Downpatrick,
County Down BT30 7LS

1953 | [icons]

High on a hillside with views across the tranquil waters of Strangford Lough, the Gothic and classical collide at Castle Ward. This eccentric 18th-century mansion within an extensive walled demesne is one of the most peculiar architectural compromises between two people. In the farmyard, visit the water-powered cornmill or stroll among flowers and subtropical plants in the restored Sunken Garden. The laundry, tack room and dairy give an insight into life

Castle Ward, County Down: a striking Gothic interior in the eccentric mansion

'below stairs'. Discover more on the 21 miles of multi-use trails, while the Woodland and Adventure playgrounds and Secret Shore Nature Trail are great for children. **Note**: 1 March to 30 November, access to livestock grazing areas may be restricted.

Parking: on site.

Dog rating: 🐾 🐾 🐾 **Best** – Welcome on leads (restrictions apply in livestock grazing areas). Enclosed dog exercise area available.

Access: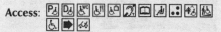

The colourful Sunken Garden at Castle Ward,
above, and peaceful lough shore, right

Find out more: 028 4488 1204 or
castleward@nationaltrust.org.uk
nationaltrust.org.uk/castle-ward

Castle Ward		M	T	W	T	F	S	S
House								
18 Mar–30 Oct	11–4	·	·	·	·	F	S	S
Parkland, trails and garden								
Open all year	9–6	M	T	W	T	F	S	S
Tea-room, gift shop and second-hand bookshop								
Open all year	11–4	M	T	W	T	F	S	S

House: times subject to change, please check before visiting.
Everything closed 25 December.

Crom

Upper Lough Erne, Newtownbutler, County Fermanagh BT92 8AJ

1987 🏛🏠🎫🌿🦌☕🏕

Home to islands, ancient woodland and historical ruins, this 800-hectare (2,000-acre) demesne sits in a tranquil landscape on the peaceful southern shores of Upper Lough Erne. One of Ireland's most important conservation areas, it has many rare species and is rich in wildlife, including fallow deer, red squirrels and pine martens. An ideal spot for relaxing walks, cycling and boat trips. Visit the outbuildings, such as the summerhouse and boathouse. Jetty area available to use nearby. Turn your visit into a holiday with a stay in one of our holiday cottages (dog-friendly), award-winning glamping pods or campsites. **Note**: 19th-century castle not open to public.

Parking: 100 yards.

Dog rating: 🐾 🐾 🐾 **Best** – Under control.

Access: 🅿♿🚻♿♿♿♿➡♿

Crom in County Fermanagh, this page and above right: on Upper Lough Erne's tranquil shores

Find out more: 028 6773 8118 or
crom@nationaltrust.org.uk
nationaltrust.org.uk/crom

Crom		M	T	W	T	F	S	S
Visitor centre and tea-room								
5 Mar–10 Apr	11–4*						S	S
15 Apr–24 Apr	11–4*	M	T	W	T	F	S	S
30 Apr–31 May	11–4*	M	T	W	T	F	S	S
1 Jun–31 Aug	11–5*	M	T	W	T	F	S	S
1 Sep–30 Sep	11–4*	M	T	W	T	F	S	S
1 Oct–30 Oct	11–4*						S	S
Grounds								
1 Jan–28 Feb	10–4	M	T	W	T	F	S	S
1 Mar–1 Nov	10–6	M	T	W	T	F	S	S
2 Nov–31 Dec	10–4	M	T	W	T	F	S	S

*Last admission one hour before closing.
Open Bank Holiday Mondays, Wednesday 17 March
and all other public holidays in Northern Ireland.

The Crown Bar

46 Great Victoria Street, Belfast,
County Antrim BT2 7BA 1978

Belfast's most famous pub remains one
of the finest examples of a high-Victorian
gin palace complete with period features.
Note: run by Mitchells & Butlers.
Open daily, 11:30 to midnight
(opens 12:30 on Sunday).

Find out more: 028 9024 3187 or
info@crownbar.com
nationaltrust.org.uk/crown-bar

Cushendun

County Antrim

1954

Set at the mouth of the River Dun
(Brown River) at the foot of Glendun,
Cushendun is a very charming historic
village steeped in character and folklore.
The surrounding hills are a patchwork
of farms, small fields, hedgerows and
traditional stone walls. Sheltered harbour
and beautiful beach. Views of Scotland.

Satnav: use BT44 0PH.
Parking: car park adjacent to Corner House
tea-room and at Glenmona House.

Dog rating: 🐾 **Standard** – Dogs welcome
in all areas on a lead.

Find out more: 028 7084 8728 or
cushendun@nationaltrust.org.uk
nationaltrust.org.uk/cushendun

The bay at Cushendun in County Antrim

Derrymore House

Bessbrook, Newry,
County Armagh BT35 7EF

1953 🏠👥🌳🏃

Derrymore House in County Armagh

Resting peacefully in a landscaped demesne, this 18th-century thatched cottage is rich in history. Explore the park and woodlands and discover the children's play area.

Parking: on site.

Dog rating: ❀ Standard – Dogs on leads and only in grounds.

Access: ♿🚻

Find out more: 028 8778 4753 or derrymore@nationaltrust.org.uk
nationaltrust.org.uk/derrymore-house

Derrymore House	
Grounds	
Open every day all year*	Dawn–dusk

House: open by appointment only or private group booking (minimum numbers apply), please email to arrange.
*Grounds: closed 25 and 26 December.

Divis and the Black Mountain

Hannahstown, near Belfast, County Antrim

2004 🏠👥☕🌳🏃

Sitting in the heart of the Belfast Hills, this 809-hectare (2,000-acre) mosaic of upland heath and blanket bog is a great place for a wild countryside experience. There are three walking trails to explore, affording panoramic views across Belfast and a wealth of flora, fauna and archaeological remains to discover. **Note**: cattle roam freely during summer months. Mountain environment and weather conditions can change rapidly.

Satnav: use BT17 0NG.
Parking: beside The Barn or in the car park on Divis Road, opposite entrance gates.

Dog rating: ❀ Standard – Welcome on leads only.

Access: ♿🚻🧴🚶♿♿

Find out more: 028 9082 5434 or divis@nationaltrust.org.uk
nationaltrust.org.uk/divis

Divis and the Black Mountain	
Barn café	
Open every day all year	10–5

Closed 25 and 26 December. Opens 9:30 at weekends.

Divis and the Black Mountain in County Antrim

Florence Court

Enniskillen, County Fermanagh BT92 1DB

| 1954 | 🏠 🏡 ❀ 🛏 ☕ ⛺ 🚶 |

Florence Court enjoys a majestic countryside setting in West Fermanagh, surrounded by lush parkland with Benaughlin Mountain rising in the background. There is something for everyone to enjoy at this extensive and welcoming place. Inside the Georgian mansion you can hear stories about the Earls of Enniskillen and their staff, who lived here for more than 250 years. Outdoors take a gentle walk or long cycle along 10 miles of trails in the adjoining forest park and see fascinating industrial heritage features, including the water-powered sawmill and blacksmith's forge. The gardens are home to the mother of all Irish yew trees, as well as the kitchen garden, which is being restored to its 1930s character.

The Walled Garden, above, and Servants' Hall, below, at Florence Court in County Fermanagh

Florence Court: exploring the Library, above, inside the Georgian mansion, below

Parking: 200 yards to visitor centre.

Dog rating: 🐾 🐾 **Good** – Welcome on leads in walled garden.

Access: 🅿️ 🐕 ♿ 🚻 VT ♿ 🎧 📷 🔦 ♿ ➡️ 🚫

Find out more: 028 6634 8249 or florencecourt@nationaltrust.org.uk
nationaltrust.org.uk/florence-court

Florence Court		M	T	W	T	F	S	S
House, tea-room and visitor centre								
5 Mar–10 Apr	11–5						S	S
15 Apr–24 Apr	11–5	M	T	W	T	F	S	S
25 Apr–31 May	11–5	M	T	W	T		S	S
1 Jun–31 Aug	11–5	M	T	W	T	F	S	S
1 Sep–1 Oct	11–5	M	T	W	T		S	S
8 Oct–23 Oct	11–5						S	S
24 Oct–31 Oct	11–5	M	T	W	T	F	S	S
5 Nov–31 Dec*	11–4						S	S
Gardens and park								
1 Jan–28 Feb	10–4	M	T	W	T	F	S	S
1 Mar–1 Nov	10–6	M	T	W	T	F	S	S
2 Nov–31 Dec	10–4	M	T	W	T	F	S	S

House: admission by guided tour (last tour one hour before closing). *House and tea-room: closed November and December. Open Bank Holiday Mondays and all other public holidays in Northern Ireland. Grounds closed 25 December.

Giant's Causeway

44 Causeway Road, Bushmills,
County Antrim BT57 8SU

| 1962 |

Follow in the legendary footsteps of giants at Northern Ireland's iconic UNESCO World Heritage Site. The famous basalt columns of the Causeway landscape, left by volcanic eruptions 60 million years ago, are home to more than Finn McCool. Its nooks and crannies are dotted with dainty sea campion, and defensive fulmars protect their cliff nests. Windswept walking trails wind through this Area of Outstanding Natural Beauty, with an all-accessible walk at Runkerry Head and more challenging terrain along the Causeway Coast Way. The interactive exhibition and innovative audio-guides unlock secrets of the landscape and regale visitors with legends of giants. **Note**: due to popularity, all visitors, including members, are recommended to book before visiting.

Magnificent basalt columns at The Giant's Causeway in County Antrim

Discovering The Giant's Causeway

The Giant's Causeway: inside the Visitor Centre

Parking: on-site car park for Visitor Experience ticket holders. Causeway Coast Way car park on Causeway Road for walkers with PayByPhone system.

Dog rating: 🐾 🐾 🐾 **Best** – Fully dog friendly. Welcome on leads in Visitor Centre and on guided tours.

Access:

Find out more: 028 2073 1855 or
giantscauseway@nationaltrust.org.uk
nationaltrust.org.uk/giants-causeway

Giant's Causeway		M	T	W	T	F	S	S
Stones and coastal path								
Open all year	Dawn–dusk	M	T	W	T	F	S	S
Visitor Centre								
1 Jan–31 Mar	10–4		M	T	W	T	F	S	S
1 Apr–31 Oct	10–5		M	T	W	T	F	S	S
1 Nov–31 Dec	10–4*		M	T	W	T	F	S	S

Visitor Centre: last entry one hour before closing.
*Closed 24 to 26 December.

Gray's Printing Press

49 Main Street, Strabane,
County Tyrone BT82 8AU 1966

The indelible story of printing is told behind this Strabane Georgian shop front, once reputed to be Ireland's printing capital. **Note**: appointment only or private group booking (minimum numbers), please email.

Find out more: 028 8674 8210 or grays@nationaltrust.org.uk
nationaltrust.org.uk/grays-printing-press

Islandmagee

near Larne, County Antrim 1996

An Area of Special Scientific Interest, this peninsula has some of Northern Ireland's largest colonies of cliff-nesting seabirds. **Note**: paths are uneven and steep in places. For satnav use BT40 3TP.

Find out more: 028 9064 7787 or islandmagee@nationaltrust.org.uk
nationaltrust.org.uk/islandmagee

Lisnabreeny and Cregagh Glen

near Belfast, County Down 1938

On the edge of Belfast, paths through a wooded glen cross farmland, emerging at a rath on the Castlereagh Hills. **Note**: uneven paths and steps. For satnav use BT8 6SA.

Find out more: 028 9064 7787 or lisnabreeny@nationaltrust.org.uk
nationaltrust.org.uk/lisnabreeny

Minnowburn

near Belfast, County Down

1952

Two views of Minnowburn, County Down, which sits in the heart of the Lagan Valley

Nestled in the heart of Lagan Valley Regional Park, where meadows and woodlands roll down to the River Lagan. Perfect for a short stroll or longer walk. Climb Terrace Hill to discover the garden built by linen merchant Ned Robinson, and stop for a picnic and to admire the views. **Note**: trails are uneven and steep in places.

Satnav: use BT8 8LD. **Parking**: on site.

Dog rating: ❖ **Standard** – On leads only.

Find out more: 028 9064 7787 or minnowburn@nationaltrust.org.uk
nationaltrust.org.uk/minnowburn

Mount Stewart

Portaferry Road, Newtownards,
County Down BT22 2AD

1976

Voted one of the world's top 10 gardens, Mount Stewart reflects a rich tapestry of design and planting artistry bearing the hallmark of its creator. Edith, Lady Londonderry's passion for bold planting schemes coupled with the mild climate of Strangford Lough mean rare and tender plants from across the globe thrive in this

The glorious garden at Mount Stewart, County Down, has been voted one of the world's top 10

celebrated garden, with the formal gardens exuding a distinct character and appeal. Explore the exquisite house, recently restored to glory. Hear fascinating stories about the Londonderry family, and enjoy a world-class collection of paintings and many other internationally significant items. For a different view of Mount Stewart, stroll around miles of walking trails and discover a landscape lost in time.

Satnav: access via second gate into Mount Stewart, identified by brown sign.
Parking: 200 yards from main car park. Overflow car park approximately 465 yards. Accessible and family parking spaces in main car park.

Access: ⓅⒹⓌⒸ♿🚻🍴♿♿♿➡♿

Find out more: 028 4278 8387 or mountstewart@nationaltrust.org.uk
nationaltrust.org.uk/mount-stewart

Mount Stewart		M	T	W	T	F	S	S
1 Jan–31 Mar	10–4	M	T	W	T	F	S	S
1 Apr–31 Oct	10–4:30	M	T	W	T	F	S	S
1 Nov–31 Dec*	10–4	M	T	W	T	F	S	S

Temple of the Winds: open once a month, April to September. *Everything closed 25 and 26 December. Please note: all visitors must leave the site at closing time.

Dog rating: 🐾 🐾 **Good** – Welcome on short leads in grounds and gardens. Off lead in dog exercise area. Elsewhere, assistance dogs only.

Mount Stewart contains world-class collections, while outside, above, there are miles of trails to discover

The Mournes

near Newcastle, County Down

1992

These famous, wildlife-rich mountains are crossed by coastal and mountain paths. Great for exploring, the National Trust-maintained paths stretch from the shore into the heart of the Mournes, offering views over Dundrum Bay to the Isle of Man on a clear day.

Satnav: use BT33 0EU for Slieve Donard and BT33 0LA for Bloody Bridge.
Parking: for Slieve Donard, park in Newcastle; for Bloody Bridge, park on A2.

Dog rating: ❖ **Standard** – Welcome on leads.

Find out more: 028 4375 1467 or mournes@nationaltrust.org.uk
nationaltrust.org.uk/mournes

Walking on The Mournes in County Down

Murlough National Nature Reserve

near Dundrum, County Down

1967

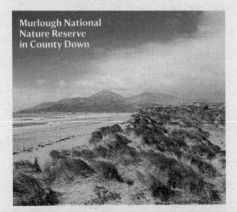
Murlough National Nature Reserve in County Down

Home to seals, Neolithic sites and Ireland's first nature reserve, Murlough is one of the most extensive examples of dune landscape in the country and an important wildlife conservation site. Paths and boardwalk wind through ancient dunes, woodland and heath, making the reserve ideal for relaxed walks and wildlife spotting. **Note**: limited toilet facilities with seasonal opening.

Satnav: use BT33 0LW. **Parking**: on site.

Dog rating: ❖ **Standard** – Welcome on leads. Access restricted during ground-nesting bird season or when cattle are grazing.

Access:

Find out more: 028 4375 1467 or murlough@nationaltrust.org.uk
nationaltrust.org.uk/murlough

Murlough

Car park: open daily; October to February, 8 to 5, and March to September, 8 to 7.

Mussenden Temple and Downhill Demesne

Mussenden Road, Castlerock,
County Londonderry BT51 4RP

1949 [icons]

The sheltered, vibrant gardens, cliff-edge landmark and striking ruins of a grand headland mansion bear testament to the eccentricity of the Earl Bishop who once made this 18th-century demesne his home. Mussenden Temple, perched atop sheer cliffs, offers panoramic views of the famous north coast and is a great place for walking and kite-flying.
Note: Mussenden Temple is not open.

Satnav: use BT51 4RP for Lion's Gate.
Parking: for Downhill Demesne at Lion's Gate.

Dog rating: 🐾 **Standard** – On leads only.

Access: [icons]

Find out more: 028 7084 8728 or mussendentemple@nationaltrust.org.uk
nationaltrust.org.uk/mussenden-temple

Mussenden Temple and Downhill

Downhill Demesne grounds: open every day all year (excluding 25 December), dawn to dusk. Open Bank Holiday Mondays and all other public holidays in Northern Ireland.

Mussenden Temple and Downhill Demesne, County Londonderry: the ruined mansion, above, and Temple

Patterson's Spade Mill

751 Antrim Road, Templepatrick,
County Antrim BT39 0AP

1991

The red-hot forge at Patterson's Spade Mill in County Antrim

Travel back in time and witness history literally forged in steel at the last working water-driven spade mill in daily use in the British Isles. Dig up the history and culture of the humble spade and discover the origin of the phrase 'a face as long as a Lurgan spade'.

Parking: 50 yards.

Dog rating: ❧ Standard – On leads only.

Access: 🅿️ 🅳 🚾 ♿ 🐾 ♿

Find out more: 028 9443 3619 or pattersons@nationaltrust.org.uk
nationaltrust.org.uk/pattersons-spade-mill

Patterson's Spade Mill
Open by appointment only (please email).

Portstewart Strand

Portstewart, County Londonderry

1981

Sweeping along the edge of the north coast, this 2-mile stretch of golden sand is one of Northern Ireland's finest beaches and affords uninterrupted views of the coastline. It's an ideal place for lazy picnics, surfing and long walks into the wildlife-rich sand dunes.

Satnav: use BT55 7PG. **Parking**: on beach.

Dog rating: ❧ Standard – Welcome on leads before post 10; exercise area beyond.

Access: 🅿️ 🅳 🚾 ♿ 🐾 ➡️

Find out more: 028 7083 6396 or portstewart@nationaltrust.org.uk
nationaltrust.org.uk/portstewart-strand

Portstewart Strand
Beach: open to pedestrians every day all year.
Car park (on beach) and facilities: opening days and times vary throughout year (weather and tide dependent), please check before visiting. Closed 25 December.

Looking down on the golden sands at Portstewart Strand in County Londonderry

Rowallane Garden

Saintfield, County Down BT24 7LH

1956 ❈▣▦

Carved into the County Down drumlin landscape since the mid-1860s, this inspirational 21-hectare (52-acre) garden is waiting to be discovered. The passion and shared vision of the Reverend John Moore, and later his nephew Hugh Armytage Moore, created a garden where you can leave the outside world behind and immerse yourself in nature's beauty. The formal and informal garden spaces are home to magical features mingled with native and exotic plants, such as drifts of rare rhododendrons. Follow in the footsteps of plant-hunters and explore the sights and scents of their discoveries in the garden today.

Home to native and exotic plants, Rowallane Garden in County Down, above and below, is inspirational

Follow in the footsteps of passionate plant-hunters at Rowallane Garden

Parking: on site.

Dog rating: 🐾 🐾 🐾 **Best** – Welcome on leads in garden. Dogs off lead in exercise area.

Access: [icons]

Find out more: 028 9751 0131 or rowallane@nationaltrust.org.uk
nationaltrust.org.uk/rowallane

Rowallane Garden		M	T	W	T	F	S	S
Garden								
1 Jan–28 Feb	10–4	M	T	W	T	F	S	S
1 Mar–30 Sep	10–6	M	T	W	T	F	S	S
1 Oct–31 Dec*	10–4	M	T	W	T	F	S	S
Café								
1 Jan–28 Feb	10–3:30	M	T	W	T	F	S	S
1 Mar–30 Sep	10–5	M	T	W	T	F	S	S
1 Oct–31 Dec*	10–3:30	M	T	W	T	F	S	S

Open Bank Holiday Mondays and all other public holidays in Northern Ireland. *Closed 25 and 26 December.

Springhill

20 Springhill Road,
Moneymore, Magherafelt,
County Londonderry BT45 7NQ

[1957] [icons]

Springhill, County Londonderry: the grounds, top, and 17th-century 'Plantation' home, above

Home to the Lenox-Conyngham family for 10 generations, this 17th-century plantation house is regarded as 'one of the prettiest houses in Ulster'.

Parking: 50 yards.

Dog rating: 🐾 **Standard** – Welcome on leads in grounds and garden.

Access: [icons]

Find out more: 028 8674 8210 or springhill@nationaltrust.org.uk
nationaltrust.org.uk/springhill

Springhill		M	T	W	T	F	S	S
House and visitor reception								
6 Mar–10 Apr	11–5	.	.	.	.	.	.	S
15 Apr–19 Apr	11–5	M	T	.	.	F	S	S
24 Apr–26 Jun	11–5	.	.	.	.	.	.	S
1 Jul–29 Aug	11–5	M	.	.	.	F	S	S
4 Sep–30 Oct	11–4	.	.	.	.	.	.	S
Grounds								
Open all year*	11–5	M	T	W	T	F	S	S

House: last entry one hour before closing; also open 19 and 20 February, 11 to 5. *Grounds: closed 25 and 26 December.

Strangford Lough

County Down 1969

The tidal treasures of the UK's largest sea lough and one of Europe's key wildlife habitats await discovery.
Note: for satnav use BT22 1RG.

Find out more: 028 4278 7769 or strangford@nationaltrust.org.uk
nationaltrust.org.uk/strangford-lough

Wellbrook Beetling Mill

20 Wellbrook Road, Corkhill, Cookstown, County Tyrone BT80 9RY

 1968

Discover how yarn was spun at Northern Ireland's last working water-powered linen beetling mill and enjoy a woodland river walk.

Parking: 10 yards.

Dog rating: 🐾 **Standard** – On leads in grounds only.

Access:

Wellbrook Beetling Mill in County Tyrone is still spinning today

Find out more: 028 8674 8210 or wellbrook@nationaltrust.org.uk
nationaltrust.org.uk/wellbrook-beetling-mill

Wellbrook Beetling Mill		M	T	W	T	F	S	S
Mill								
3 Jul–28 Aug	1–5	.	.	.	.	.	.	S
Grounds								
Open all year	Dawn–dusk	M	T	W	T	F	S	S

White Park Bay

near Ballintoy, County Antrim 1939

Once home to Neolithic settlements, this arc of white sand and ancient dunes is home to a myriad of wildlife.
Note: for satnav use BT54 6NH.

Find out more: 028 7084 8728 or whiteparkbay@nationaltrust.org.uk
nationaltrust.org.uk/white-park-bay

You and your Trust

More for members

Have you found your dedicated members' area on the website? You'll find previews, videos and behind-the-scenes stories.
And you'll be the first to see new features on the website, such as:

- seasonal recipes from our chefs' kitchens, and 'what's in season' food advice

- podcasts that unearth the stories behind everything from landscapes to literature

- tips from our gardeners, wildlife experts and curators

- spotlights on collections, conservation work and recent discoveries

- upcoming shop and holiday offers, and member events

- information you need for planning your next visit

nationaltrust.org.uk/ members-area

Data protection – our promise to you

We have to store your data to keep in touch with you, but we promise we'll keep your details safe and never send you anything that you haven't agreed to receive. And we promise we'll never sell your personal data to third parties.

You can change your mind at any time – about how you want to hear from us or what you want to hear about – by calling 0344 800 1895.

How else can you stay in touch?
Keep an eye on our social media channels and podcasts.

 @nationaltrust

Alphabetical index

Additional coast and countryside car parks

If you like to explore off the beaten track, here's a list of our additional coast and countryside car parks. You'll also find this online at **nationaltrust.org.uk/carparks**

Cornwall	Postcode	OS reference
Cadsonbury	PL17 7HL	SX346678
Carn Galver	TR20 8YX	SW421364
Chapel Carn Brea	TR19 6JD	SW388283
Chyvarloe	TR12 7PY	SW652236
Coombe Farm	PL23 1HW	SX109511
Cot Valley	TR19 7NS	SW356308
Cotehele Quay	PL12 6TA	SX424681
Degibna	TR12 7PR	SW653251
Hendersick	PL13 2LZ	SX235520
Kiberick (Nare Head)	TR2 5PH	SW921380
Lamledra (Vault Beach)	PL26 6JS	SX010411
North Cliffs – Basset's Cove	TR14 0HE	SW638440
North Cliffs – east (Deadman's Cove)	TR14 0HE	SW622430
North Cliffs – Fishing Cove	TR27 5EE	SW599427
North Cliffs – Hudder Down	TR27 5EE	SW610428
North Cliffs – middle (Derrick Cove)	TR14 0HE	SW619429
North Cliffs – Reskajeage	TR14 0HE	SW625431
North Cliffs – west (Derrick Cove)	TR14 0HE	SW618428
Park Head	PL27 7UU	SW85270
Penrose Hill	TR13 0RE	SW638258
Rinsey	TR13 9TS	SW591271
Rotterdam Beach, Talland Bay	PL13 2JA	SX226515
Trencrom	TR27 6NP	SW517359
Wheal Charlotte (Towan Cross)	TR4 8PZ	SW703484

Devon and Dorset	Postcode	OS reference
Devon		
Barna Barrow (Countisbury)	EX35 6NE	SS752496
Combe Park	EX35 6LF	SS740477
Danes Wood	EX5 3LH	SX968992
Dunsland	EX22 7AA	SS415052
East Titchberry	EX39 6AU	SS244270
Ellerhayes	EX5 4PY	SS975012
Exmansworthy	EX39 6AR	SS270266
Hartland: Brownsham	EX39 6AN	SS285259
Hembury Woods	TQ13 7RY	SX730680
Holne Woods	TQ13 7NT	SX711708
Man Sands	TQ6 0EF	SX913531
Prawle Point	TQ7 2BX	SX774355
Ringmore	TQ7 4HR	SX650456
Salcombe Hill	EX10 0NY	SY139882
Scabbacombe	TQ6 0EF	SX912523
Snapes Point	TQ8 8NQ	SX739401
Steps Bridge	EX6 7EQ	SX802883
Stoke	PL8 1JG	SX556465
Torrs Walk, Ilfracombe	EX34 8BA	SS512475
Trentishoe Down	EX34 0PF	SS635480
Woody Bay	EX31 4QU	SS675486
Dorset		
Cogden	DT6 4RJ	SY504882
Lambert's Castle	DT6 5QJ	SY366988

Somerset and Wiltshire	Postcode	OS reference
Somerset		
Ivy Thorn, Polden Hills	BA16 0TZ	ST480345
King's Wood, Mendip Hills	BS25 1DH	ST421560
Quarts Moor	EX15 3UZ	ST151169
Sand Point	BS22 9UD	ST330660
Staple Plain, Quantock Hills	TA4 4DQ	ST117410
Stourhead – King Alfred's Tower car park	BA12 6QX	ST748353
Walton Hill, Polden Hills	BA16 9RD	ST466350
Woodlands Hill, Holford	TA5 1SE	ST158406
Wiltshire		
Cley Hill	BA12 7QU	ST837442
Overton Hill	SN8 1QG	SU119681
Pepperbox Hill	SP5 3QL	SU211248
Whitesheet Hill	BA12 6RP	ST797350
Win Green Hill	SP5 5AW	ST923204

The Cotswolds, Buckinghamshire and Oxfordshire	Postcode	OS reference
Buckinghamshire		
Ivinghoe Beacon	LU6 2EG	SP96341
Pulpit Wood, Whiteleaf Fields	HP27 0NB	SP832045
Gloucestershire		
Dover's Hill	GL55 6UN	SP136395
May Hill	GL17 0RF	SO691221
Oxfordshire		
Buscot village	SN7 8DE	SU230976

Berkshire, Hampshire and the Isle of Wight

	Postcode	OS reference
Berkshire		
Cookham Common	SL6 9SB	SU892853
Simon's Wood	RG45 6AB	SU813635
Isle of Wight		
Bembridge and		
Culver Downs	PO36 8QY	SZ634856
Borthwood Copse	PO36 0LD	SZ566843
Highdown	PO39 0HY	SZ324855
Ventnor Downs	PO38 1AH	SZ565784
Windy Gap	PO38 2NP	SZ494758

Kent, Surrey and Sussex

	Postcode	OS reference
East Sussex		
Crowlink	BN20 0AY	TV549979
Kent		
Oldbury Hill	TN15 0ET	TQ577564
One Tree Hill	TN15 0SN	TQ559532
Toys Hill	TN16 1QG	TQ469516
Surrey		
Black Down	GU27 3BJ	SU920308
Fourwents Pond,		
Blackbrook Road	RH5 4NX	TQ183454
High Chart	RH8 0TW	TQ426521
Hydon's Ball		
and Heath	GU8 4BB	SU979402
Outwood Common	RH1 5PW	TQ326456
Witley and Milford		
Commons	GU8 5QA	TQ932406
West Sussex		
Lavington Common	GU28 0QL	SU948187
Woolbeding		
Countryside	GU29 9RL	SU874218

West Midlands

	Postcode	OS reference
Comer Wood		
(Dudmaston)	WV15 6QL	SO741899
Hampton Loade	WV15 6HD	SO747866
Hawksmoor	ST10 3AW	SK039441
Sawmill	WV15 6QW	SO756889

The Lakes

	Postcode	OS reference
Borrowdale and Derwent Water		
Ashness Bridge	CA12 5UN	NY269196
Bowder Stone	CA12 5XA	NY253168
Great Wood	CA12 5UP	NY272213
Kettlewell	CA12 5UN	NY266195
Rosthwaite	CA12 5XB	NY257148
Seatoller	CA12 5XN	NY246137
Surprise View	CA12 5UU	NY268189
Watendlath	CA12 5UW	NY275163

Buttermere Valley

	Postcode	OS reference
Honister Pass	CA12 5XN	NY225135
Lanthwaite Green	CA13 9UY	NY158207
Coniston		
Glen Mary	LA21 8DP	SD321998
The Langdales		
Old Dungeon Ghyll	LA22 9JY	NY285062
Ullswater		
High Cascades	CA11 0JY	NY397211
Park Brow	CA11 0JY	NY397206

Wales

	Postcode	OS reference
Brecon Beacons		
Cwm Gwdi	LD3 8LE	SO024248
Llŷn Peninsula		
Carreg nr Porthor	LL53 8LH	SH162289
Mynydd Mawr,		
Uwchmynydd	LL53 8DD	SH141256
Monmouthshire		
Skirrid	NP7 8AP	SO329164
Pembrokeshire		
Bosherston Lakes	SA71 5DR	SR967948
Broad Haven South	SA71 5DR	SR975938
Lodge Park Woods	SA71 5DE	SR976962
Porth Clais	SA62 6RR	SM739242
Snowdonia		
Cregennan	LL39 1LX	SH657143
Nantmor	LL55 4YG	SH597461

Northern Ireland

	Postcode	OS reference
Belfast		
Glenoe	BT40 3LG	NW537517
East Down		
Kearney	BT22 1QF	NW739043
Strangford Lough		
(Greyabbey)	BT22 2RU	NW697211
Mid Ulster		
Ballymoyer	BT60 2LA	SB067898
North Coast		
Cushendun	BT44 0PH	NW424887
Dunseverick	BT57 8SY	NR179025
Fair Head and		
Murlough Bay	BT54 6RG	NW378987
South Down		
Dundrum		
Coastal Path	BT33 0NG	SB501921

Need to get in touch?

@ enquiries@nationaltrust.org.uk

⌨ nationaltrust.org.uk/
help-centre

✉ PO Box 574, Manvers,
Rotherham, S63 3FH

☎ 0344 800 1895

0344 800 4410 (minicom)

9am to 5.30pm weekdays

9am to 4pm weekends
and Bank Holidays.

President
HRH The Prince of Wales

Deputy Chair
Orna NiChionna Turner

Director-General
Hilary McGrady

Central Office
The National Trust
Heelis, Kemble Drive,
Swindon, Wiltshire
SN2 2NA

Editor
Lucy Peel

Content management
**Roger Shapland
Dave Buchanan**

Project manager
Lisa Howe

Artworking
Steers McGillan Eves

Origination
Zebra

Printed
Walstead UK Ltd

©MAPS IN MINUTES™ 2021.
Contains Ordnance Survey data
©Crown Copyright and
database right 2020.

ISBN: 978-0-70-780463-7

Special thanks to
**Royal Oak Foundation
Historic House Hotels Ltd
National Lottery Heritage Fund**

MIX
Paper from
responsible sources
FSC® C010219

Places and facilities key

 Historic house

 Castle/fort

 Other buildings

 Garden

 Countryside/park

 Coast

 Nature reserve

 Shop or bookshop

 Food outlet

 Picnic area

 Nature trail

 Guided tour

 Assistance dogs only